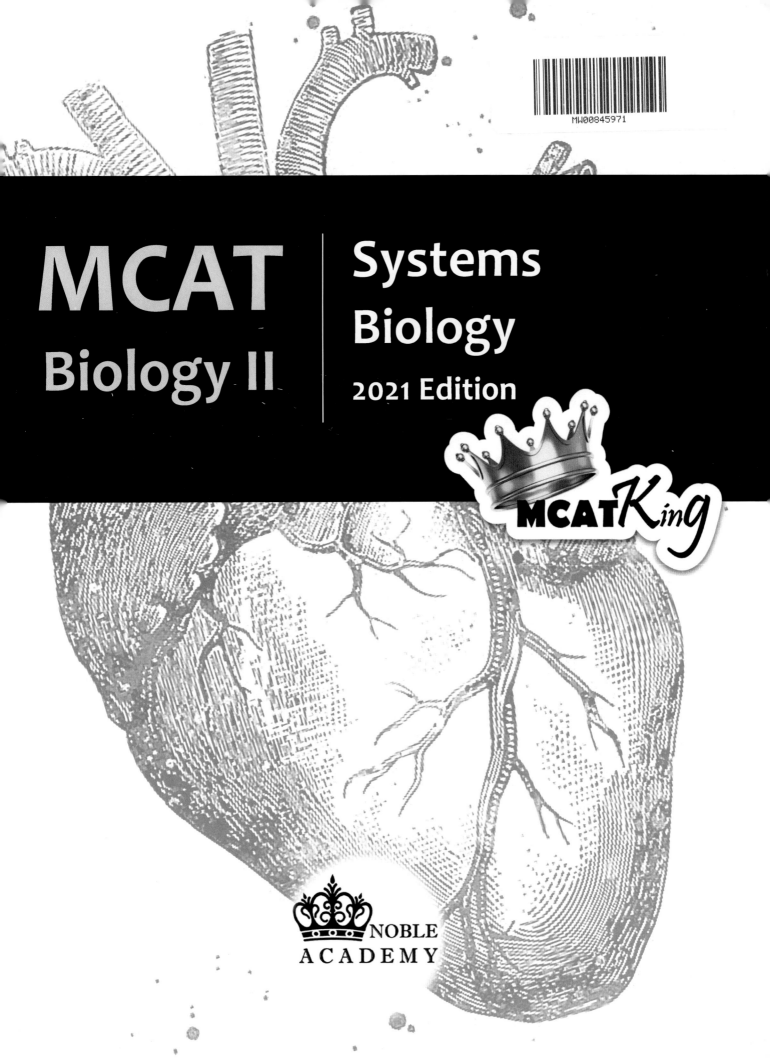

MCAT
Biology II

Systems
Biology
2021 Edition

MCAT King

NOBLE
ACADEMY

Published by MCAT® KING INC
NOBLE ACADEMY CENTER
213 W 35th St #600A,
New York, NY 10001

ISBN-13: 978-1-7339906-1-5

ISBN-10: 1-7339906-1-5

Table of Contents

Chapter 5: Cardiovascular System

Chapter 6: The Respiratory System

Chapter 7: Lymphatic System

Table of Contents

Chapter 8: The Immune System

Chapter 9: Urinary System

Chapter 10: Muscular System

We'd love to hear your feedback!

Please send comments and feedback to us at

feedback@mcatking.com

Meet the Team!

Prof. Farnad Noble Zaghi
Founder of MCAT KING
Columbia University
Yeshiva University | Lander College

Contributing Authors

Marissa LoCastro
University of Rochester School of Medicine

Jerrin Peter
Stony Brook University School of Medicine

Jasmine Levine
Harvard University

Anjali D'Amiano
Johns Hopkins University

Ammar Hamid
New York University

Editorial & Art Committee

Dania Halperin
Editor in Chief
Sackler School of Medicine

Tanya Alex
Index Manager
University of Maryland

Cassia L Rand
Art Production Manager
Touro College

Or Mossaiov
Assistant Editor
Yeshiva University

Anna Frolova
Illustrator
SUNY Binghamton

Kathryn A. Dotterweich
Illustrator
University of Virginia

Lindsay Chevlin
Illustrator
Barnard College

Sayak Ghosh
Copy Editor

New York University

Review Committee

Elizabeth Aleksanov
Marymount Manhattan
college

Karla Reid
Columbia University

Avital Tenenbaum
New York University

Oliya Clarkson
University of Oxford

Vicky Vasiliki Delengos
Fordham University

Samuel Zverev
Cornell University

Matthew Peng
University Of Pennsylvania

Maximilian P. Oljanenko
Brooklyn College CUNY

Commissioned Artists: Kateryna Zghola, Marcus DoCarmo

Ready?

Let's Get That White Coat™

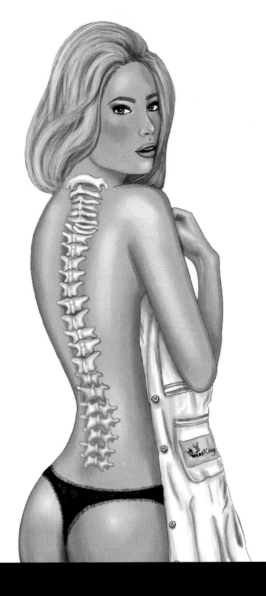

Chapter 1
The Nervous System

Chapter 1
The Nervous System

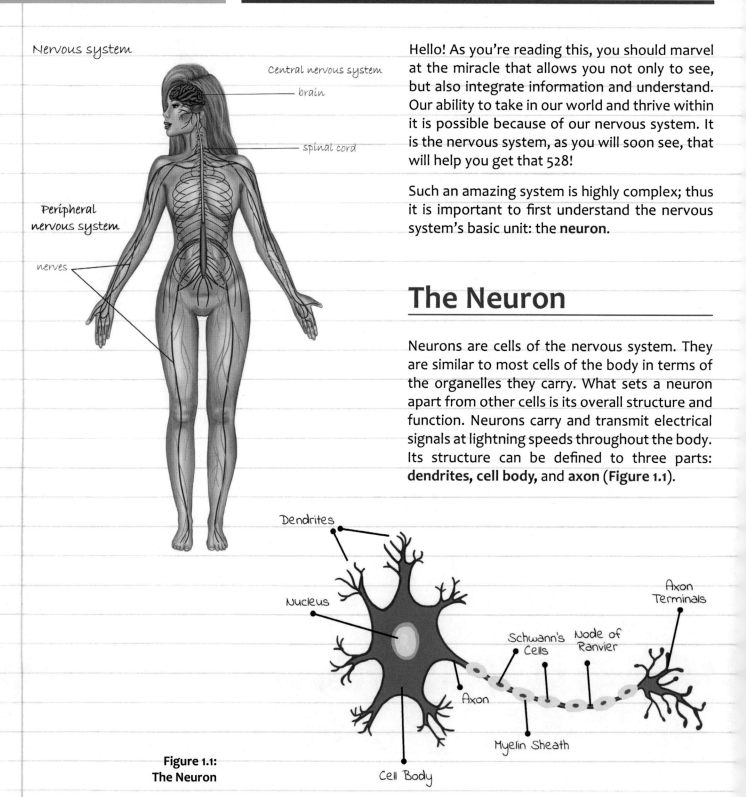

Nervous system

Central nervous system

brain

spinal cord

Peripheral
nervous system

nerves

Hello! As you're reading this, you should marvel at the miracle that allows you not only to see, but also integrate information and understand. Our ability to take in our world and thrive within it is possible because of our nervous system. It is the nervous system, as you will soon see, that will help you get that 528!

Such an amazing system is highly complex; thus it is important to first understand the nervous system's basic unit: the **neuron.**

The Neuron

Neurons are cells of the nervous system. They are similar to most cells of the body in terms of the organelles they carry. What sets a neuron apart from other cells is its overall structure and function. Neurons carry and transmit electrical signals at lightning speeds throughout the body. Its structure can be defined to three parts: **dendrites, cell body,** and **axon (Figure 1.1).**

Dendrites

Nucleus

Axon

Schwann's
Cells

Node of
Ranvier

Axon
Terminals

Myelin Sheath

Cell Body

**Figure 1.1:
The Neuron**

1. **Dendrites:** branches that receive information from other neurons and bring it toward the cell body.

2. **Cell body:** the command center of the neuron. The cell body contains the nucleus, endoplasmic reticulum, ribosomes, and other organelles that are required for the neuron to function. All proteins are made in the cell body and if need be, transferred to the axon using microtubules and microfilaments.

3. **Axons:** long branch that carries information away from the cell body and onward toward the next cell. The **axon hillock** is the name of the point from which the axon emerges from the cell body. Interestingly, this part lacks ribosomes and endoplasmic reticulum and thereby does not conduct **translation**. The axon is covered by a special insulator called the **myelin sheath** that allows electrical signals to travel through the axon quickly and effectively. Myelin sheath is produced by **Schwann cells** (covered later on) as shown in **Figure 1.1**.

Now that we have reviewed the structure of the neuron, let's contemplate: how does communication occur between the cells of the nervous system? To understand this, we need to see the events that occur within the cell. Follow along on **Figure 1.2**.

Neurons

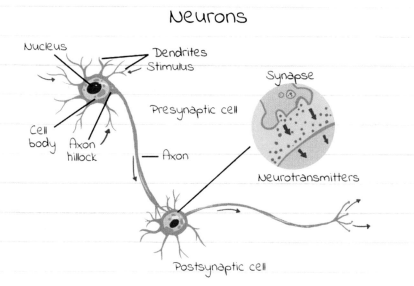

Figure 1.2:
Neurons and the Synapse.
Presynaptic neurons transmit signals across a synapse to the postsynaptic neuron.

First the dendrites receive the signal. The signal then travels to the cell body. Dendrites can receive signals from many neurons and thus, the neural cell can communicate with multiple other neurons. After the integration of the signal, the axons carry the signal out of the cell body. The signal travels down the axon to the **axon terminal,** also known as the **synaptic knob,** where the neurotransmitters are released across the synapse toward the dendrites of another neural cell. The region where the axon meets its target cell is known as the **synapse.** The cell that transmits the signal carrying the message is called the **presynaptic cell** since it is before (pre) the synapse. The cell that receives the signal is known as the **postsynaptic cell.** Notice the space between the pre and postsynaptic cell on **Figure 1.2**. The space is called the **synaptic cleft.**

Figure 1.3: Glia

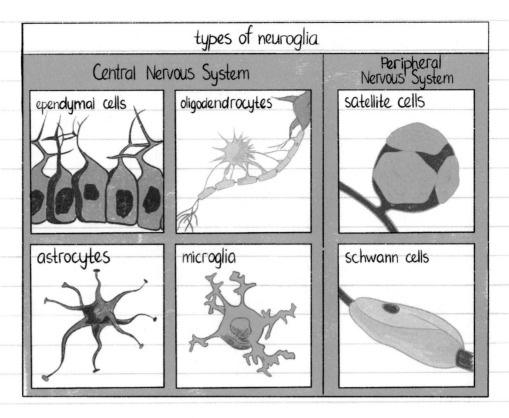

Glia, or **neuroglia,** are another type of cell in the nervous system that provide neurons with structural and metabolic support. Earlier, we mentioned one type of glial cell called Schwann cells. Let us look at all the types of glial cells that contribute to overall maintenance and successful functioning of the nervous system:

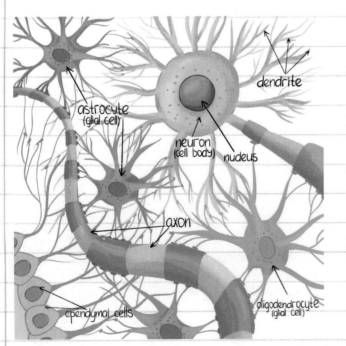

1. **Oligodendrocytes:** produce myelin for the central nervous system.

2. **Schwann cells:** produce myelin for the peripheral nervous system.

3. **Astrocytes:** provide nutrients and minerals as well as physical support to neurons.

4. **Microglia:** macrophages of the central nervous system that clean up debris.

5. **Ependymal cells:** epithelial cells that line the spinal cord and the ventricles of the brain. They are involved in producing cerebrospinal fluid.

6. **Satellite cells:** cells that surround the sensory, sympathetic, and parasympathetic ganglia. They help regulate the chemical environment.

Figure 1.4:
Glia in the Nervous System

You are now an expert on the neuron. Let us now discuss how neurons communicate via cell potentials!

Membrane Potential

The neuron's resting membrane potential, or voltage across the membrane, is **-70 mV**. This means at rest, the outside of the cell is relatively more positively charged compared to the inside of the cell. The difference in charge across the membrane is due to two factors:

1. The unequal distribution of ions

2. The membrane permeability of those ions.

The ions that are involved in the overall resting membrane potential are sodium, potassium, calcium, chloride, and organic anions. There is a greater concentration of sodium, calcium, and chloride ions outside the cell versus inside the cell; there is a greater concentration of potassium and organic anions inside the cell versus outside the cell. The cell is most permeable to potassium. As you will soon see, sodium and potassium ions are the two main players that contribute to the overall resting membrane potential of the neuron. Let us take a look at how these ions create the resting membrane potential of -70 mV.

Let us begin with potassium and assume that the cell is ONLY permeable to potassium at the moment. The resting membrane potential begins with the **Na^+/K^+ pump** creating the concentration gradient for potassium and sodium. The **Na^+/K^+ pump** moves two potassium ions into the cell and three sodium ions out of the cell at the expense of ATP. The potassium concentration inside the cell becomes larger relative to the concentration outside of the cell; thus forming a concentration gradient, also known as a **chemical gradient,** that drives potassium out of the cell. The potassium leaves the cell via special channels in the membrane called **potassium leak channels.** Leak channels are always open. For every positively charged potassium ion that leaves the cell, the inside of the cell becomes more negative (less positive) while the outside of the cell becomes more positive. In other words, an **electrical gradient (electrical potential)** is created across the membrane.

Since the outside of the cell is relatively more positive than the inside, the positively charged potassium ions will find it much more difficult to leave the cell since like charges repel. The potassium ions will also find it hard to leave the cell because the positively charged potassium ions are attracted to the organic anions (negatively charged ions) inside the cell. As the electrical force pushing potassium ions into the cell equals the chemical force pushing potassium out of the cell, the system reaches an **equilibrium.** The membrane potential of potassium at equilibrium is -90 mV. This value represents the voltage across the membrane if the cell were ONLY permeable to potassium. The membrane potential is negative because it represents the cell becoming less positive (more negative) when the potassium ions leave the cell due to the chemical (concentration) gradient. Only a small amount of potassium needs to leave the cell to achieve this membrane potential; thus, there is still a greater amount of potassium inside the cell versus outside the cell.

Now let us look at sodium and assume that the cell is ONLY permeable to sodium. **There are more sodium ions outside the cell than inside the cell due to the Na⁺/K⁺ pump that moves three sodium ions out of the cell and two potassium ions into the cell.** The chemical gradient will cause sodium ions to move into the cell via **sodium leak channels**. With each sodium ion moving into the cell, the inside of the cell becomes more positive while the outside of the cell becoming more negative (less positive). Like with potassium, this forms an electrical gradient that makes it difficult for sodium ions to move into the cell. As the electrical force pushing sodium ions out of the cell equals the chemical force pushing sodium ions into the cell, the system reaches an equilibrium. The membrane potential of sodium at equilibrium is +60 mV. This value represents the voltage across the membrane if the cell were ONLY permeable to sodium. The membrane potential is positive because it represents the cell becoming more positive (less negative) when the sodium ions enter the cell due to the chemical (concentration) gradient. Only a small amount of sodium needs to enter the cell to achieve this membrane potential; thus, there is still a greater amount of sodium outside the cell versus inside the cell.

Considering that sodium and potassium are the two most important ions that contribute to the overall cell membrane potential, we can simply average the two ion membrane potentials and acquire a number close to -70 mV (resting membrane potential), correct? Nope! The average of -90 mV and +60 mV is -15 mV. So what are we missing?

Remember, the overall cell membrane potential is dependent on both the unequal distribution of ions AND the membrane permeability of those ions. **The neuron is more permeable to potassium than it is to sodium** because there are far, far more potassium leak channels than there are sodium leak channels; thus, more potassium is able to leave the cell than sodium is able to enter. Since more positively charged potassium ions are able to leave the cell, the cell becomes more negative, going from +15 mV to -70 mV.

As a general rule, the ion for which the cell is **most permeable** more heavily sways the overall membrane potential towards the potential of that ion. For example, the membrane is most permeable to potassium. The potential for potassium is -90 mV and the membrane potential of the cell at rest is -70 mV. Pretty close! A useful metaphor to consider involves isotopes: the atomic mass of an element is actually the average of the masses of all of its possible isotopes found in nature. The most abundant isotope affects the average the most. The same concept applies here. **The more permeable the cell membrane is for a particular ion, the closer the overall membrane potential is to the potential of that ion.**

To maintain the gradients of the two most important ions that form this resting membrane potential, the **Na⁺/K⁺ pump** constantly pumps three sodium ions out of the cell and two potassium ions into the cell. **Figure 1.5** demonstrates how all these channels and pumps work in unison to establish the neuronal membrane potential.

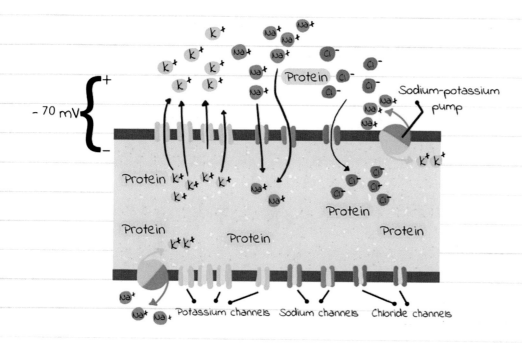

Figure 1.5:
Establishing Neuron Membrane Potential. The sodium-potassium pump establishes the initial gradient that pushes the flow of ions across the ion channels.

The Nernst equation

The **Nernst equation** allows us to predict the membrane potential of a cell when permeable to a single ion, given the concentrations of that ion on both sides of the membrane. In physics, we learn that a potential is a voltage between two plates. In the context of the cell, the potential is the maintenance of a small voltage across the membrane. Most likely, you won't be required to use this equation to calculate anything on the exam. It is more important to understand the Nernst equation conceptually.

$$E_{cell} = \frac{RT}{zF} \ln \frac{[Ion_{outside}]}{[Ion_{inside}]}$$

or

$$E_{cell} = 2.3 \frac{RT}{zF} \log \frac{[Ion_{outside}]}{[Ion_{inside}]}$$

In the Nernst equation, E_{cell} is the cell potential; **R** is the gas constant of $8.315 \frac{J}{mol \cdot K}$; **T** is the temperature in Kelvin (310 K in the body); **z** is the valence of the ion (i.e. +1 for Na^+); and **F** is Faraday's constant of $96,500 \frac{C}{mol}$.

At equilibrium, the following extracellular and intracellular concentrations for sodium and potassium are found below.

ION	Extracellular Concentration	Intracellular Concentration	Ratio of Extracellular Concentration over Intracellular Concentration
Potassium	5	150	0.0333
Sodium	145	15	9.6666

IN-TEXT QUESTION:
What would happen to the resting membrane potential of the cell if the permeabilities of potassium and sodium were flipped?

Answer:
If their permeabilities were to be flipped, then the resting membrane potential would most reflect the equilibrium membrane potential of sodium, which is 60 mV. However, because there is still some permeability to potassium when this flip occurs along with some other ions, the resting membrane potential would not be quite as high, most likely closer to 50 mV.

Using the Nernst equation, we can plug in the values above to find the cell membrane potential when the cell is permeable to only that ion. Let us use potassium as an example.

$$E_{cell} = \frac{(8.315 \frac{J}{mol \cdot K})(310K)}{(+1)(96.500 \frac{C}{mol})} \ln \frac{5M}{150M}$$

$$E_{cell} = (0.0267) \ln (0.0333)$$

$$E_{cell} = -0.09083 \, V = -90.83 \, mV$$

As you can see, when we plug in the concentrations for potassium inside and outside of the cell into the Nernst equation, we achieve the cell potential if the cell is only permeable to potassium!

Action Potentials

An action potential is an impulse sent through a cell due to a change in membrane potential. It is important to understand how an action potential is triggered. Follow the picture below (**Figure 1.6**).

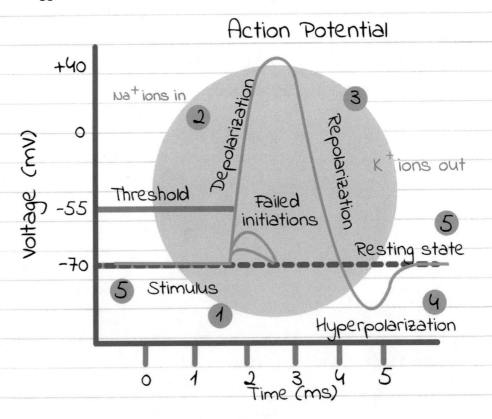

Figure 1.6:
The Action Potential

1. A signal acts on a neuron and causes positive ions to flow into its cell body and depolarize the cell. The signal typically comes in the form of a **neurotransmitter** (which we will cover later on).

2. Upon membrane potential reaching the threshold of -55 mV (**action potential threshold**) at the axon hillock, voltage-gated sodium channels quickly open and sodium begins to rush into the cell, down its concentration gradient. As more sodium enters the cell, the membrane potential becomes even more positive (**depolarized**).

3. At +40 mV, the voltage-gated sodium channels inactivate and voltage-gated potassium channels open causing the release of potassium from the cell. This **repolarizes** the cell. Voltage-gated potassium channels begin to close as the membrane potential crosses -55 mV.

4. Voltage-gated potassium channels in general take a longer time to close than voltage-gated sodium channels. As extra potassium leaves the cell, the cell **hyperpolarizes** to about -90 mV. Hyperpolarization means that the cell's membrane potential becomes even more negative than its resting potential.

5. At -90 mV, the voltage-gated potassium channels fully close. The cell returns to its normal resting membrane potential of -70 mV due to the concentration gradients that are reestablished thanks to the sodium potassium pump.

Look at **Figure 1.6**. If the MCAT were to give you a blank graph, you should be able to identify and explain what occurs in each step of an action potential. Give it a shot! Based on what we learned above, fill in what process occurs in each of the 5 steps.

In many biology books, action potentials are referred to as **all-or-none events** because they either occur at full strength or not at all. There is no in between. If the action potential is an "all-or-nothing" event, and action potentials are the same "strength," then an interesting question arises. How do we know which signals are a priority? Which signal requires our attention right now? Well, that all depends on the frequency with which the action potentials are fired. More signals cause action potentials to be fired at higher frequencies. For example, when we place our hand on a hot stove, neurons will fire action potentials at a higher rate compared to when we place our hand on a stove that is at room temperature. There is a limiting factor, however, on how frequent an action potential can be fired called **refractory periods**. During the refractory period of an action potential, a second action potential will not be initiated no matter how strong a second signal may be.

What causes refractory periods? The answer lies in the 3 states of the sodium channels:

    A. Closed

    B. Open

    C. Inactivated

Figure 1.7:
The Voltage-Gated Sodium Channel

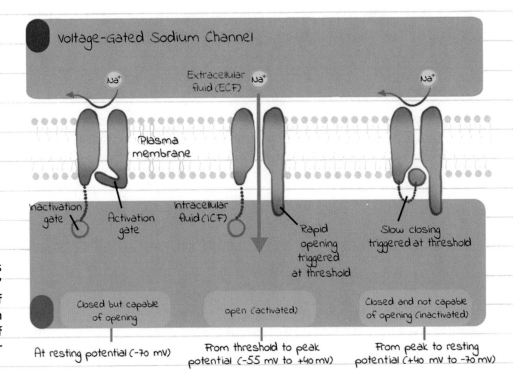

IN-TEXT QUESTION:

Some voltage-gated K⁺ channels are known as "delayed rectifiers" as a result of the timing of their opening during an action potential. What would occur if these channels took much longer than normal to open?

Answer:

Generally, voltage-gated K⁺ channels open 1 ms after membrane depolarization. The resulting change in potassium conductance "rectifies" the membrane potential back towards threshold. The reason these channels are called "delayed" rectifiers is because of the 1 ms delay in rectifying the membrane potential after depolarization. If these channels took longer than normal to open, the width of the action potential would increase, meaning that the neuron would remain at peak potential for longer and that it would take longer for the neuron to repolarize.

Follow along on **Figure 1.7.** During a normal resting potential, the sodium channel is **closed**. In this state, its activation gate is closed, and the inactivation gate is open. This is the only state of a sodium channel at which an action potential can be triggered. Once the cell is depolarized to threshold, the activation gate opens, allowing more sodium ions to enter. At this point, the sodium channels are considered **open**. As the membrane potential approaches +40 mV, the inactivation gates begin to close, preventing more sodium from entering the cell. At this point the sodium channels are deemed **inactive**. During the time between depolarization and repolarization, an action potential cannot occur due to the fact that all of the sodium channels are in either an **open** or **inactive state**. This is called the **absolute refractory period.** As the cell hyperpolarizes and returns to its resting membrane potential, the sodium channels begin to return to their **closed** states. During this time, if a stimulus occurs that is strong enough to reach the threshold, an action potential can be initiated. This period is called the **relative refractory period**. At resting membrane potential, the sodium channels are returned to their **closed** states where another action potential can be initiated normally again.

Graded Potentials

It is important to note that not every signal causes the membrane potential to reach threshold potential. Some signals cause only slight changes in membrane potential. Graded potentials are the sum of these weaker potentials caused by these signals. They can be depolarizing or hyperpolarizing. If a graded potential causes the cell to be less negative and therefore more likely to have an action potential, it is **excitatory**. The resulting shift in membrane potential is called an **excitatory postsynaptic potential** (EPSP).

Chapter 1 The Nervous System

Conversely, if the graded potential causes the cell to be more negative and therefore less likely to have an action potential, the graded potential is considered **inhibitory**. The resulting shift in membrane potential is called an **inhibitory postsynaptic potential** (IPSP). Notice **Figure 1.8**!

Graded potentials move towards the integrating region called the **trigger zone**, located at the axon hillock. If the graded potential is above the threshold once it reaches the trigger zone, then the voltage-gated sodium channels open and an action potential is initiated. Potentials contributing to a graded potential do not contain a refractory period, so many of them can occur simultaneously and be summed together. Notice on **Figure 1.9** how a once graded potential at the axon hillock reaches the threshold of -55 mV, an action potential is stimulated!

Graded potential summation: Graded potentials are created in two ways: **temporal summation** and **spatial summation**. Temporal means time. **Temporal summation** occurs when signals from *one* neuron acting on a postsynaptic neuron are sent consecutively in a short period of time, causing the potentials created from these signals to be added together. **Spatial summation** occurs when signals from adjacent synapses *(multiple neurons)* occur at the same time and their corresponding potentials add. For example, if two presynaptic neurons interact with one postsynaptic neuron. Check out **Figure 1.10**.

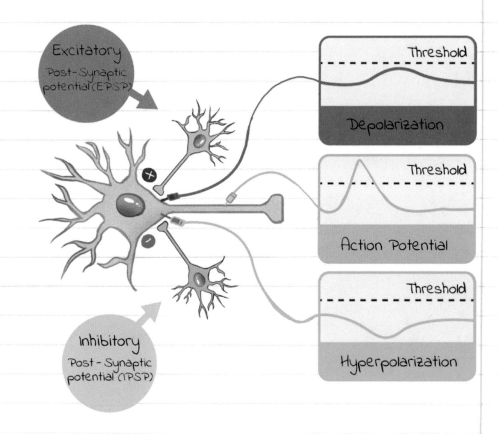

Figure 1.8:
Graded Potentials. EPSP increases the likelihood of an action potential. IPSP decreases the likelihood of an action potential.

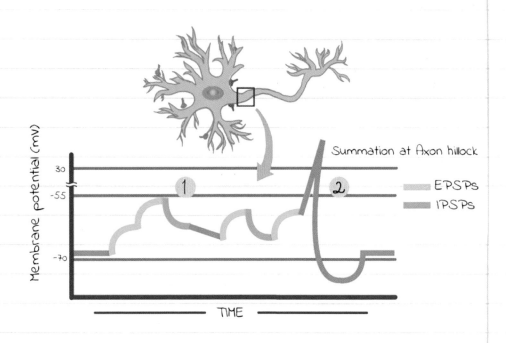

Figure 1.9:
Graded Potentials at the Axon Hillock over Time.

Types of Summation

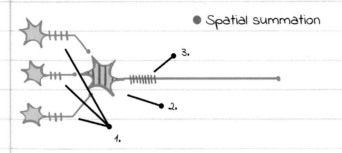

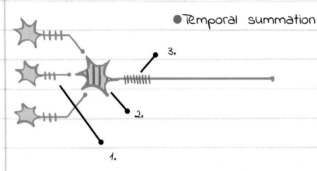

Figure 1.10:
Graded Potential Summation.

Spatial Summation:

1. Simultaneous stimulation by several presynaptic neurons

2. EPSPs spread from several synapses to axon hillock

3. Postsynaptic neuron fires.

Temporal Summation:

1. High frequency stimulation by one presynaptic neuron

2. EPSPs spread from one synapse in axon hillock

3. Postsynaptic neuron fires

Below is a table discussing the difference between graded potentials and action potentials:

	Action Potential	Graded Potential
Location	Axon hillock and Axon	Dendrites and cell bodies
Change in membrane potential	Depolarizing	Depolarizing or hyperpolarizing
Stimulus	Triggered by membrane depolarization	Triggered by external stimuli
Strength	All-or-none; stimuli that are greater than threshold will produce same strength action potentials	Depends on intensity of stimulus; decreases with distance from stimulus
Refractory period	Yes, a second action potential will not be initiated no matter how strong the signal may be with the exception of the relative refractory period.	None
Types of channels involved	Voltage-gated and ligand-gated ion channels	Ligand-gated
Summation	None	Temporal and spatial

Action potential velocity

The two factors that determine the speed at which a signal travels down the axon are the diameter of the axon and myelination of the axon. The larger the diameter of the axon, the faster the action potential travels. The larger the diameter, the more space for ions to travel and less probability that ions will bump into other molecules. An axon with a larger diameter,

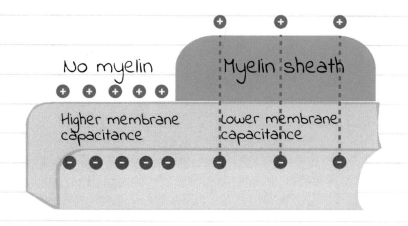

No myelin

Myelin sheath

Higher membrane capacitance

Lower membrane capacitance

WITHOUT MYELIN

More cations are concentrated along the inner surface of the membrane

WITH MYELIN

Less cations are concentrated along the inner surface of the membrane

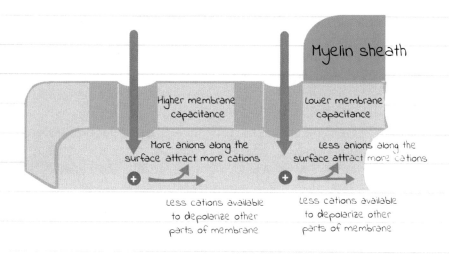

Myelin sheath

Higher membrane capacitance

Lower membrane capacitance

More anions along the surface attract more cations

Less anions along the surface attract more cations

Less cations available to depolarize other parts of membrane

Less cations available to depolarize other parts of membrane

therefore, effectively offers less resistance than an axon with a smaller diameter.

An action potential also travels faster down myelinated axons. Myelin is composed mostly of lipids and is formed by **oligodendrocytes** in the central nervous system and by **Schwann cells** in the peripheral nervous system. Myelin acts like an insulator and increases the speed in which the signal propagates down the axon. This is because the myelin REDUCES axonal membrane capacitance (see **Figure 1.11**). The total number of charges (anions or cations) along each side of the membrane is the membrane's "capacitance". The thinner the barrier (membrane) between opposite charges, the more they will attract. The more attracted they are, the more charges are able to crowd on each side of the membrane. Thus, a membrane with a thick sheet of myelin that separates opposite charges across the membrane **decreases** capacitance. A neuron at resting membrane potential is relatively more negative than outside the neuron due to the relative abundance of positive ions outside the neuron versus inside the neuron. Positively charged ions line up on the outside of the membrane. At unmyelinated parts of the neuron, negatively charged ions within the cell

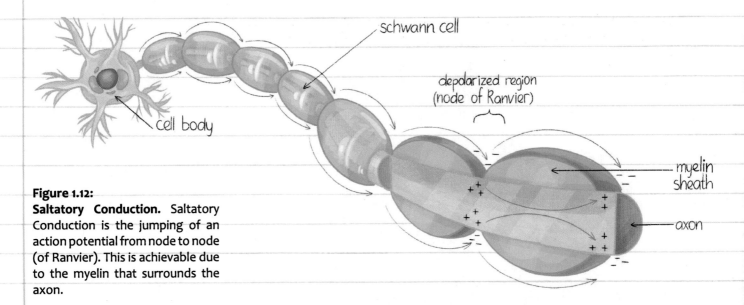

schwann cell

depolarized region
(node of Ranvier)

cell body

myelin
sheath

axon

Figure 1.12:
Saltatory Conduction. Saltatory Conduction is the jumping of an action potential from node to node (of Ranvier). This is achievable due to the myelin that surrounds the axon.

become attracted to these positive ions that have lined up on the other side of the membrane. When an action potential is stimulated, positively charged sodium ions rush into the cell. Its ability to depolarize a cell is quickly counteracted by the large number of negatively charged ions crowded by the membrane. However if these sodium ions in the cell pass through a myelinated section of the axon where there are less negative ions crowded around the membrane (decreased capacitance), depolarization can occur faster and with less resistance. Thus, an action potential can be propagated quickly to the next unmyelinated section where depolarization can occur again. These unmyelinated sections are called the **nodes of Ranvier.** The act of depolarization from node to node is called **saltatory conduction (Figure 1.12).**

Neuronal Communication

We understand how an electrical signal travels down the axon, but what happens once that signal reaches the end of the axon? How does the next neuron receive the message so that neurons can communicate with each other?

We mentioned that the space in between the axon of one neuron and the dendrites of another neuron is called the **synapse**. The synapse is where chemical messages from the presynaptic neuron, called **neurotransmitters,** are passed onto the postsynaptic neuron. The chemical message, when it stimulates a dendrite of the postsynaptic neuron, is converted into an electrical message. The postsynaptic neuron is then depolarized and an action potential is initiated. Let us take a deeper look at how neurons communicate.

Within the axon terminal of the presynaptic cell are many vesicles filled with neurotransmitters. Upon depolarization of the region due to an action potential, voltage-gated calcium channels in the cell membrane of the presynaptic neuron open, allowing calcium INTO the cell. This influx of calcium causes the synaptic vesicles to fuse with the membrane of the axon terminal, releasing neurotransmitters into the synapse. The neurotransmitters diffuse across the synaptic cleft and bind to membrane receptors on the postsynaptic cell (**Figure 1.13**).

Figure 1.13:
Neuron Communication at the Synapse.

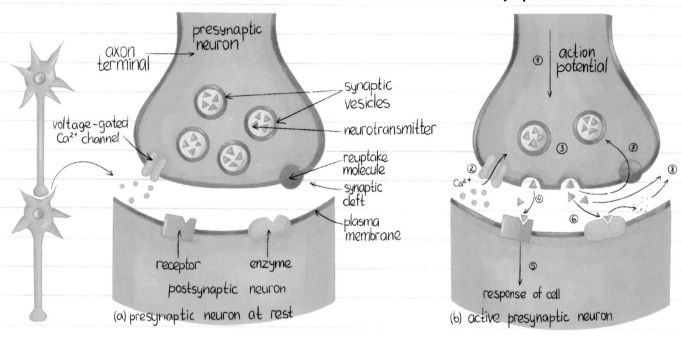

(a) presynaptic neuron at rest

(b) active presynaptic neuron

It is important to know for the MCAT that the same neurotransmitter can have varied effects. How is that so? It all depends on the receptor the neurotransmitter binds to. **The same neurotransmitter bound to two different types of receptors can elicit two different responses.**

Like all biological processes, neuronal signaling needs to be regulated. We want to be able to turn on the switch, but also turn it off. Otherwise, the neuron will be incapable of returning to its resting potential. If the neuron never returns to its resting potential state, a new action potential cannot be initiated. Once a signal is no longer needed, what is done with all the neurotransmitters in the synapse? Neurotransmitters cannot be left in the synapse because if they are, they will continue binding to the postsynaptic neuron and cause action potentials to be continually initiated. There are three major ways that the cell deals with the neurotransmitters once the signal is no longer needed (**Figure 1.14**).

Figure 1.14: Neurotransmitter Signal Termination Mechanisms.

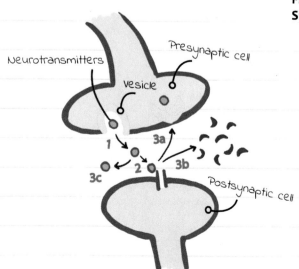

1 Neurotransmitter release

2 Binding and cellular response

3 Effect termination

   a. Reuptake

   b. Degradation

   c. Diffusion

The neurotransmitters can:

1. Be reuptaken into the presynaptic neuron, recycled, and reused.

2. Be inactivated or metabolized by special enzymes.

3. Diffuse out of the synaptic cleft.

All three ways result in the same end result: lingering neurotransmitters are removed from the cleft and the signal stops being initiated. This allows the neural cell to return to its resting potential.

Neurotransmitters

Neurons secrete a wide array of neurotransmitters. For the MCAT exam we do not need to know every single one, but instead can group them into four major classes based on their chemical structure.

1. **Acetylcholine**: This molecule is synthesized from choline and acetyl Coenzyme A. Acetylcholine is used in the neuromuscular junction to trigger a muscle contraction and is also used to elicit a parasympathetic response in the peripheral nervous system. This is an example of how the receptor determines the effect of the neurotransmitter.

2. **Amines**: Amine neurotransmitters are derived from amino acids and those contain one or more amine groups (Nitrogen with a lone pair). Amine neurotransmitters derived from tyrosine are called **catecholamines** and include **dopamine, norepinephrine,** and **epinephrine**. **Histamine** is derived from **histidine** and **serotonin** is derived from tryptophan.

   a) **Dopamine**: responsible for the reward system and movement. The substantia nigra (covered later) in the brain is known for secreting **dopamine** for movement. The lack of dopamine secreting neurons in the substantia nigra is commonly associated with **Parkinson's Disease**. Another part of the brain, called the **ventral tegmental area**, is known for secreting dopamine when we expect or receive a reward.

   b) **Norepinephrine** and **Epinephrine**: also known as **adrenaline**. These neurotransmitters aid in the fight or flight response.

   c) **Histamine**: released in response to an injury, or due to an allergic and inflammatory response.

   d) **Serotonin**: regulates mood, sleep, appetite, sexual function, and the reward system.

3. **Amino Acids:** The amino acids themselves can function as neurotransmitters. This contrasts with amines (amino acids that are modified into a new form). Amino acids that act as neurotransmitters include:

   a) **Glutamate:** A primary excitatory neurotransmitter in the central nervous system.

b) **Aspartate**: An excitatory neurotransmitter.

c) **Gamma-aminobutyric Acid (GABA)**: A major inhibitory neurotransmitter in the brain.

d) **Glycine**: A primary inhibitory neurotransmitter of the spinal cord.

4. **Purines**:

a) **AMP** and **ATP** can also act as signaling molecules. They are called purines due to their adenine ring.

How do neurotransmitters cause a cell's ion concentrations to change so that an action potential is induced? There are two types of channels involved (**Figure 1.15**). Let us take a look:

1. **Voltage-Gated Ion Channels**: Like most channels, voltage-gated ion channels are selectively permeable. There are voltage-gated ion channels for Na^+, K^+, Ca^{2+}, and Cl^-. As their name suggests, these channels respond to changes in voltage. Upon initiation of a membrane potential, the voltage channels will open (or close, depending on the channel), allowing ions into the cell. The popular example we discussed is the Na^+ channel of an action potential.

2. **Ligand-Gated Ion Channel**: These channels open once the appropriate ligand, such as a neurotransmitter, binds to the receptor. Remember, a ligand is a molecule that binds to a receptor. Once the ligand binds to the receptor, the ion channel opens and allows for the influx or efflux of specific ions.

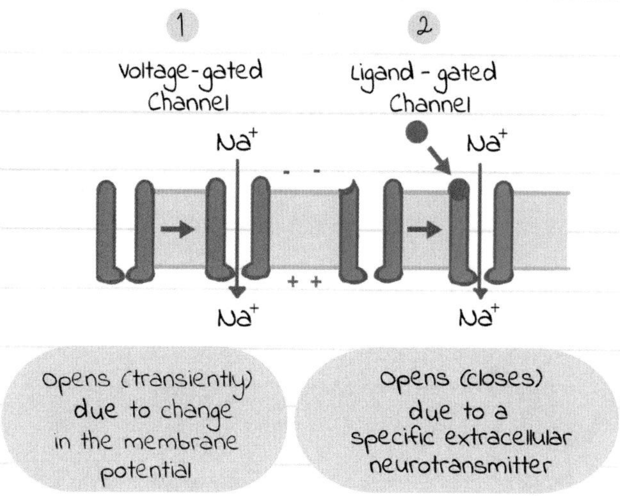

Figure 1.15: Membrane Channels in the Neuron. These channels are responsible for altering ion concentration in the cell, thereby altering the membrane potential.

There are other receptors that you should be familiar with for the MCAT:

3. **Enzyme-Linked Receptor**: These channels are also called catalytic receptors. It is a transmembrane receptor, but the nuance is that upon ligand binding, enzymatic activity will be initiated on the intracellular side. There will be two important domains: an **extracellular binding domain** and an **intracellular catalytic domain** that has catalytic capabilities. The binding of the ligand causes a conformational change on the internal catalytic domain that activates its enzymatic activity.

4. **G-Protein-Coupled Receptors (GPCR):** G-protein-coupled receptors are transmembrane proteins. Most of the physiological responses in the body (responses to hormones and neurotransmitters) are thanks to GPCRs. These are only found in eukaryotes. Humans have over 1,000 different types of these receptors. If no ligand binds to the receptor, the G-protein inside the cell remains inactive.

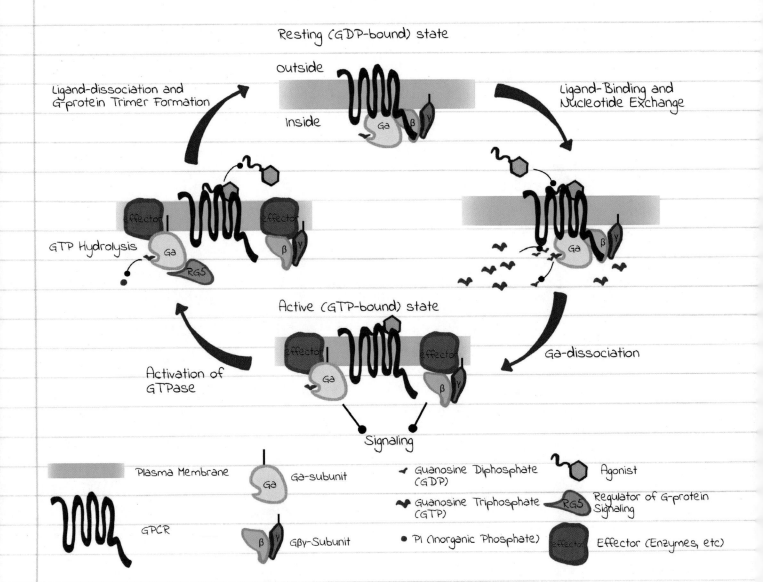

Resting (GDP-bound) state

Ligand-dissociation and G-protein Trimer Formation

Ligand-Binding and Nucleotide Exchange

outside

Inside

GTP Hydrolysis

Gα-dissociation

Activation of GTPase

Active (GTP-bound) state

Signaling

	Plasma Membrane		Gα	Gα-subunit		Guanosine Diphosphate (GDP)		Agonist
	GPCR		βγ	Gβγ-Subunit		Guanosine Triphosphate (GTP)	RGS	Regulator of G-protein Signaling
					•	PI (Inorganic Phosphate)	effector	Effector (Enzymes, etc)

Figure 1.16:
G-Protein Coupled Receptors (GPCRs).

In the **inactive** state, the G-protein will be bound to **GDP** (guanosine diphosphate). The G-protein bound to the GDP is a heterotrimeric protein, meaning that it is composed of three subunits: an alpha subunit, a beta subunit, and a gamma subunit.

Once the ligand binds, everything changes. The GPCR is now in an **activated** mode and the GDP that is bound to the G-protein is exchanged for a **GTP**. This causes the heterotrimeric protein to separate into two pieces: one piece is the alpha subunit bound to the GTP and the other is the beta and gamma units bound together. Both the alpha/GTP and beta/gamma subunits can initiate a cellular response by interacting with other proteins in the cell. The alpha subunit eventually hydrolyzes the GTP back to GDP and the G-protein will once more return to the inactive state, reassembling into the heterotrimer (**Figure 1.16**).

Now that we have covered the neuron, let us look at its role in the function of the entire nervous system!

The nervous system is divided into two parts: **the central nervous system and the peripheral nervous system.**

IN-TEXT QUESTION:
Why is an excitatory synapse on the soma more effective in triggering action potentials in the postsynaptic neuron than an excitatory synapse on the tip of the dendrite?

Central Nervous System

The Central Nervous System (CNS) is composed of the brain and the spinal cord.

Spinal Cord

The spinal cord functions as a bridge between the peripheral nervous system and the brain. Information from the environment is picked up by sensory neurons, sent to the spinal cord, and brought up to the brain to be integrated and interpreted. Information is then sent back down through the spinal cord to somatic motor neurons that elicit a response in muscles.

The spinal cord also acts as a reflex center. Information that needs immediate attention has the ability to skip processing in the brain; instead, a response will occur immediately from motor neurons in the spinal cord. The response is later registered in the brain as a memory of the event. A good example of this is the knee-jerk reflex. This will be covered later on in the chapter.

Answer:
A current entering the sites of synaptic contact must not only reach a zone in the axon where an action potential can be initiated but also must be strong enough to cause a depolarization beyond the threshold potential in order to generate an action potential. Furthermore, the strength of a current decays as a function of distance along the neuron. As a result, the effectiveness of an excitatory synapse to trigger an action potential is directly dependent on its distance from the axon. Since in most neurons, the soma is closer to the axon than the dendrite, an excitatory synapse on the soma is more effective for evoking action potentials than an excitatory synapse on the tip of a dendrite.

Organization of the Spinal Cord

The spine can be divided into four main regions: the **cervical, thoracic, lumbar, and sacral regions.** Looking at a cross section of the spinal cord shows that there are two roots: ventral and dorsal. The **dorsal** (meaning backside) **root** is located toward the back of one's body. The **ventral** (meaning front) **root** is located toward the front of one's body. The type of nerve that enters each root differs. Sensory nerves **ENTER** the spinal cord through the dorsal root and motor nerves **EXIT** through the ventral root. Neurons of the ventral root carry information to glands, tissues, and organs. Unfortunately, individuals with severe spinal cord injuries can lose sensation from their skin and muscles and even become paralyzed.

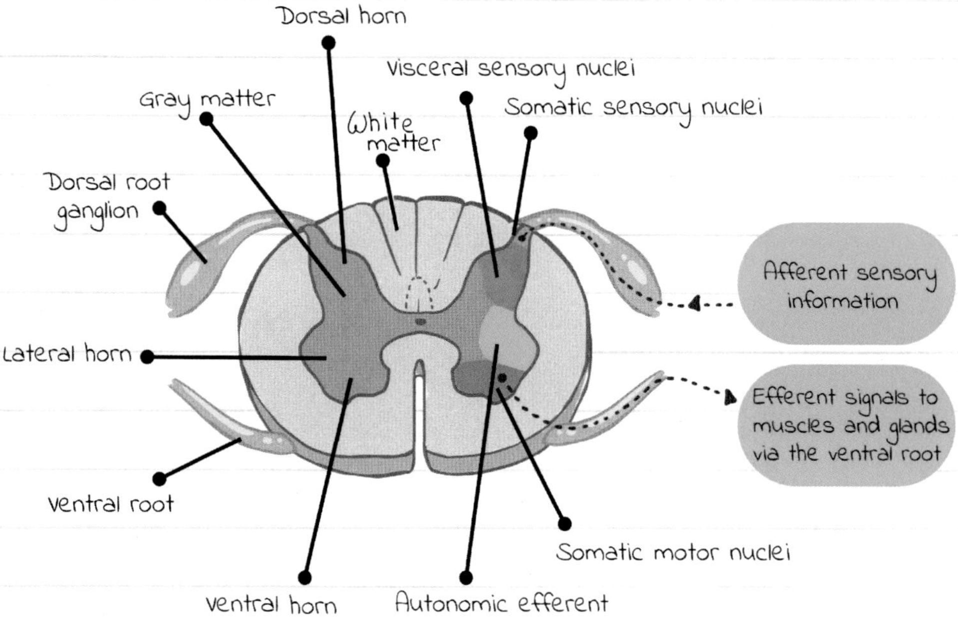

Looking at the cross section of the spinal cord on **Figure 1.17**, we see a butterfly shape of **gray matter** surrounded by a rim of **white matter.** Gray matter contains cell bodies and dendrites of the neuron. Usually, the neurons in the gray matter are organized in clusters called **nuclei.**

Figure 1.17:
Cross Section of the Spinal Cord.

White matter contains the axons. It looks white due to the abundance of **myelin** in the myelin sheath of axons.

Sensory neurons of the dorsal root synapse with interneurons in the dorsal horn of the gray matter. The ventral horn of the gray matter contains cell bodies of motor neurons and carries efferent signals to the muscles and glands.

The Brain

The brain needs no introduction. The brain is in charge of all of our thoughts, memories, movements, speech, and many organs inside our bodies. In addition to gray and white matter the brain has two other notable structures you should know:

1. **Sulci:** The depressions, or "valleys," of the brain.

2. **Gyri:** The bumps, or "hills," of the brain.

In the brain, gray matter surrounds white matter. This is in contrast with the spinal cord where the white matter surrounds the gray matter (**Figure 1.18**).

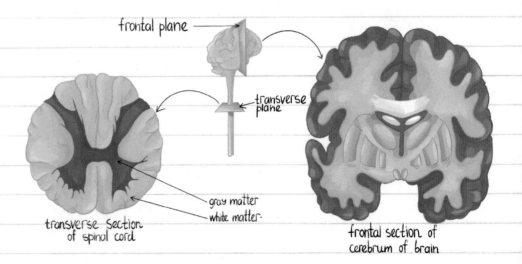

Figure 1.18:
Gray and White Matter in the CNS.

Organization of the Brain

1. **Forebrain:** The forebrain contains **the telencephalon (cerebrum)** and the **diencephalon (thalamus** and **hypothalamus)**. See **Figure 1.19**.

    ‣ **Telencephalon (Cerebrum)**

        • The cerebrum looks like what we think of when we envision a typical brain: the wrinkly, pink good stuff. The cerebrum can be divided into two hemispheres — the right and the left. Almost all of our cognitive function is possible thanks to the cerebrum; including smell, sight, reasoning, planning, and thinking. The left and right hemispheres of the brain communicate with each other using a structure called the **corpus callosum**. The cerebrum consists of both white and gray matter. The

Chapter 1 The Nervous System

cerebral cortex is the outer layer of gray matter surrounding the cerebrum. The cerebrum can be divided into four lobes:

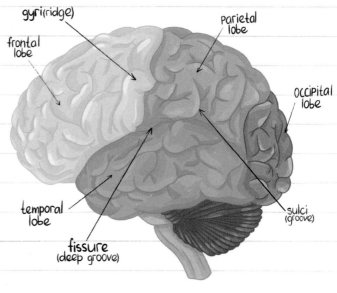

> **Frontal lobe**: As the name indicates, the frontal lobe is in the front of the brain, directly behind the forehead. The structure and functions of the frontal lobe include:

>> **Broca's area**: This is a region in the frontal lobe in the left hemisphere that helps us translate our thoughts into words. Damage to Broca's area can cause **expressive aphasia**, resulting in a patient's inability to produce language. Language comprehension, however, usually remains intact.

**Figure 1.19:
The Forebrain.**

   o Motor skills such as coordination of voluntary movement.

   o Categorization and classification of objects.

   o Memory formation and storage of long-term memories.

   o Reasoning, planning, and judgement.

> **Parietal lobe**: The parietal lobe is responsible for processing information related to touch, temperature, and taste. This lobe is known as the **somatosensory cortex**.

> **Occipital lobe**: Primarily responsible for processing visual information. The occipital lobe maps the visual world, processing spatial reasoning and visual memory. It also assists with other visual details such as color, distance, shape, size, and depth. We also recognize faces thanks to the occipital lobe.

> **Temporal Lobe**: Functions in processing auditory information and language comprehension.

>> **Wernicke's Area**: This area in the temporal lobe is responsible for language comprehension. Wernicke's aphasia can occur when this area is damaged. The patient may speak fluent sentences, but the sentences will lack any meaning or contextual sense (i.e. they are speaking total gibberish)

▸ **Diencephalon (Figure 1.20)**

• **Thalamus**: The thalamus is the prime relaying center of sensory information (except smell). Upon receiving the sensory information, the thalamus will direct the signals to appropriate parts of the brain.

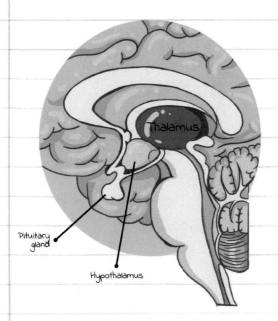

Figure 1.20:
The Diencephalon.

- **Hypothalamus:** We will discuss the hypothalamus in depth in the endocrine chapter in regards to its endocrine function. Let us summarize the hypothalamus in its neural context. The main function of the hypothalamus is to keep the body in homeostasis. It regulates emotions, sleep cycles, sex drive, digestion, blood pressure, heart rate, and so much more.

▸ Additional structures of the forebrain:

- **Pineal Gland:** The pineal gland is mainly responsible for producing melatonin. Melatonin is the famous sleep-regulating hormone that we all need and love.

- **Basal Ganglia:** The basal ganglia are a group of nuclei (clusters of neurons) that are located at the base of the forebrain. They control voluntary motor movements and procedural/habitual learning. The basal ganglia also consists of the substantia nigra, which plays an important role in reward and movement. the

- **Limbic System:** The limbic system is composed of the **amygdala** and the **hippocampus**. The amygdala is responsible for emotions, particularly fear, and survival instincts. The hippocampus is associated with storing short term memory and converting short term memory into long term memory to be stored in the frontal lobe.

2. **Brainstem:** The brainstem is composed of 3 structures (**Figure 1.21**).

   ▸ **Medulla**

   - The first structure above the spinal cord. The medulla performs all of the life sustaining functions such as breathing, heart rate, and swallowing. It also carries information from the cerebrum to the spinal cord, where the signals are transmitted to different parts of the body. **Pyramids** are a structure within the medulla that contain motor fibers that help control motor functions of the body.

   ▸ **Pons**

   - The pons sits directly above the medulla. It relays messages from the cerebrum to the cerebellum. It also plays an important role in sleep and dreaming, particularly REM sleep.

   ▸ **Midbrain:** The midbrain helps us in our auditory and visual reflexes. When we hear a loud and sudden sound, the midbrain is the reason we quickly turn our heads toward that sound! The midbrain also contains the substantia nigra that connects with the frontal lobe and other areas that control motor function. The substantia nigra produces and secretes dopamine in the brain via dopaminergic neurons. As mentioned previously, a lack of dopamine production in the substantia nigra has been shown to be linked with Parkinson's Disease.

3. **Cerebellum**
   ▸ The cerebellum sits right under the cerebrum (**Figure 1.21**) and is responsible primarily for **motor control**; in particular, muscle tone and balance information are monitored by the cerebellum. Consuming alcohol, for example, will impact the cerebellum and result in loss of balance and coordination!

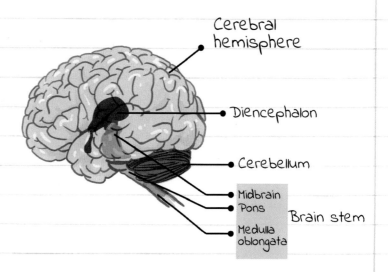

Figure 1.21:
Brainstem and Cerebellum.

The Peripheral Nervous System (PNS)

The PNS consists of the Autonomic and Somatic divisions:

1. Autonomic division: controls the smooth and cardiac muscles, glands, and other types of tissues. Think of autonomic as automatic. We have no control over these organs and they function automatically and involuntarily.

2. Somatic Division: contains neurons that control skeletal muscles that help us conduct voluntary movement.

The Autonomic Division

The autonomic nervous system can be further subdivided into the:

1. **Sympathetic branch**

2. **Parasympathetic branch**

To understand the functional differences between them, let us present some scenarios. It's been a hard week at work and finally it's the weekend. You're chilling, and after eating an entire pie of pizza, you watch some Netflix. You feel relaxed. Right now, your parasympathetic nervous system is in control.

Suddenly, you feel a little itchy on your leg. You extend your arm and your shrieks are heard all the way down the block. A spider has just jumped across the room and you feel your heart pumping intensely, your brow sweating, your mouth is slightly dry. You are ready to run like you've never run before. This is your sympathetic nervous system in control. The fight or flight mode has turned on.

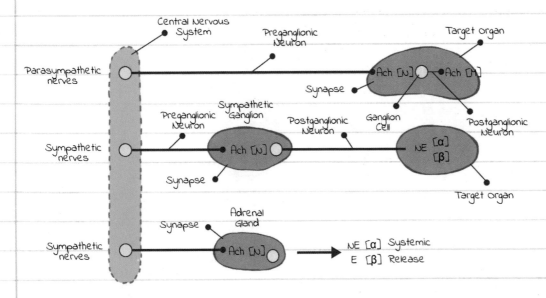

Figure 1.22:
Sympathetic vs. Parasympathetic Nerves. Notice that the preganglionic neurons in both the parasympathetic and sympathetic nervous systems are cholinergic (they release nicotinic acetylcholine to the receptor on the ganglion, designated by Ach[N]). The postganglionic neuron of the parasympathetic nervous system releases muscarinic acetylcholine (the receptor is denoted by Ach [M]). The postganglionic portion of the sympathetic nervous system is adrenergic (it releases norepinephrine, the receptor is designated by NE). The adrenal glands release norepinephrine and epinephrine (E), in response to cholinergic input from the sympathetic nervous system. Alpha (α), and Beta (β) denote norepinephrine receptor subtypes.

Notice that the effects of the sympathetic and parasympathetic branches are opposite to one another. This opposite control, where one system has an excitatory effect and the other system has an inhibitory effect, is referred to as **antagonistic control.** Both the sympathetic and parasympathetic branches have a **preganglionic neuron** with an origin in the CNS. It extends to communicate with an autonomic ganglion which is outside the CNS called the **postganglionic neuron.** The postganglionic neuron acts on the target glands.

The sympathetic and parasympathetic branches differ in more ways than just their function (**Figure 1.22**). First, they differ in where their presynaptic neuron synapses with their postsynaptic neuron. They also differ in the type of receptors on the postsynaptic neuron and target gland. In the sympathetic branch, the cell body of the presynaptic neuron synapses with the cell body of the postsynaptic neuron located closer to the spinal cord than the target gland. In the parasympathetic branch, the cell body of the presynaptic branch is also located within the spinal cord, but it extends from the spinal cord and synapses with the cell body of the postsynaptic neuron that is farther from the spinal cord and closer to the target gland.

There are two types of receptors on the postsynaptic neuron and/or target gland: **cholinergic** and **adrenergic. Cholinergic receptors** can be split into **muscarinic** or **nicotinic receptors. Cholinergic receptors** respond to **acetylcholine** while **adrenergic receptors** respond to **epinephrine/norepinephrine.** Sympathetic preganglionic neurons release acetylcholine onto nicotinic receptors on postganglionic neurons. These postganglionic neurons release epinephrine/norepinephrine onto adrenergic receptors on effector organs. In contrast, parasympathetic preganglionic neurons release acetylcholine onto nicotinic receptors on postganglionic neurons. These parasympathetic postganglionic neurons release acetylcholine onto muscarinic receptors on effector organs.

Another important fact to understand is that the nerves of the sympathetic and parasympathetic branches exit the spinal cord in different regions (**Figure 1.23**). The parasympathetic nervous system exits through the **sacral region** and the **cervical regions** of the spinal cord, while the sympathetic nervous system exits through the **thoracic** and **lumbar** regions of the spinal cord. One final difference to note is the speed at which the signals travel. The reaction of the parasympathetic system is slower, whereas the sympathetic responses are very fast. Now let's move onto the somatic division!

Chapter 1 The Nervous System

	Sympathetic System	Parasympathetic System
General function	Fight or flight response; prepares body to cope with stress	Rest and digest; stores energy; helps body to restore after stressful situations
Location of ganglia	Located closer to the spinal cord than the target gland	Farther from the spinal cord and closer to the target gland
Neurotransmitters released	Preganglionic neurons: acetylcholine Postganglionic neurons: norepinephrine	Preganglionic neurons: acetylcholine Postganglionic neurons: acetylcholine
Output of the preganglionic neuron	Thoracic and lumbar regions of the spinal cord	Cervical and sacral regions of the spinal cord
Rate of effects	Very fast	Slower than sympathetic

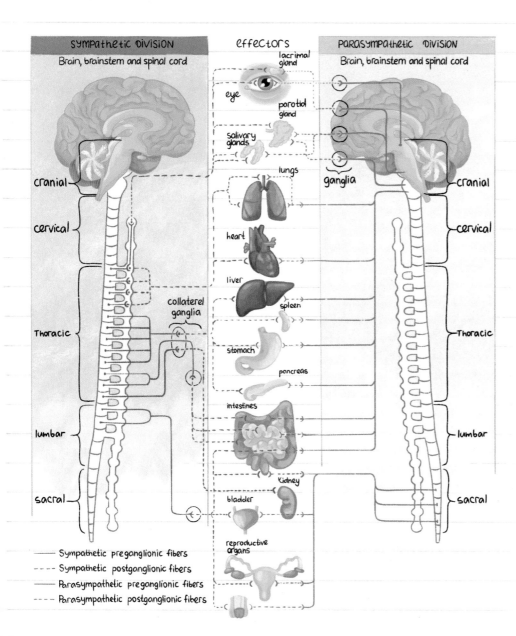

Figure 1.23: Sympathetic and Parasympathetic Origins.

Somatic Nervous System

As mentioned above, the CNS is the command center of the body, the place where all signals are integrated and interpreted. The CNS determines whether a response is needed. Signals come into the CNS via the **afferent branch** (think afferent — A for ARRIVES), or sensory neurons, of the peripheral nervous system. The sensory neuron then synapses with an interneuron in the CNS that can send information to the brain. If the brain determines that a response is needed, signals exit the CNS via an interneuron that synapses with the **efferent branch** (think efferent — E for EXIT), or motor neuron. This motor neuron then acts on a muscle.

The cell body (soma) of a motor neuron is located in the spinal cord. The motor neuron extends to the target muscle, innervates it, and releases acetylcholine onto cholinergic receptors on the muscle (**Figure 1.24**).

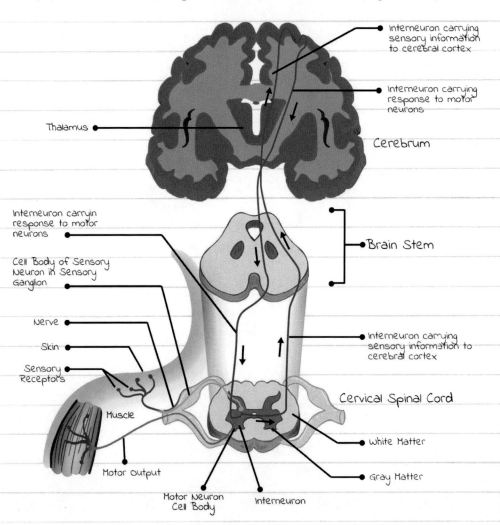

**Figure 1.24:
Somatic Nervous System.**

Reflexes

Reflexes are an example of the somatic nervous system in action. They are unique in that they are movements that occur without conscious thought. Reflexes are typically used when something needs our immediate attention and brain processing would take too long. But, how is it that we can have a response without wanting to respond?

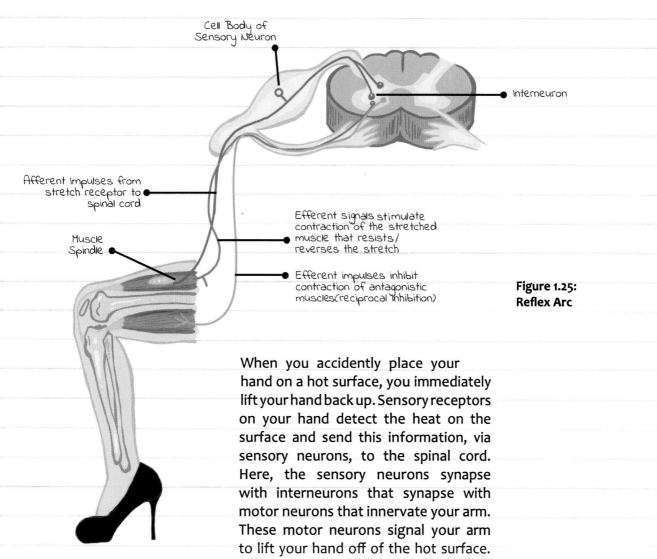

Cell Body of
Sensory Neuron

Interneuron

Afferent Impulses from
stretch receptor to
spinal cord

Efferent signals stimulate
contraction of the stretched
muscle that resists/
reverses the stretch

Muscle
Spindle

Efferent impulses inhibit
contraction of antagonistic
muscles (reciprocal inhibition)

**Figure 1.25:
Reflex Arc**

When you accidently place your hand on a hot surface, you immediately lift your hand back up. Sensory receptors on your hand detect the heat on the surface and send this information, via sensory neurons, to the spinal cord. Here, the sensory neurons synapse with interneurons that synapse with motor neurons that innervate your arm. These motor neurons signal your arm to lift your hand off of the hot surface. The interneuron also sends this information to the brain for it to process afterward. Had you waited for your brain to tell your arm to move, your hand would have burned!

Another reflex you've probably experienced occurs during your regular checkups. The doctor bumps your knee with his little hammer and your leg shoots up. This response is called the **knee-jerk reflex** and occurs because the doctor hit your patellar tendon right below your knee. This stretches the quadriceps of your thigh and stimulates the sensory neurons. Axons from these neurons extend to the spinal cord where they connect to motor neurons that innervate the quadricep, causing them to fire. As a result, the quadriceps contracts and straightens the leg at the knee. What is the role of the hamstring in this situation? We know that the function of the hamstring is to flex the leg at the knee. Thus, the hamstring MUST be relaxed for the quadriceps to contract and straighten the leg. When the doctor hits your patellar tendon, the sensory neuron that has its axon extended into the spinal cord activates interneurons. These interneurons inhibit (hyperpolarize) motor neurons that innervate the hamstring, causing the hamstring to relax. This contraction-relaxation dynamic of antagonistic muscles is called **reciprocal inhibition (Figure 1.25)**.

IN-TEXT QUESTION:
What is the purpose of having sulci and gyri rather than just having a smooth brain?

Answer:
Brain gyri and sulci serve two very important functions: the first is to increase the surface area of the cerebral cortex. This allows the packing of a greater quantity of neurons into the cortex to confer increased efficiency in processing information. The second function is that they form brain divisions. By creating boundaries between the lobes of the brain, sulci and gyri allow for brain function to be more localized and modular.

Chapter 1 The Nervous System

Sensory Information

Eye and Vision

The eyes allow us to enjoy the beautiful complexity of the world around us, including that hot babe you see in the mirror. You can think of your eyes as mini cameras. The process of vision is quite complex; but what we must know in respect to the MCAT is a little simpler.

Follow along on **Figure 1.26**!

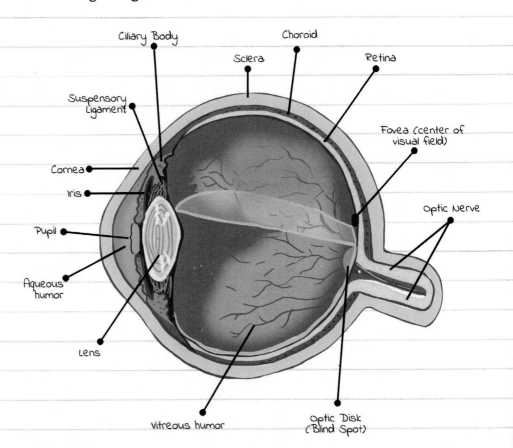

Figure 1.26:
The Anatomy of the Eye.

Light enters the eye through the **cornea**, a transparent disk of tissue that is the outermost layer. The cornea plays a significant role in focusing the light as it enters the eye. The light then passes through the aqueous humor, where it is refracted because the aqueous humor has a greater density than air. Let us remember our physics! When a light enters a medium of different density, it will bend (refact).

Following, light passes through the pupil and strikes the lens. At the lens, the light is further focused onto the retina. The light travels through a gelatinous fluid, called **vitreous humor,** as it passes from the lens to the retina. The retina contains numerous photoreceptors that capture light and convert it into an electrical signal. The electrical signals converge at the **optic disc** and exit to the brain via the **optic nerve**.

Light doesn't just randomly enter the eye, however. Before reaching the retina, light is modified in two ways:

1. The amount of light entering is altered by changes in pupil size caused by the movement of the iris. When you're in a dark place, and more light is needed to see, the pupil dilates to let in as much light as possible. When there is too much light, on the other hand, the pupil constricts.

2. The cornea and the lens focus, or angle, the incoming light onto the retina.

The Lens

As mentioned, the lens functions to focus, or angle, light onto the retina. To understand how this works, we must go back to physics!

The lens in our eyes are convex (converging) lenses. When rays of light pass through a convex lens, the point where the rays converge is called the **focal point**. The distance from the center of the lens to its focal point is the **focal length**. When light passes through the lens of the eye, the focal point must fall on the retina if the object is to be seen in focus. Otherwise, the image would either be very blurry or not seen at all.

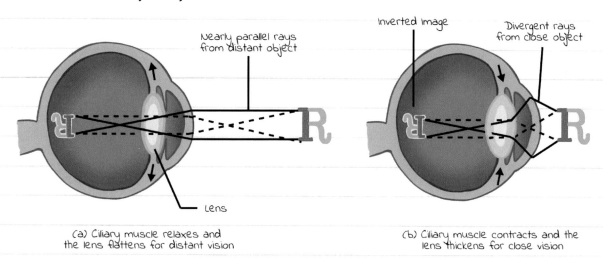

(a) Ciliary muscle relaxes and the lens flattens for distant vision

(b) Ciliary muscle contracts and the lens thickens for close vision

By adjusting the shape of the lens, the eye can keep images of objects from varying distances in focus. This process of adjusting the lens shape to maintain clarity is called **accommodation**. The closest distance at which the eye can focus an object is known as the **near point of accommodation**. The lens is capable of flattening and expanding and can move the focal point either forward or backward, ensuring the image is constantly focused on the retina. The lens can change its shape thanks to the **ciliary muscles**. The ciliary muscle is a ring of smooth muscle that surrounds the lens and is attached via inelastic ligaments called **zonules,** or **suspensory ligaments**. If no tension is on the lens, it is in its natural rounded shape. If the ciliary muscle relaxes and the ligaments pull, the lens flattens and assumes the shape required for distance vision. If the ciliary muscle contracts, the lens thickens to assume the shape required for near vision (**Figure 1.27**).

Figure 1.27:
Accommodation at the Lens. By altering the shape of the lens through contraction and relaxation of ciliary muscle, we can focus an image of an object onto the retina at varying distances.

Figure 1.28:
Vision Disorders. Vision disorders are characterized by the inability of the eye to focus incoming light onto the retina.

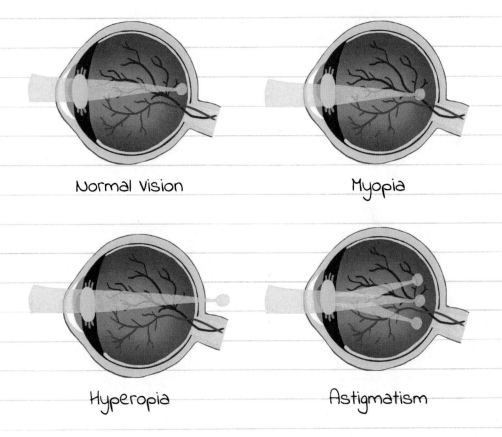

Normal Vision

Myopia

Hyperopia

Astigmatism

The MCAT expects you to understand the different types of vision weaknesses and how to combat them. Follow **Figure 1.28** and **Figure 1.29** as you read!

1. **Myopia:** Nearsightedness. This occurs when the focal point falls in **front** of the retina. This is typically due to one's eyeball being too long in relation to the focusing power of the cornea and lens. In this condition, near objects are seen clearly but objects far away are blurry. To correct myopia, **concave** lenses are used to push the focal point back and onto the retina!

2. **Hyperopia:** Farsightedness. This occurs when the focal point falls **behind** the retina. This is typically due to one's eyeball being too short in relation to the focusing power of the cornea and lens. Farsightedness is a condition in which distant objects are seen clearly but objects nearby may be blurry. To correct hyperopia, **convex** lenses are used to bring the focal point forward and onto the retina.

3. **Astigmatism:** A condition in which the cornea is irregularly shaped and causes a distorted image due to the light rays being unable to meet at a common focus. A special type of glasses that can bend light towards one direction is often prescribed.

4. **Presbyopia:** Condition where there is a loss of accommodation that makes it harder for the eye to focus images that are relatively close to one's eye. The loss of accommodation typically occurs as people age. Reading glasses, which contain **convex** lenses, are given to those with presbyopia (**Figure 1.29**).

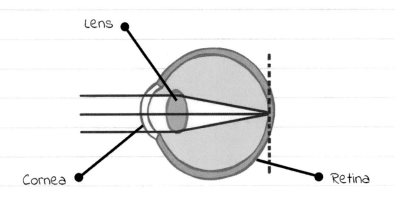

Normal Vision

Lens

Cornea

Retina

Figure 1.29:
Concave and Convex lenses in vision disorders.

Nearsighted Vision

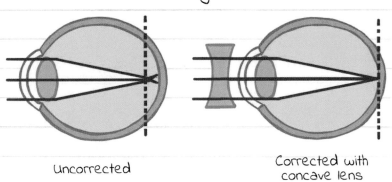

Uncorrected

Corrected with
concave lens

Farsighted Vision

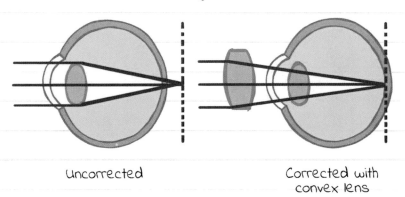

Uncorrected

Corrected with
convex lens

Phototransduction

How are we able to take light that hits the retina and turn it into electrical signals? The process of converting light energy into electrical signals is called **phototransduction**.

The cells that make this possible are called **photoreceptors** located on the retina. The two main types of photoreceptors are:

1. **Rods:** function best in **dark** environments when objects are seen in black and white rather than in color. There are about 20 times more rods than cones. Rods are located on the periphery of the retina.

2. **Cones:** responsible for sharp vision and **color** vision during daytime. The **macula** is an area on the retina that is particularly dense with cones. The **fovea** is located at the center of the macula; it contains the highest density of cones and is the area of sharpest vision.

Figure 1.30:
Rods and Cones. Rods and Cones are photoreceptors located on the retina.

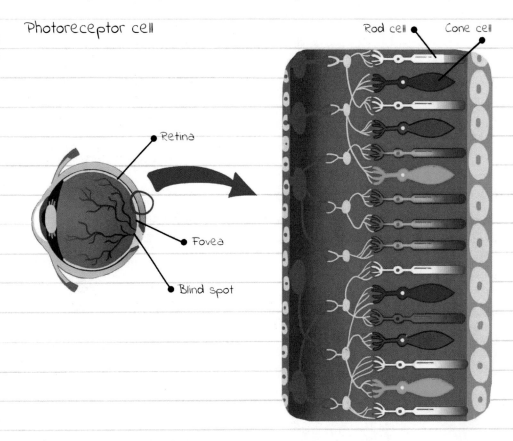

Pigments are found in photoreceptors and are responsible for absorbing specific wavelengths of light while reflecting all others. These pigments convert light energy into a membrane potential as we will discuss. Rods have the pigment **rhodopsin.** Cones have 3 different pigments that can either absorb blue, green, or red light. It makes sense that cones are specialized for different colors since they have more than one type of pigment.

In the genetics chapter of MCAT Biology I, we spoke about the fact that color-blindness is an X-linked recessive trait. But what is color-blindness exactly? An individual with color-blindness has defective cones and has difficulty distinguishing between certain colors. The most common is **red-green color blindness**. As the name suggests, these individuals have trouble distinguishing between red and green.

Phototransduction Cascade

We will discuss the **phototransduction cascade**, the method by which light is converted into electrical signals, for rhodopsin. The phototransduction cascade is similar for the three pigments in cones as well. Within rhodopsin, there are two molecules:

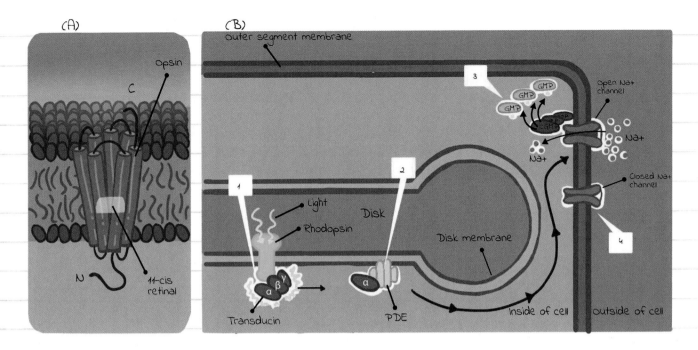

1. **Transducin:** a heterotrimeric G-protein containing an alpha, beta, and gamma subunit.

2. **Retinal:** This is a derivative of vitamin A and is the light-absorbing portion of the pigment. Retinal is the main protein of interest as we discuss the phototransduction cascade.

Follow along on **Figure 1.31**. In the absence of light, retinal and transducin are bound to rhodopsin. When a photon of light hits retinal, retinal changes

Figure 1.31:
Phototransduction Cascade.
1) Light stimulates rhodopsin which activates the G-protein called transducin.
2) Alpha subunit of transducin binds to phosphodiesterase (PDE)
3) PDE hydrolyzes cGMP to GMP, reducing cGMP concentration.
4) The reduction of cGMP concentration causes the closure of Na+ channels.

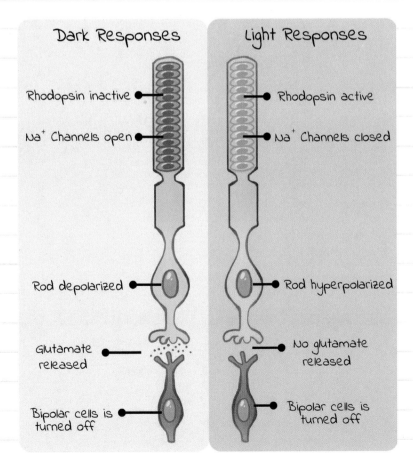

Figure 1.32:
Photoreceptor Response to Light.
When there is no light, glutamate is released by the rod onto the bipolar cell and turns bipolar cell off. When light is present, the rod does not release glutamate onto the bipolar cell and the bipolar cell turns on.

shape (from cis to trans). This causes rhodopsin to change shape as well. Rhodopsin's shape change causes transducin, specifically the alpha subunit of transducin, to break off and activates a phosphodiesterase that converts cyclic GMP (cGMP) to GMP. cGMP binds to membrane sodium channels in the rod that allow the influx of sodium and the rod's depolarization. When the rod is depolarized, it releases glutamate and turns off the bipolar cell. Conversion of cGMP to GMP prevents cGMP from binding to the sodium channels, thereby closing them. This causes the rod to hyperpolarize and turn off. Turning off the rod prevents the release of glutamate and turns on the bipolar cell. Yup you read that correctly. When the rod is turned on, the bipolar cell is turned off! Thus, light turns on our vision by turning off our photoreceptor cells! See **Figure 1.32**.

Light's Journey to the Brain

From bipolar cells, a signal is sent to **ganglion cells**. The ganglion cells collect the electrical signals and bring them to the **optic disk**. The **optic disk** is where the retinal neurons involved form the **optic nerve** and exit the eye towards the brain. The optic disk is also called the **blind spot** because there are no photoreceptors here. If light hits the optic disk, we will not be able see that corresponding image. See **Figure 1.33** and **Figure 1.34**.

Figure 1.33:
1) Light enters through the pupil of the eye
2) Light hits photoreceptors of the retina and phototransduction occurs.
3) Electrical signals from the photoreceptors travel through cells of the retina (shown in Figure 1.33).
4) Electrical signals converge at the optic disk (blind spot).
5) Electrical signals travel to the brain via the optic nerve.

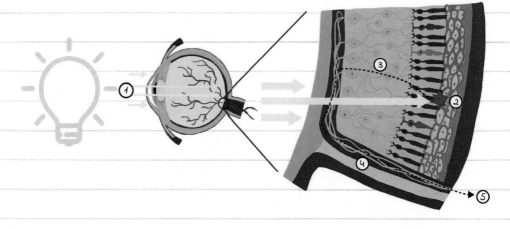

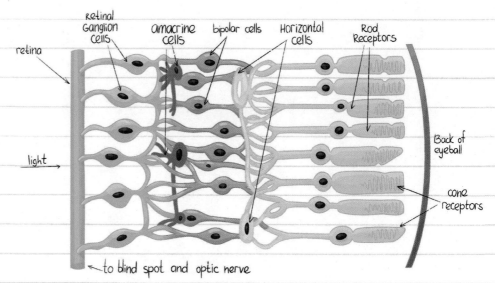

Figure 1.34:
Cells of the Retina

Chapter 1 The Nervous System

The optic nerves proceed to the **optic chiasm,** a structure in the brain that looks like the letter X due to the crossing over of the optic nerves (**Figure 1.35**).

Here's where things get interesting. Specific regions of the brain process specific areas of the image. These areas of the image are called **visual fields.** The information from the right visual field of both eyes is processed on the left side of the brain and the information from the left visual field is processed on the right side of the brain. Eventually, the signal gets processed in the visual center of the brain: **the occipital lobe.**

Look at **Figure 1.36.** Do not make the common misconception that the right eye information is the left brain and the left eye is the right brain. The left visual field of both the right and left eye is processed by the right side of the brain, and conversely, the right visual field of both the right and left eye is processed by the left side of the brain.

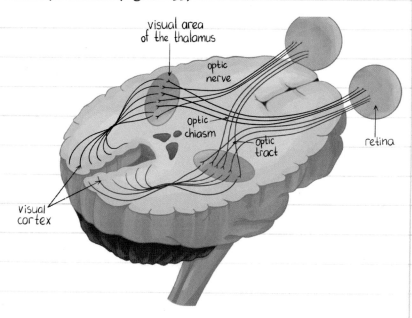

Figure 1.35:
The Optic Nerve. The optic nerves cross over at the optic chiasm.

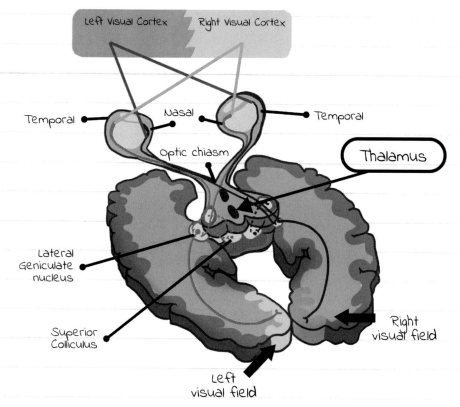

Figure 1.36:
Processing of Visual Fields in the Brain. The left visual field (orange) is processed in the right visual cortex of the occipital lobe. The right visual field (green) is processed in the left visual cortex of the occipital lobe.

Before we move on from vision, there is something we cannot LOOK past.

There are two types of ganglion cells that you must know for the MCAT:

1. **Magnocellular cells:** sensitive to information about movement. When you look at a fast moving car, you are using your magnocellular cells. You are not able to view all the fine details of the car. But you are able

to make out that the moving object is a car. Thus, magnocellular cells cannot detect fine details.

2. **Parvocellular cells**: more sensitive to signals that have to do with fine detail, like the texture of objects. You are using parvocellular cells when you look at a still object and are able to make out all of its little details. Parvocellular cells do not work on moving objects.

Hearing

Our ability to hear allows us to take in all the sounds of the environment and the moans of the bedroom. Just as the eyes are to vision, the ear is the main structural component of hearing. However, the ear functions beyond hearing and is responsible also for positional equilibrium and balance. Before we discuss how the ear does its magic, let us first go over its basic structure.

Structure of the Ear

Figure 1.37: Anatomy of the Ear.

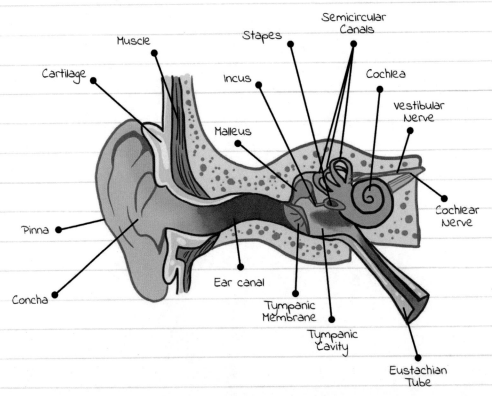

Follow along on **Figure 1.37**. The first structure is the *external ear* which includes the **outer ear**, known as the **pinna,** and the **ear canal.** The inner end of the ear canal is sealed by the ear drum, called the **tympanic membrane.** This membrane separates the external ear from the middle ear.

Next is the **middle ear.** The middle ear consists of an air-filled cavity that connects with the pharynx via the **eustachian tube.** This tube opens up when chewing, swallowing, and yawning in order to make sure that the pressure of the middle ear equilibrates with atmospheric pressure. There are three small important bones in the middle ear which function to conduct sound from the outer environment to the inner ear. These bones are the **malleus** (also known as the **hammer**), the **incus** (also known as the **anvil**), and the **stapes** (also known as the **stirrup**).

The inner ear contains the **vestibular apparatus** consisting of the **semicircular canals, utricle** and **saccule** (not shown in **Figure 1.37**), and **cochlea.** The **cochlea** contains sensory receptors that tell the brain, through the **cochlear nerve**, what sound we are hearing.

Sound exists as waves, called sound waves. However, sound does not simply enter the brain as sound waves for it to be processed. Instead sound waves enter through the external ear and are converted to mechanical energy by the middle ear. From the middle ear to the inner ear, the mechanical energy is turned into electrical signals. The electrical signals then travel to the brain to be processed. It is important to know that the brain recognizes frequency of the sound wave as pitch, and the intensity of the sound wave as loudness. Intensity, or loudness, is a function of the amplitude of the sound wave. To remember this, let us think of the bedroom. The larger his package, or amplitude of a sound wave, the louder the bedroom will be!

Let us now take a deeper look at how exactly sound waves are converted into electrical signals as it travels through the ear.

The Auditory Pathway

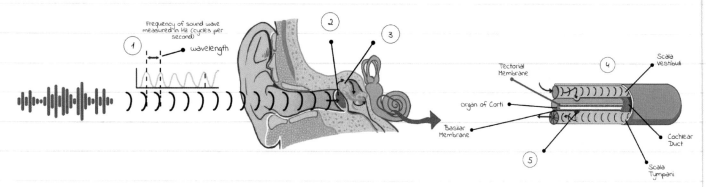

Follow along on **Figure 1.38**. The source of sound creates a wave that hits the tympanic membrane and causes it to vibrate. The energy of the vibrations causes the malleus, incus, and stapes to vibrate. Since the stapes touches the oval window, the vibrations are transferred to the fluid within the cochlea. The cochlea contains an organ called the **organ of corti.** It is an organ containing many hair cells that all assist in the transduction of sound into signals. These cells are composed of the hair cell receptors.

There are two membranes in the cochlea that respond to vibrations: the **basilar membrane** and the **tectorial membrane**. The movement of the fluid due to vibrations from the middle ear causes vibrations of the basilar membrane. This, in turn, causes movement of the hair cells on the Organ

Figure 1.38:
The Auditory Pathway.
1) Sound waves representing areas of high and low pressure travel to the external auditory canal.
2) The tympanic membrane vibrates in response to the sound wave.
3) Vibrations are amplified across ossicles.
4) Vibrations against the oval window set up standing waves in the fluid of the vestibule.
5) Pressure bends the membrane of the cochlear duct at a point of maximum vibration of a given frequency, causing hair cells in the basilar membrane to vibrate.

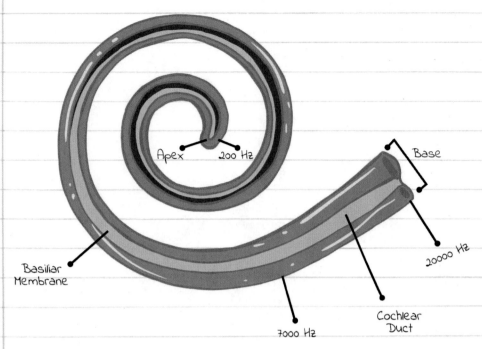

of Corti against the tectorial membrane. The movement of the hair cells causes the hair cells to bend, membrane ion channels open, and ion influx. This depolarizes the hair cell and causes an action potential to follow. The electrical signal from the hair cells are then sent through the **cochlear nerve**, which merges with the **vestibular nerve** to form the **vestibulocochlear nerve (auditory nerve)**, and sent to the brain.

It is important to note that the base of the cochlea is thicker and responds to higher frequency sounds. The apex of the cochlea is thinner and responds to lower frequency sounds (**Figure 1.39**). To remember this, think of the cochlea as a curvy girl: thin at the top, thick at the base. Since the base is much thicker, it can handle a much higher frequency of action.

Figure 1.39:
The Cochlea. The base of the cochlea is connected to the middle ear. The middle ear transmits energy from sound waves to the cochlea, causing cochlear fluid to move.

Hair cells

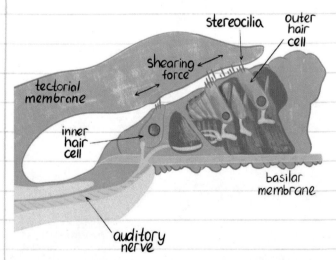

We briefly discussed earlier how hair cells convert mechanical energy into electrical signals. But how exactly does this occur?

Hair cells are sensory cells. They have little cilia on their tips called **stereocilia** that look like small hairs, hence the name (**Figure 1.40**). They are arranged in ascending height with the longest stereocilia called the **kinocilium**, embedded in the tectorial membrane. Movement of the basilar membrane also moves the kinocilium and other stereocilia of the hair cell. The stereocilia on hair cells are attached to each other by protein bridges called **tip links**. Tip links are also connected to gates that open and close ion channels in the cilia membrane. When the hair cells are in a neutral position, very few of the gates are open and there are few signals being sent to the brain. What happens when the hair moves?

Figure 1.40:
The Organ of Corti. Stereocilia are small hairs on hair cells. Kinocelium is the longest stereocilia that is attached to the tectorial membrane. Movement of the stereocilia opens ion channels that cause the depolarization of the hair cells.

Upon movement and as the hair cells bend, the tip links will be pulled and will open more channels, causing calcium and potassium to enter the cell. This will depolarize the hair cell and result in a signal being sent to the CNS via the auditory nerve. The **auditory cortex**, located in the **temporal lobe**, is the main sound processing center of the brain.

Chapter 1 The Nervous System

The Vestibular Apparatus

We briefly mentioned how the ears do more than just allow us to hear. The ears are also able to help us maintain balance and let us know our position in space using the **vestibular apparatus**. There are two important structures that make up the vestibular apparatus: **saccule** and **utricle**. Additionally, there are three **semicircular canals** that connect the utricle at its base. The saccule and utricle tell the brain about the vertical and horizontal acceleration of our body, respectively, as well as relative head position. The semicircular canals are important for sensing rotational acceleration. This movement and positional information is sent to the **cerebellum** in order to regulate balance. See **Figure 1.41**.

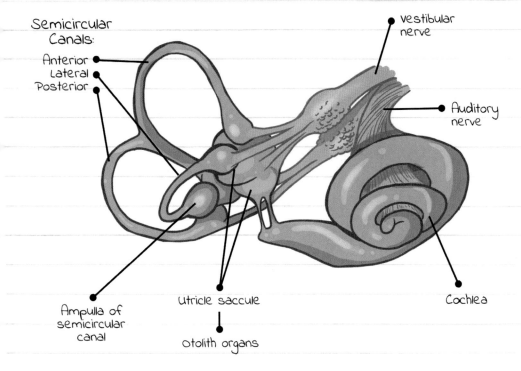

Figure 1.41:
The Vestibular Apparatus. The utricle and saccule detect linear acceleration and head positioning. The semicircular canals detect rotational acceleration.

Taste and Smell

There are two more sensations that you must know for the MCAT: taste and smell.

The scientific name for smell is called **olfaction**. The forebrain has an extension called the **olfactory bulb** that receives signals from the olfactory neurons in the nose (**Figure 1.42**).

The odorant receptors are G-protein cAMP linked membrane receptor proteins. When an odorant binds to the receptor, the G-protein, called G_{olf}, is activated and increases the concentration of cAMP within the cell. This causes cation channels to open and depolarize the cell, triggering a signal that travels along the olfactory axon to the olfactory bulb.

How do we smell different odors?

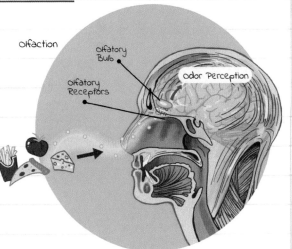

Figure 1.42: Olfaction.

IN-TEXT QUESTION:

Given that chemicals that have bitter, sweet, and umami tastes all activate the exact same intracellular signaling molecules, how does the nervous system distinguish between these three tastes?

Answer:

These three taste pathways all utilize the exact same second messenger pathways that eventually transfer signals to afferents that lead to the brain. However, these three different taste receptors are expressed in three different taste cells, and each receptor is selective for its given taste molecule. Furthermore, each taste receptor cell projects to a unique gustatory axon that receives information for only one class of taste receptor proteins to deliver a unique message to the relevant brain area.

Different odor receptors bind to different odorant chemicals. The brain uses the information from hundreds of different olfactory receptor cells in different combinations to create the perception of many different smells.

Taste is closely linked to smell. Remember the last time you had a stuffy nose because of the flu? Eating was much less pleasing because you couldn't taste anything. The reason this occured is because our perception of flavor is a combination of the taste and smell of the food that we eat! Each taste bud contains specialized cells that contain receptors for one of the five taste sensations: **bitter, salty, sweet, sour,** and **umami**. Umami is the ability to taste glutamate. Thus, wherever there is a taste bud on your tongue, you will be able to taste any of the five flavors.

Sour and salty cells rely on ion channels; bitter, sweet, and umami cells rely on GPCR receptors. From the taste cells, signals are sent to the thalamus, where they are relayed to the **gustatory cortex** located deep within the cerebrum.

Questions

1) **Which of the following is true?**
   a. Schwann cells myelinate purkinje axons
   b. Oligodendrocytes myelinate pyramidal neurons in the cortex
   c. Schwann cells myelinate schaffer collaterals in the hippocampus
   d. Oligodendrocytes myelinate cochlear hair cells

2) **What kind of cells support the immune system of the brain?**
   a. Satellite cells
   b. Ependymal cells
   c. Microglia
   d. Astrocytes

3) **Why is the resting membrane potential -70 mV?**
   a. Because there is more sodium outside the cell than inside the cell and the membrane is most permeable to potassium
   b. Because there is more sodium inside the cell than outside the cell and the membrane is most permeable to sodium
   c. Because there is more potassium outside the cell than inside the cell and the membrane is most permeable to sodium
   d. Because there is more potassium inside the cell than outside the cell and the membrane is most permeable to potassium

4) **If potassium leak channels were to be blocked, how would that affect the membrane potential?**
   a. The resting membrane potential would become more negatively charged, as potassium would accumulate outside of the cell
   b. The resting membrane potential would become more positive, as potassium would accumulate inside of the cell
   c. The resting membrane potential would become more negatively charged, as potassium would accumulate inside of the cell
   d. The resting membrane potential would become more positively charged, as potassium would accumulate outside of the cell

5) **How does an action potential occur?**
   a. Sodium enters the cell causing the cell to hyperpolarize
   b. Potassium enters the cell causing the cell to hyperpolarize
   c. Sodium enters the cell causing the cell to depolarize
   d. Potassium enters the cell causing the cell to depolarize

6) **Why can't two action potentials be fired in close temporal succession?**
   a. No new action potential can be initiated until the inactivation gate opens on the voltage-gated sodium channel
   b. Time must pass before the voltage-gated potassium channels close, allowing the membrane to depolarize to threshold
   c. No new action potential can be initiated until the activation gate opens on the voltage-gated sodium channel
   d. After an action potential both the activation gate and the inactivation gate are closed

7) *Tetraethylammonium* (TEA) has been found to block voltage-gated potassium channels by blocking the channel opening. If TEA is applied to a neuron along with a significant inward current, which of the following will occur?
   1. Potassium leak channels would allow for net potassium influx
   2. An action potential would occur without a fast repolarization
   3. Voltage-gated sodium channels would remain constitutively open
      a. I only
      b. II only
      c. I and II only
      d. II and III only

8) In what kind of axon would an action potential travel the fastest?
      a. Large diameter, large capacitance
      b. Large diameter, small capacitance
      c. Small diameter, large capacitance
      d. Small diameter, small capacitance

9) Serotonin is an important neurotransmitter to regulate mood, and *selective serotonin reuptake inhibitors* (SSRIs) are a common treatment for depression. What makes SSRIs effective in treating depression?
      a. By clearing and taking up serotonin that has been released, the presynaptic neuron is in a better position to initiate another neurotransmitter release
      b. Reuptake inhibitors reduce the amount of time that the neurotransmitter spends in the synaptic cleft
      c. Reuptake inhibitors increase the concentration of neurotransmitter in the synaptic knob
      d. By allowing serotonin to remain in the synaptic cleft, its signal to the postsynaptic neuron persists for a longer period of time

10) Which of the following neurotransmitters are released at the neuromuscular junction?
      a. Norepinephrine
      b. Glutamate
      c. Acetylcholine
      d. Dopamine

11) What is the first thing that occurs after a ligand binds to its respective G-protein coupled receptor?
      a. The G-protein bound GDP gets exchanged for a GTP
      b. The alpha subunit of the G-protein hydrolyzes GDP into GTP
      c. The G-protein separates into the alpha and the beta-gamma subunits
      d. The beta-gamma subunit breaks off to initiate a cellular response

12) Order the regions of the spinal cord from top to bottom:
      a. Thoracic → cervical → lumbar → sacral
      b. Thoracic → lumbar → cervical → sacral
      c. Cervical → thoracic → sacral → lumbar
      d. Cervical → thoracic → lumbar → sacral

13) Why do axons and dendrites appear white?
    a. Extensive myelination appears white in color
    b. Highly concentrated solutions of sodium give the exterior a white color
    c. Fast electric signal emit electromagnetic radiation that appears white
    d. None of the above

14) If a patient presents with issues involving gustation, and deficits in the peripheral nervous system have been ruled out, in which of the following areas of the cortex does the patient MOST likely have an issue?
    a. Frontal lobe
    b. Parietal lobe
    c. Temporal lobe
    d. Occipital lobe

15) A patient presents with difficulty in speaking. When you greet him, he says "problem number planets can't make elephants run." What area of his brain is most likely to be damaged?
    a. Amygdala
    b. Broca's area
    c. Wernicke's area
    d. Thalamus

16) All of the following release acetylcholine as their neurotransmitter EXCEPT
    a. Parasympathetic preganglionic neurons
    b. Sympathetic postganglionic neurons
    c. Parasympathetic postganglionic neurons
    d. Sympathetic preganglionic neurons

17) What kind of receptors are utilized by the auditory system?
    a. Nociceptors
    b. Mechanoreceptors
    c. Chemoreceptors
    d. Electromagnetic receptors

18) Which of the following is the correct pathway of light after it hits the eye?
    a. Cornea → aqueous humor → vitreous humor → retina
    b. Cornea → vitreous humor → aqueous humor → retina
    c. Cornea → retina → aqueous humor → vitreous humor
    d. Cornea → retina → vitreous humor → aqueous humor

19) When you are trying to make out the details of a house, which group of cells are you utilizing the most?
    a. Hair cells
    b. Magnocellular cells
    c. Stereocilia
    d. Parvocellular cells

20) All of the following sensory pathways utilize a G-protein coupled receptor system EXCEPT
   a. Vision
   b. Audition
   c. Olfaction
   d. Gustation

Answers

1) **Answer: B**

   Explanation: Oligodendrocytes myelinate the CNS while Schwann cells myelinate the PNS. Pyramidal neurons are multipolar neurons found in the cortex, amygdala, and the hippocampus, existing in the CNS, making B the correct answer. Purkinje cells are in the cerebellum and schaffer collaterals are in the hippocampus, both in the CNS, eliminating A and C. Cochlear hair cells are not neurons and are part of the PNS, eliminating D.

2) **Answer: C**

   Explanation: Microglia are macrophages of the central nervous system that clean up debris, serving an immune function and making C correct. Satellite cells regulate the chemical environment, eliminating A. Ependymal cells are involved in producing cerebrospinal fluid, eliminating B. Astrocytes provide nutrients and minerals as well as physical support to neurons, eliminating D.

3) **Answer: D**

   Explanation: The neuronal membrane is most permeable to potassium, eliminating B and C. As a result, potassiums equilibrium potential has the maximal influence on the overall resting potential. There is far more potassium inside of the cell than outside the cell due to the Na^+/K^+ ATPase; and because the cell is very permeable to potassium via leak channels, potassium tends to exit the cell. Because potassium is a cation, this exit leaves the cell more negatively charged than it was before, eliminating A and making D the correct answer.

4) **Answer: B**

   Explanation: The sodium-potassium pump ensures that 2 potassium cations enter the cell for every 3 sodium cations that exit the cell, resulting in a buildup of potassium inside of the cell. If leak channels were to be blocked, this buildup would not be relieved and the resting membrane potential would become more positive, making B the correct answer. None of the other answer choices reflect this.

5) **Answer: C**

   Explanation: Once threshold is reached, voltage gated sodium channels open. Since the equilibrium potential of sodium is +50 mV, sodium rushes into the cell in hopes to achieve that potential. This increase in potential from -70 mV is a depolarization as the charge of the cell is becoming less polar, making C the correct answer and eliminating all of the other choices.

6) **Answer: A**

> **Explanation**: During the absolute refractory period, a neuron will not fire another action potential no matter how the magnitude of a membrane depolarization, as the voltage-gated sodium channels have been inactivated, eliminating B and making A the correct answer. Even if the activation gate is closed, an action potential can be initiated to cause it to reopen so long as the absolute refractory period has passed, eliminating C. There is no point of time at which both the activation gate and the inactivation gate are closed but even if so, answer choice D does not explain why two action potentials cannot be fired in temporal succession, eliminating it.

7) **Answer: B**

> **Explanation**: In this scenario, since voltage-gated sodium channels are unblocked, an action potential would occur in response to an inward current that raises the membrane potential to the threshold. The cell would depolarize and reach its maximum potential around 50 mV at which point the voltage-gated sodium channels will inactivate as inactivation is time-dependent, making statement III untrue and eliminating D. At that point, normally, voltage-gated potassium channels open, allowing the cell to quickly repolarize back down to the resting membrane potential and beyond. However, since TEA is present, those channels will not be able to open and fast repolarization would not occur. True, some repolarization would occur due to potassium leak channels, but that would be the result of potassium efflux not influx, as the membrane potential is becoming more negative, making statement I untrue and eliminating A and C. Rather than having a fast repolarization, these potassium leak channels would allow for a very slow repolarization, making statement II true and B the correct answer.

8) **Answer: B**

> **Explanation**: Remember from physics - for parallel-plate capacitors, capacitance is inversely proportional to the distance between the plates (in this case, the charges on opposing sides of the membrane). If one were to increase the distance between the charges they would, in effect, reduce the capacitance. Myelin accomplishes this by increasing the effective diameter of the axon, and allowing charge to flow at a higher rate, eliminating A, C and D and making B the correct answer.

9) **Answer: D**

> **Explanation**: Normally, once neurotransmitters are released, they are removed from the cleft in a timely manner to terminate the signal. If they are left in the synapse, they will continue binding to the postsynaptic neuron and cause action potentials to be continually initiated. In the case of someone dealing with depression,

this effect is actually desirable, as increased serotonin signalling should improve mood. By inhibiting reuptake, SSRIs potentiate the serotonergic signal, eliminating A and B and making D the correct answer. Reuptake inhibition actually decreases the concentration of neurotransmitters in the synaptic knob as it remains in the cleft, eliminating C.

10) Answer: C

Explanation: All somatic motor neurons innervate skeletal muscle cells and use acetylcholine as their neurotransmitter, eliminating A, B and D and making C the correct answer.

11) Answer: A

Explanation: Once the ligand binds, GDP that is bound to the G-protein is exchanged for a GTP, making A the correct answer. GDP cannot be hydrolyzed into GTP, eliminating B. The separation of the GPCR complex into the two pieces succeeds the exchange of GDP for GTP, which is then succeeded by a downstream pathway, eliminating C and D.

12) Answer: D

Explanation: From top to bottom, the spinal cord is organized from cervical to thoracic to lumbar to sacral, making D the correct answer.

13) Answer: A

Explanation: Myelin is the reason that white matter appears to be white, making A the correct answer. Neither B or C are true statements.

14) Answer: B

Explanation: Remember the 3 Ts for parietal - touch, taste and temperature!

15) Answer: C

Explanation: This patient is able to produce speech, yet the speech is incoherent, signaling deficits in comprehension. This points towards damage to Wernicke's area, as that is the area responsible for language comprehension, making C the correct answer. The amygdala is primarily responsible for fear and survival instincts, so damage to that area would not cause errant speech, eliminating A. Broca's area is responsible for speech production, not comprehension, so damage to that area would result in inability to speak at all, eliminating B. The thalamus has numerous functions, primarily as a sensory relay, and there are no sensory deficits present in the patient, eliminating D.

16) Answer: B

Explanation: If you refer back to Figure 1.23, you can see that parasympathetic preganglionic and postganglionic neurons release ACh as their neurotransmitter as well as sympathetic preganglionic neurons, eliminating A, C and D. Only sympathetic postganglionic neurons release norepinephrine as their neurotransmitter, making B the correct answer.

17) Answer: B

Explanation: Although not mentioned in the chapter, pain receptors are nociceptors that are able to detect intensity of pain, eliminating A. Both gustatory and olfactory receptors are chemoreceptors that detect the presence of specific molecules, eliminating C. The visual systems utilize photoreceptors which are able to transduce electromagnetic radiation, eliminating D. The vibration of the basilar membrane in the cochlea causes the hair cells to move back and forth. This movement causes mechanosensitive transduction channels on the tips of the stereocilia open and close, making them mechanoreceptors, as they respond to mechanical stimuli, making B the correct answer.

18) Answer: A

Explanation: Light enters the idea at the cornea, and then travels through the aqueous humor and vitreous humor getting subsequently refracted at each step until finally reaching the retina, making A the correct answer. None of the other answer choices reflect this.

19) Answer: D

Explanation: Stereocilia are part of hair cells and are involved in addition, eliminating A and C. Magnocellular cells have a larger receptive field making them most useful for detecting motion, eliminating B. Parvocellular cells have a smaller receptive field and as a result are most useful in processing fine details of an object, making D the correct answer.

20) Answer: B

Explanation: In the visual system, photoreceptors contain retinal which undergoes a cis-trans isomerization when it absorbs light and activates transducin, a heterotrimeric G-protein, eliminating A. In the olfactory system, the odorant receptors are G-protein cAMP linked membrane receptor proteins and release G_{olf} upon odorant binding, eliminating C. Similarly, other than detecting salt or sour, the other three categories of taste (bitter/sweet/umami) all utilize GPCR systems, eliminating D. In audition, voltage gated channels open in response to the displacement of stereocilia in one direction, which causes a depolarization that results in glutamate being released to spiral ganglion cells - all accomplished without a GPCR system, making B the correct answer.

Chapter 2
Endocrine System

Chapter 2

Endocrine System

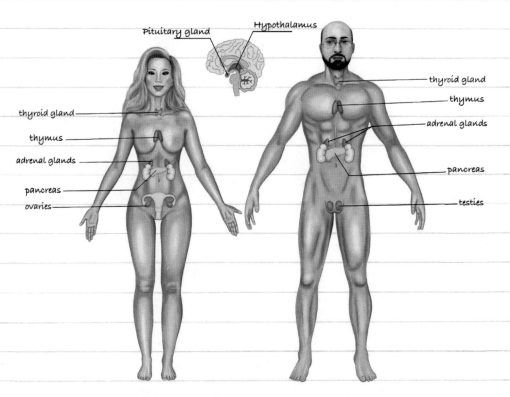

The body is immensely complex. But an interesting question arises: how can it be that this massively complex system functions so harmoniously? How is the body capable of maintaining such strict regulatory control? The system responsible for maintaining homeostasis is called the **endocrine system.** The endocrine system is the series of glands and chemical messengers that regulate our internal processes in response to stimuli from the external world. External stimuli are received by the sensory nervous system and interpreted at the central nervous system (CNS). The nervous system functions intimately with the endocrine system to ensure that everything is tightly regulated. From the CNS, efferent neurons act on endocrine glands to secrete special chemical messengers called **hormones** that travel through the blood, act on receptors, and create a response in the body. The organ they affect is called the **target**. Unlike other chemical messengers, hormones create long-term effects on their target cells lasting hours, days, or even weeks.

Exocrine glands differ from endocrine glands in that they secrete chemicals, instead of hormones, into epithelial lining (external environment) via ducts (**Figure 2.1**). Sweat, oil, mucus, and digestive enzymes are all examples of exocrine gland secretions that will be covered more in depth in later chapters. But we're here to talk about the endocrine system. Let us now look more in depth at the communicators of the endocrine system, **hormones!**

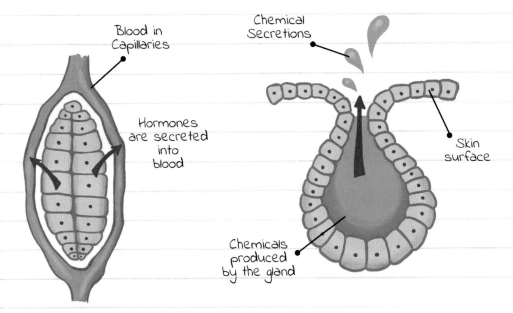

Blood in Capillaries

Chemical Secretions

Hormones are secreted into blood

Skin surface

Chemicals produced by the gland

Endocrine Gland

Exocrine Gland

Hormones

Hormones are released into the blood from endocrine glands. There are three types of hormones: **peptide, steroid hormones,** and **amino acid derivatives.**

Peptide Hormones

Peptide hormones are derived from polypeptide chains, produced on the ribosomes of the rough endoplasmic reticulum, and modified into their final form in the Golgi apparatus. As polar molecules, peptide hormones are unable to diffuse through the non-polar plasma membrane of target cells and instead act on membrane-bound receptors. The binding of a peptide hormone to its corresponding receptor activates an intracellular enzyme that activates **second messenger systems** such as cAMP, cGMP, or calmodulin. The activation of these second messenger systems cause a cascade of events that result in the modification of specific enzymatic activities in the cell (**Figure 2.2**). Let us look at a real world example to explain how a second messenger system works:

Figure 2.2:
Second messenger system. Peptide hormones bind to extracellular receptors. Upon binding of the ligand, the receptor changes conformation and activates an intracellular enzyme to produce second messengers. In this case, ATP is converted to cAMP. The second messenger then activates an enzyme cascade that produces an end product that will leave the cell.

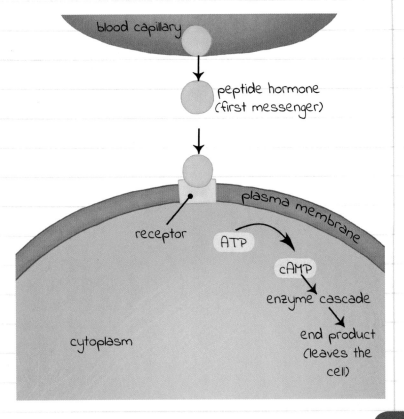

blood capillary

peptide hormone (first messenger)

receptor

ATP

cAMP

enzyme cascade

end product (leaves the cell)

cytoplasm

plasma membrane

Imagine you're walking in the street and all of a sudden, a man or woman in front of you collapses to the ground, shocked by the sight of your smoking hot body. Since you're not a doctor yet, you quickly take out your phone and dial 911. Within minutes, an ambulance arrives and EMTs rush to the scene. They rush the individual to the hospital. In effect, an entire series of events was initiated by you.

This above situation is analogous to a second messenger system. The hormone, or you in this case, initiated a series of events. The second messengers would be the EMTs and the hospital staff. A peptide hormone is the primary messenger, but it is not the one that necessarily enacts the response.

Numerous peptide hormones are running throughout our body at any given time. The MCAT, however, wants us to know these specific ones:

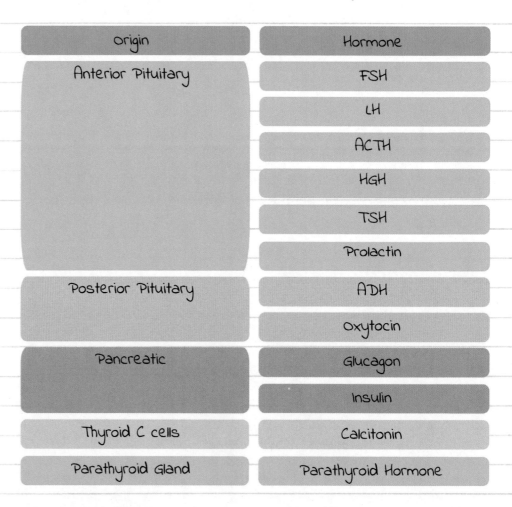

Origin	Hormone
Anterior Pituitary	FSH
	LH
	ACTH
	HGH
	TSH
	Prolactin
Posterior Pituitary	ADH
	Oxytocin
Pancreatic	Glucagon
	Insulin
Thyroid C cells	Calcitonin
Parathyroid Gland	Parathyroid Hormone

Take note of the above table. As we move through the chapter and learn more about our hormones, we shall add more columns with information about the hormones' specific targets and functions!

Steroid Hormones

Steroid hormones are derived from **cholesterol** and are synthesized in the smooth ER. **For the MCAT, make sure you can recognize a cholesterol**

molecule. Notice the structure of cholesterol and the examples of steroid hormones in **Figure 2.3** and **Figure 2.4**. Can you see the similarities? You do not need to know specifics but make sure you can recognize that the four fused rings indicate a cholesterol or a cholesterol-derived molecule.

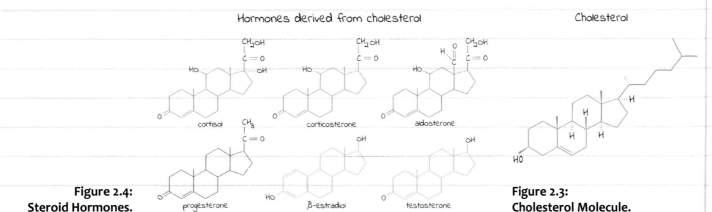

Hormones derived from cholesterol

cortisol · corticosterone · aldosterone

progesterone · β-estradiol · testosterone

Cholesterol

Figure 2.4:
Steroid Hormones.

Figure 2.3:
Cholesterol Molecule.

Steroid hormones are hydrophobic and lipid-soluble, allowing them to diffuse across the nonpolar membrane of target cells and bind to an intracellular receptor in the cytosol or nucleus (**Figure 2.5**).

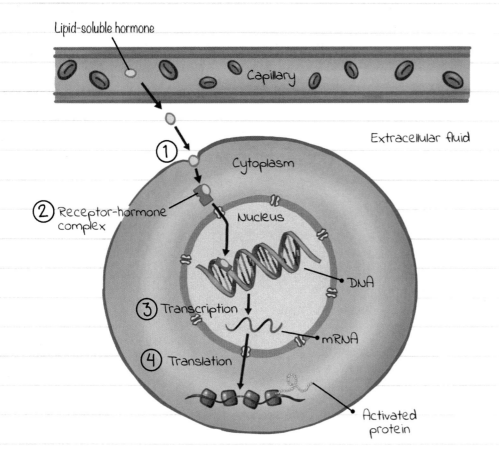

Lipid-soluble hormone

Capillary

Extracellular fluid

① Cytoplasm

② Receptor-hormone complex

Nucleus

DNA

③ Transcription

mRNA

④ Translation

Activated protein

Figure 2.5:
Lipid-soluble transport.
1) First, Lipid-soluble hormones diffuse through the plasma membrane.
2) The binding of the hormone with its receptor in the cytoplasm forms a receptor-hormone complex.
3) This complex enters the nucleus and triggers gene transcription.
4) The mRNA transcript then undergoes translation to form a protein that will alter cell activity.

Blood, on the other hand, is aqueous and not an ideal environment for nonpolar lipid molecules. Steroid hormones and other lipids therefore require a carrier protein to travel throughout the bloodstream. The binding of a steroid hormone to its corresponding receptor in the cell causes a cascade of events that result in the up or down-regulation of certain genes. These are the specific steroid hormones you must know for the MCAT:

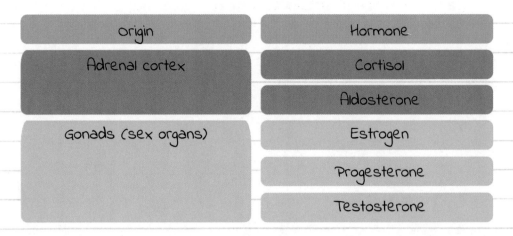

Origin	Hormone
Adrenal cortex	Cortisol
	Aldosterone
Gonads (sex organs)	Estrogen
	Progesterone
	Testosterone

In the table above, we see that the adrenal cortex releases the steroid hormones cortisol and aldosterone. **Cortisol** and **aldosterone** are known as **glucocorticoids** and **mineralocorticoids**, respectively.

Amino Acid Derivatives

These small guys are derived from amino acids — particularly **tyrosine** and **tryptophan** (**Figure 2.6**). Below are the tyrosine derivatives you must know for the MCAT:

Origin	Hormone
Thyroid gland	T3 (triiodothyronine)
	T4 (thyroxine)
Adrenal medulla	Epinephrine
	Norepinephrine
Pineal Gland	Melatonin

Thyroid hormone (T3/T4) is a **nonpolar molecule** that can diffuse across the plasma membrane of target cells and binds to receptors in the nucleus where it regulates the transcription of many genes. Just like steroid hormones, thyroid hormones require a carrier protein to travel throughout the blood.

Epinephrine and **norepinephrine** are **polar molecules** that dissolve in the blood. They bind to receptors on target cells and initiate the second messenger cAMP. Notice the difference in polarity between thyroid hormone and epinephrine/norepinephrine!

Melatonin is an amphiphilic molecule (soluble in both aqueous and lipid environments) derived from tryptophan and is produced in the **pineal gland**. This hormone, which we all need more of, regulates the sleep cycle.

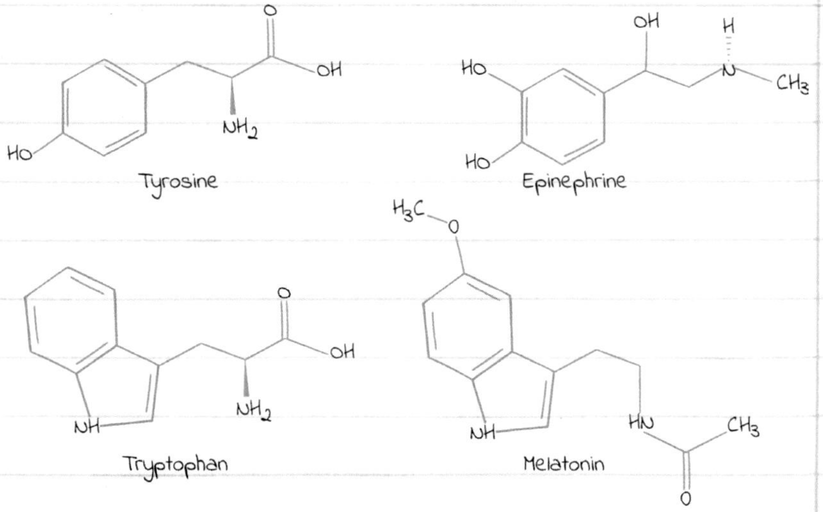

Hydrophilic vs. Hydrophobic Hormones

In the previous sections, we discussed how the polarity of a hormone determines how the hormone travels throughout the blood and acts on its target cell. Polarity also determines the onset and duration of a hormone. Since polar hormones dissolve in the blood, they are able to travel quickly to their target and cause an action. However, they are also quickly washed out of the body. Polar hormones, therefore, have a short duration of action in the body.

Since nonpolar hormones require a carrier protein to travel throughout the blood, they take much longer to reach their target tissue. In addition, nonpolar hormones act at the level of transcription, causing a more sustained action in comparison to the modifications of enzymatic activity we see caused by polar hormones.

Figure 2.6:
Amino Acid Derivatives.
Epinephrine is a derivative of the amino acid tyrosine. Melatonin is a derivative of tryptophan.

Below is a table summarizing the three types of hormones:

	Steroid Hormone	Peptide Hormone	Tyrosine Derivatives
Originates from	Cholesterol	Polypeptide chains	Prohormones (inactive precursor to a hormone)
Solubility	Non-Polar Lipophilic Needs carrier protein to travel in blood	Polar Soluble in water travel freely in blood	Polar or Nonpolar
Where are the receptors?	Intracellular receptors that directly affect gene expression	Receptors on cell membrane. Effects initiated by second messengers	Receptors are on the cell membrane if it is a polar hormone. Receptors are in the cytoplasm if it is a nonpolar hormone
Effects' duration	Slow onset, long duration	Fast onset, shorter duration	Fast and short for polar hormone, but slow and long for nonpolar
Examples	Testosterone, estrogen	Insulin, Glucagon	Epinephrine (polar), Norepinephrine (polar), T3 and T4 (nonpolar)

Endocrine Glands

Now that we have talked about the messengers of the endocrine system, hormones, let us discuss the glands that secrete them.

Hypothalamus

The **hypothalamus** is considered the master controller of the endocrine system. It is special in that it has both neural and endocrine functions. Below the hypothalamus is the pituitary gland that is split in two: the **anterior pituitary**, composed of glandular tissue, and the **posterior pituitary**, composed of neural tissue. The neural function of the hypothalamus involves controlling hormones released from the anterior pituitary; the endocrine function involves creating hormones and storing it in the posterior pituitary.

Figure 2.7:
Posterior Pituitary. The neurons of the hypothalamus create the hormones oxytocin and ADH. These neurons extend into the posterior pituitary, where oxytocin and ADH is stored. When called for, the posterior pituitary secretes these hormones into the blood via capillaries.

Posterior Pituitary

The **posterior pituitary** is an extension of the hypothalamus: neuronal cell bodies of the hypothalamus extend their axons into the posterior pituitary. This gives the posterior pituitary its other name, the *neurohypophysis*.

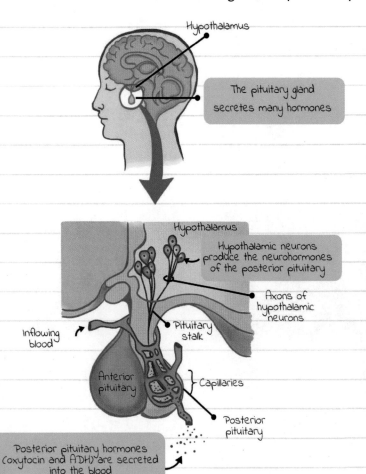

The posterior pituitary does not directly synthesize hormones, but it does store and secrete hormones that are produced by the hypothalamus. When the appropriate signal is initiated by the nervous system, these hormones are released into the bloodstream (**Figure 2.7**). The hormones of the posterior pituitary gland include **oxytocin** and **antidiuretic hormone (ADH)**. Oxytocin is involved in increasing uterine contractions and the ejection (not production) of milk from breasts. **ADH** increases blood pressure by increasing the permeability of the collecting duct in the nephron of the kidney to water. When blood pressure is low, ADH, also known as **vasopressin**, causes water to be reabsorbed back into the blood vessels. As the volume of fluid in the blood vessels increases, the pressure inside of the blood vessels increases as well. Alcohol is an ADH blocker; that is why you may have frequently urinated after your tequila shots last weekend!

Anterior Pituitary

The **anterior pituitary,** in contrast to the posterior pituitary, does synthesize hormones. The hormones released by the anterior pituitary are controlled by the hormones released by the hypothalamus. Thus, many of the hormones released by the hypothalamus onto the anterior pituitary are regulatory hormones. Hormones that have other endocrine glands as their target are called **tropic hormones.** The network of blood vessels that connect the anterior pituitary to the hypothalamus is called the **hypophyseal portal system (Figure 2.8).** Think of this system as a shortcut that allows the quick transport of hormones to the anterior pituitary without the hormones having to travel through the systemic blood system. Below are the main tropic hormones released by the hypothalamus that act on the anterior pituitary:

- **Gonadotropin-releasing hormone (GnRH):** stimulates the release of **follicle-stimulating hormone (FSH)** and **luteinizing hormone (LH).**

- **Growth hormone-releasing hormone (GHRH):** stimulates the release of **growth hormone (GH).**

- **Thyrotropin Releasing Hormone (TRH):** stimulates the release of **thyroid-stimulating hormone (TSH).**

- **Corticotropin-releasing factor (CRF):** stimulates the release of **adrenocorticotropic hormone (ACTH).**

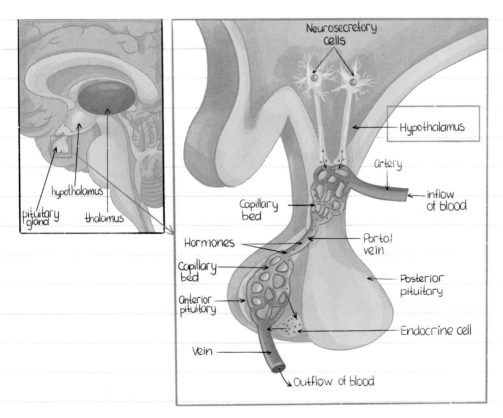

Figure 2.8:
Hypophyseal Portal System. The hypothalamus secretes tropic hormones into the hypophyseal portal system. These hormones travel to the anterior pituitary and stimulate the anterior pituitary to release its own hormones.

The anterior pituitary secretes seven different hormones. The first four mentioned below are tropic hormones, which are those that act on another endocrine gland to release hormones; the rest are direct hormones that cause an action in cells themselves.

⊘ **Follicle-stimulating hormone (FSH):** this hormone acts on the **ovaries** of females and the **testes** of males. In females, FSH stimulates the growth and maturation of the ovarian follicles. This prepares the follicles for ovulation (the rupturing of a follicle). In males, FSH stimulates the Sertoli cells of the testes to nourish the maturing sperm during spermatogenesis.

⊘ **Luteinizing hormone (LH):** this hormone stimulates the outer cells of the **follicle**, turns the cells into the **corpus luteum**, and maintains it. The LH surge causes **ovulation**. LH stimulates Leydig cells in males to secrete **testosterone**, the primary male sex hormone. FSH and LH functions will be covered more extensively in the Reproductive System Chapter. For now, understand that FSH and LH are tropic hormones that act on the gonads of males and females.

⊘ **Adrenocorticotropic hormone (ACTH):** this hormone acts on the adrenal cortex to release steroid hormones such as **cortisol, aldosterone, androgens,** and **estrogens.**

⊘ **Thyroid-stimulating hormone (TSH):** TSH acts on the thyroid to release thyroid hormone (T3+T4).

⊘ **Prolactin:** prolactin stimulates milk production in the mammary glands of females. **Dopamine** released from the hypothalamus, along with **estrogen** and **progesterone,** *decreases* prolactin secretion. When the placenta is removed, there is a decrease in dopamine, estrogen, and progesterone, which causes lactation to begin due to an increase in prolactin secretion

⊘ **Endorphins:** these hormones decrease pain perception and can even cause euphoria. **Opioids** are drugs that mimic the endorphins that are naturally produced in our body.

⊘ **Growth Hormone (GH):** growth hormone is also known as **somatotropin.** Growth hormone works on nearly all cells of the body and thus has

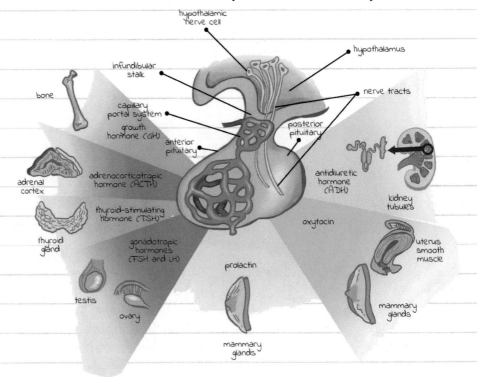

Figure 2.9:
Pituitary Hormones.

Chapter 2 Endocrine System   Copyright © 2019 MCAT King

a variety of functions. GH increases cell size, cell number, protein synthesis, fatty acid breakdown, transcription, and translation. GH decreases glucose uptake in cells, allowing for more glucose to circulate in the blood and be used by muscle and bones. A physical sign of growth hormone is its effect on bone and muscle. An excess of growth hormone in a child causes gigantism, or abnormal growth. A lack of growth hormone in a child causes dwarfism. In adults, however, an excess of growth hormone causes acromegaly, which is the increase in bone size typically of the head, hands, feet. Since acromegaly patients are adults that have closed epiphyseal plates at the ends of the long bones, the bone size increases in its diameter, not its length (**Figure 2.9**).

Figure 2.10:
Thyroid Hormone Structure. Thyroid Hormones are tyrosine derived hormones. T4 contains four iodine atoms, while T3 contains three iodine atoms.

Thyroid Gland

The thyroid gland is located near the trachea, in front of the vocal cords (**Figure 2.11**). It produces 3 hormones: **triiodothyronine (T3)**, **thyroxine (T4)**, and **calcitonin**. As shown in **Figure 2.10**, the numbers on T3 and T4 represent the number of iodine atoms attached to the tyrosine. T3 and T4 are tyrosine-derived, lipid-soluble hormones produced by the **follicular cells** of the thyroid. As such, they are able to diffuse through the lipid membrane and act on the nucleus to influence the transcription of certain genes.

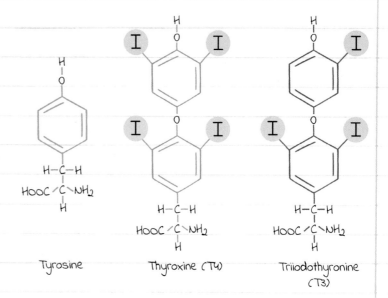

The general effect of thyroid hormones is an increase in basal metabolic rate. This causes increased cellular respiration and greater glucose, protein, and fatty acid turnover. There are two main conditions related to the thyroid: **hyperthyroidism** and **hypothyroidism**. Hyperthyroidism is the overproduction of thyroid hormones and is characterized by an increase in activity level, weight loss, sweating, heart rate, breathing, etc. Hypothyroidism is the exact opposite, and results in a lower basal metabolic rate.

Calcitonin is produced by **C-cells** (parafollicular cells) of the thyroid. **Calcitonin** decreases plasma calcium levels by decreasing **osteoclast** activity (increasing calcium storage in the bone), decreasing calcium absorption in the gut, and increasing calcium excretion from the kidneys. Osteoclasts are bone cells that degrade bone tissue, which contain calcium. Osteoclasts function to aid in the normal bone remodeling process.

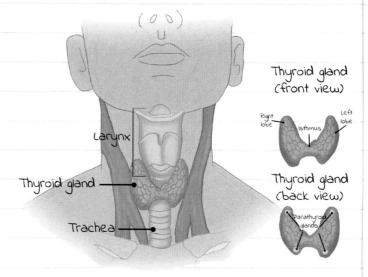

Figure 2.11:
Thyroid and Parathyroid Glands. The prefix "para" means alongside or beside. The parathyroid is located adjacent, or para, to the thyroid gland.

Answer:
As discussed, the thyroid gland produces two major hormones, T3 and T4. The activation of the thyroid stimulating hormone receptor causes the secretion of these hormones to increase. The spike in T3 and T4 levels in the bloodstream inhibits the secretion of TRH and TSH. Therefore, Grave's disease is noted for paradoxically low TRH and TSH, and high T3 and T4 levels in the bloodstream. High T3 and T4 levels would lead to hyperthyroidism. Thus, we would expect a patient to experience an increase in their basal metabolic rate causing an increase in weight loss, sweating, heart rate (tachycardia), and respiration.

Parathyroid Gland

The parathyroid gland secretes the peptide hormone, **parathyroid hormone (PTH)**. PTH opposes calcitonin by increasing plasma calcium levels. PTH increases osteoclast activity (decrease calcium storage in the bone), increases calcium absorption from the gut, and decreases calcium excretion from the kidneys. PTH has a similar effect on phosphate, with the exception of its effect on the kidneys. There is an increase in phosphate reabsorption from bone, an increase in phosphate absorption from the gut, but an increase in phosphate excretion from the kidney. Thus, PTH has little effect on phosphate levels in the blood. PTH also stimulates the formation of **calcitriol**, a steroid hormone derived from vitamin D, in the kidneys. Calcitriol aids in the increase of blood calcium levels by increasing calcium absorption from the intestine; increasing calcium release from bone by increasing osteoclast activity; and increasing calcium reabsorption at the kidneys. Parathyroid hormone and calcitonin have the same targets and similar effects on serum calcium levels.

Adrenal Glands

The adrenal glands are found on top of the kidney and are separated into two parts. The outer layer, called the cortex, and the inner layer, called the medulla (**Figure 2.12**).

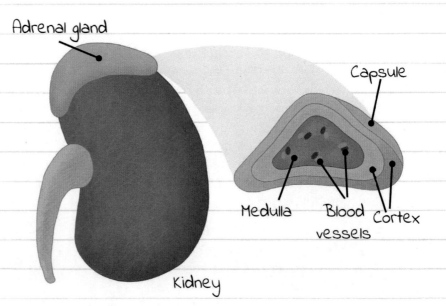

Figure 2.12:
Adrenal Gland. The adrenal gland is located on top of the kidneys. The inside of the adrenal gland, called the medulla, and the outer part, called the cortex, each secrete their own hormones.

Adrenal Cortex

The adrenal CORtex secretes steroid hormones called CORticoSTEROIDS. Corticosteroids fall into three categories: **mineralocorticoids, glucocorticoids,** and **cortical sex hormones**.

Mineralocorticoids control salt balance in the blood. Think: mineral = salt. The most important mineralocorticoid you must know for the MCAT is **aldosterone**. Aldosterone acts on the distal convoluted tubule and collecting duct of the nephron to increase sodium reabsorption. Water follows by osmosis; the increased retention of water results in an increase in blood pressure. Potassium is exchanged for the reabsorbed sodium. Hydrogen ions are also secreted into the lumen. Thus, aldosterone increases potassium and hydrogen ion excretion.

The **renin-angiotensin-aldosterone system (Figure 2.13)** controls the secretion of aldosterone and is an important pathway to know for the MCAT exam. The pathway begins when a decrease in blood pressure causes the juxtaglomerular cells of the kidney to release **renin**. Renin cleaves **angiotensinogen**, which is released by the liver, into **angiotensin I**. **Angiotensin-converting enzyme (ACE)** from the lungs converts angiotensin I to **angiotensin II**. Angiotensin II then acts on arterioles and causes vasoconstriction. It also acts on the adrenal cortex to release aldosterone. The combination of vasoconstriction along with an increase in fluid volume causes an increase in blood pressure.

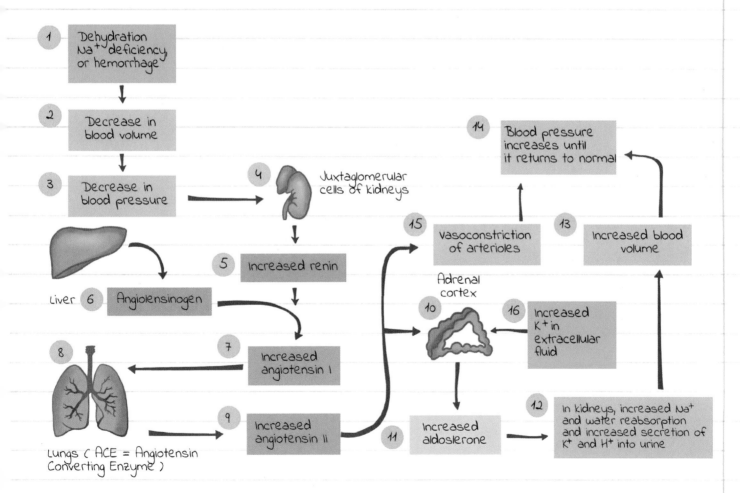

Glucocorticoids control glucose levels and protein metabolism. The main glucocorticoid hormone to know is **cortisol**, also known as the stress hormone. Cortisol stimulates gluconeogenesis in the liver, mobilizes fat to be used for energy, and breaks down protein into amino acids to serve as substrates for

Figure 2.13:
The Renin-Angiotensin-Aldosterone Pathway

gluconeogenesis. During times of stress, cortisol is very useful in providing a ready supply of energy, hence its nickname "the stress hormone". Cortisol also weakens the immune system and inflammatory response if levels are not managed long term, making one more susceptible to infection.

Another pathway to know for the MCAT exam includes the release of cortisol and other glucocorticoids. **Corticotropin-releasing factor (CRF)** is released by the hypothalamus, causing the anterior pituitary to release **adrenocorticotropic hormone (ACTH)**. ACTH then acts on the adrenal cortex to release glucocorticoids.

In terms of sex hormones, the gonads are primarily responsible for the majority of their production in both males and females. The adrenal cortex does, however, contribute slightly.

Adrenal Medulla

The adrenal medulla produces and secretes **epinephrine** and **norepinephrine,** also known as **adrenaline.** These hormones are tyrosine derivatives that belong to a group of hormones called **catecholamines. Epinephrine** and **norepinephrine** are responsible for the flight-or-fight response that occurs during highly stressful situations: increase in available glucose in the blood; increase in basal metabolic rate; increase in heart rate; dilation of the bronchi; vasodilation in the periphery of the body; and vasoconstriction of blood to the internal organs of the body. Cortisol and adrenaline are both hormones released during times of stress; however, adrenaline is released during **short periods** of stress while cortisol is released during **long periods** of stress.

Figure 2.14:
Endocrine and Exocrine Functions of the Pancreas.

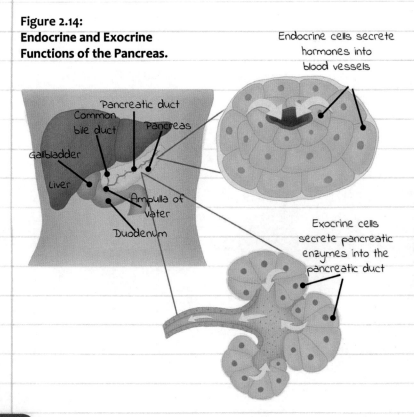

Endocrine cells secrete hormones into blood vessels

Exocrine cells secrete pancreatic enzymes into the pancreatic duct

Pancreas

The pancreas is both an exocrine and endocrine gland (**Figure 2.14**). The exocrine function comes from secreting digestive enzymes into ducts to reach newly ingested food. The endocrine function comes from hormone secretions from **alpha, beta,** and **delta cells** of the pancreas. Combined, these three groups of cells form the *islets of Langerhans.* **Insulin** and **glucagon** are the two important endocrine secretions of the pancreas you should know for the MCAT exam.

B-cells of the pancreas secrete insulin in response to high blood glucose levels. Insulin causes the uptake of glucose into muscle and liver cells, where it is converted into glycogen stores. Additionally, fat is taken up into adipose tissue and amino acids are turned into protein.

Glucagon is secreted by **alpha cells** in response to low blood glucose levels. Its function opposes that of insulin. Glucagon stimulates gluconeogenesis (synthesis of glucose) and glycogenolysis (breakdown of glycogen into glucose). In addition, glucagon causes the breakdown of fats in adipose tissue and protein in muscle.

Somatostatin is secreted by **delta cells** of the islets of Langerhans to inhibit insulin and glucagon secretion. It is also released by the hypothalamus to inhibit growth hormone.

Diabetes

Diabetes is characterized by high blood glucose levels, or hyperglycemia, caused by the underproduction of or insensitivity to insulin. **Type I** diabetes, also known as **insulin-dependent diabetes,** is an autoimmune disease that destroys insulin producing B-cells. Patients with Type I diabetes require an external source of insulin since their bodies are unable to produce it themselves. **Type II** diabetes, also known as **non-insulin-dependent diabetes,** is characterized as the insensitivity to insulin at cell receptors. Medications for Type II diabetes are given to increase the use of the patient's naturally produced insulin. If normal glucose levels are not achieved, an external source of insulin is then given to these patients.

Gonads

The gonads are the reproductive organs of the body and are covered much more extensively in the Reproductive Chapter so do not get too horny yet. We will, however, tease you a little by briefly covering the hormones released from the male gonads, the testes, and the female gonads, the ovaries.

As mentioned earlier, FSH and LH from the anterior pituitary act on the **testes**. FSH stimulates the **Sertoli cells** of the testes to nourish sperm. The **Leydig cells** of the testes produce **testosterone** in response to LH. Testosterone promotes secondary sex characteristics in males such as pubic hair growth, muscle mass, penis enlargement, deepening of voice, etc. Testosterone also causes germ cells to differentiate into sperm.

FSH and LH also stimulate the **ovaries** to produce **estrogen** and **progesterone**. Estrogen is responsible for the development of primary female sex organs and secondary sex characteristics such as breast growth, pubic hair, and body fat redistribution. Estrogen also thickens the **endometrial wall** of the **uterus** for pregnancy and interacts with LH to stimulate ovulation. Progesterone, on the other hand, is responsible for *maintaining* the thickness of the endometrial wall. Progesterone is abundant following ovulation and remains high if the female becomes pregnant. If the female is not pregnant, then the amount of progesterone drops, causing the thick uterine lining to shed which in turn causes menstruation. Both estrogen and progesterone play important roles in the menstrual cycle and in pregnancy — to be discussed further in-depth in the next chapter, the Reproductive System!

Regulation of hormones

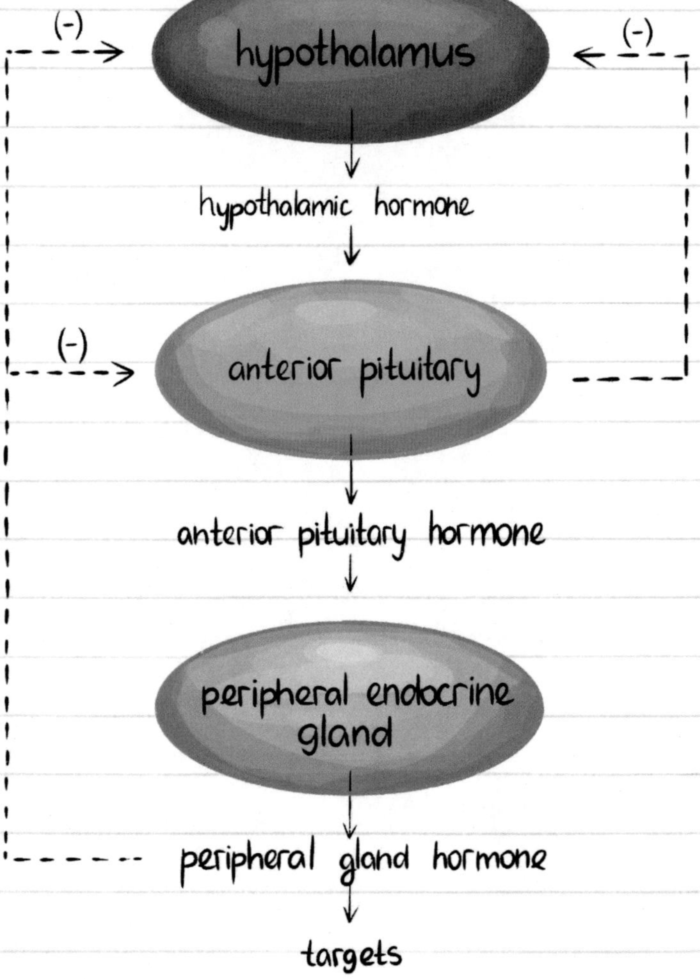

Figure 2.15:
Negative Feedback Loop. The peripheral hormones inhibit the hypothalamus and anterior pituitary to decrease the amount of peripheral hormone that is secreted.

The release of hormones needs to be tightly regulated for the maintenance of homeostasis. The way the endocrine system and hormone control are regulated is via **feedback loops**. The two types of feedback loops are negative feedback loops and positive feedback loops. Negative feedback loops are when the product of a system reduces the amount of the product that is produced. A real-world example of a negative feedback loop is how central cooling works in a home. Let's say we set our thermostat to 65 degrees when it is 70 degrees inside our house. The air conditioner remains on until the temperature reaches 65 degrees. When the temperature drops to 65 degrees or lower, the air conditioner turns off.

As can be seen in **Figure 2.15**, the hypothalamus synthesizes a certain hypothalamic hormone. The hypothalamic hormone acts on the anterior pituitary and causes it to release an anterior pituitary hormone. The anterior pituitary hormone stimulates the peripheral endocrine gland to secrete a certain hormone. Once the peripheral endocrine gland hormone reaches a certain concentration, we want to turn the switch off. Otherwise, the effect could become too pronounced. This is where the negative feedback kicks in. Once the peripheral endocrine gland hormone reaches a certain concentration, it inhibits the hypothalamus from secreting further hypothalamic hormone, resulting in the anterior pituitary to no longer release its hormone. In summary, a negative feedback loop is an inhibitory process that helps regulate hormone concentration by using the products further down the chain to inhibit further release of hormones higher up the chain. The hormone participates directly or indirectly in its own regulation.

Positive feedback is the opposite: a product later in the chain further increases its own production. These effects are similar to the amplification seen with second messengers. A good example is the production of milk by a new mother. The more the baby suckles, the more milk is produced. The nerve messages from the nipple result in the secretion of prolactin. The prolactin stimulates the mammary glands to produce even more milk.

Chapter 2 Endocrine System ‖

Table

Origin	Hormone	Type of hormone (peptide, steroid, amino acid)	Polar/ Nonpolar	Target	Function
Hypothalamus	Gonadotropin-releasing hormone (GnRH)	Peptide	Polar	Anterior pituitary	Stimulates the release of follicle stimulating hormone (FSH) and luteinizing hormone (LH)
	Growth hormone-releasing hormone (GHRH)	Peptide	Polar	Anterior pituitary	Stimulates the release of growth hormone (GH)
	Thyrotropin Releasing Hormone (TRH)	Peptide	Polar	Anterior pituitary	Stimulates the release of thyroid-stimulating hormone (TSH)
	Corticotropin-releasing factor (CRF)	Peptide	Polar	Anterior pituitary	Stimulates the release of adrenocorticotropic hormone (ACTH)
Hypothalamus (Production) Posterior Lobe of Pituitary (Storage and Release)	Oxytocin	Peptide	Polar	Uterus Mammary Glands	Stimulates uterine contraction Stimulates milk ejection
	Antidiuretic Hormone (ADH)	Peptide	Polar	Kidneys (collecting ducts)	Stimulates reabsorption of water
Anterior Lobe of Pituitary	Growth Hormone (GH)	Peptide	Polar	Most tissues	Stimulates growth of tissues; increases protein synthesis, fat metabolism; antagonizes the action of insulin.
	Prolactin (PRL)	Peptide	Polar	Mammary glands	Stimulates production of milk
	Follicle Stimulating Hormone (FSH)	Peptide	Polar	Sertoli Cells of the Testes in Males Follicle in the Ovary of Females	Stimulates nourishment of sperm during spermatogenesis Stimulates follicle maturation in females
	Luteinizing Hormone (LH)	Protein	Polar	Leydig Cells of the Testes in Males Ovary in Females	Stimulates secretion of testosterone Stimulates ovulation
	Thyroid Stimulating Hormone (TSH)	Protein	Polar	Thyroid Gland	Promotes the synthesis and secretion of thyroid hormone (T_3 and T_4)

Origin	Hormone	Type of hormone (peptide, steroid, amino acid)	Polar/ Nonpolar	Target	Function
	Adrenocorticotropic Hormone (ACTH)	Peptide	Polar	Adrenal cortex	Stimulates the release of glucocorticoids (i.e. cortisol) and moderate release of mineralocorticoids (i.e. aldosterone)
Thyroid Gland	Triiodothyronine (T_3) and Thyroxine (T_4)	Amino acid derivative	Non-polar	Most tissues	Vital for normal cellular processes; regulates metabolic rate.
	Calcitonin	Peptide	Polar	Bones	Decreases blood calcium levels by inhibiting osteoclast activity
Parathyroid Gland	Parathyroid Hormone (PTH)	Peptide	Polar	Bones	Increases blood-calcium levels by: stimulating osteoclast activity
				Digestive Tract	increasing calcitriol secretion from the kidneys, thereby increasing calcium absorption
				Kidneys	decreasing reabsorption of calcium
Pancreas (Islets of Langerhans)	Insulin	Protein	Polar	Liver, muscle, and adipose tissue	Decreases blood glucose levels; stimulates glycogen production; promotes fat storage and protein synthesis.
	Glucagon	Protein	Polar	Liver, adipose tissue	Increases blood glucose levels; stimulates breakdown of glycogen; mobilizes fat
Adrenal Medulla	Epinephrine and Norepinephrine	Amino acid derivative	Polar	Skeletal muscle, cardiac muscle, blood vessels, liver, adipose tissue	Used short term stress: increases heart rate, blood pressure, metabolic rate; increases blood glucose levels
Adrenal Cortex	Cortisol (Glucocorticoid)	Steroid	Non-polar	Liver, muscle, adipose tissue, and the pancreas	Increases blood glucose levels; used for long term stress
	Aldosterone (Mineralocorticoids)	Steroid	Non-polar	Distal convoluted tubule and collecting duct (Kidneys)	Increases sodium reabsorption and potassium excretion; increases blood pressure.
Testes	Testosterone	Steroid	Non-polar	Primary male sex structures	Develops and maintains the testes and prostate; promotes spermatogenesis
				Secondary male sex structures	Increase in bone mass, muscle mass, and pubic hair;

Origin	Hormone	Type of hormone (peptide, steroid, amino acid)	Polar/ Nonpolar	Target	Function
Ovaries	Estrogen	Steroid	Non-polar	Primary Female Sex Structures / Secondary Female Sex Structures	Stimulate growth of uterine lining / Develops and maintains breasts, hips, pubic hair, etc.
	Progesterone	Steroid	Non-polar	Uterus	Maintains uterine lining thickness
Pineal Gland	Melatonin	Amino acid derivative	Amphi-philic (Contains both polar/ non-polar regions)	Hypothalamus	Regulates sleep cycles
Atria of the heart	Atrial Natriuretic Factor/ Atrial Natriuretic Peptide	Peptide	Polar	Kidney	Promotes excretion of sodium; decreases blood pressure
Kidneys	Erythropoietin (EPO)	Peptide	Polar	Bone marrow	Stimulates the production of red blood cells

Questions

1) Non-cancerous tumors, known as adenomas, are the most common cause of hyperpituitarism. A pituitary adenoma derived from somatotrophs, the primary cell type that secretes Growth Hormone, occurs in a 35 year old male. Which of the following conditions is most likely to result?

    a. Gigantism
    b. Hypothyroidism
    c. Acromegaly
    d. Infertility

2) Cushing's syndrome, or hypercortisolism, can develop in adults after long term exposure to cortisol. The excess secretion of which of the following hormones will most likely result in Cushing's syndrome?

    a. Parathyroid Hormone
    b. ACTH
    c. Calcitonin
    d. GnRH

3) Which of the following hormones would most likely bind to a G-Protein Coupled Receptor on the outside of the cell?

    a. Estrogen
    b. Aldosterone
    c. Insulin
    d. Cortisone

4) Somatostatinomas are a rare type of malignant tumor that releases large amounts of somatostatin. These tumors most likely occur in which of the following organs?

    a. Pancreas
    b. Liver
    c. Hypothalamus
    d. Small Intestine

5) Adrenal insufficiency, commonly known as Addison's disease, is a disease that affects the adrenal cortex. Individuals with this disease have low blood serum levels of which of the following hormones?

    a. Adrenocorticotropic Hormone and Corticotropin Releasing Factor
    b. Epinephrine and Norepinephrine
    c. Follicle Stimulating hormone and Luteinizing hormone
    d. Cortisol and Aldosterone

6) An individual with untreated Addison's disease will most likely experience which of the following symptoms?

    1. Low Blood Pressure
    2. Hypokalemia

3. Hypoglycemia
   a. I only
   b. II and III
   c. I and III
   d. I, II, and III

7) **Which of the following hormones/vitamins is NOT involved in the build up and break down of bone?**

   a. Calcitonin
   b. Calcitriol
   c. Parathyroid Hormone
   d. Vitamin E

8) **Osteoporosis, a bone disease characterized by the loss and weakening of bone density, is most likely caused by which of the following conditions?**

   a. Hyperthyroidism
   b. Hyperparathyroidism
   c. Hypothyroidism
   d. Hypoparathyroidism

9) **Which of the following pairs of hormones are secreted by the posterior pituitary?**

   a. Vasopressin and Oxytocin
   b. Prolactin and Antidiuretic Hormone (ADH)
   c. Oxytocin and Aldosterone
   d. Progesterone and Estrogen

10) **Which of the following involves a positive feedback mechanism?**

    a. The effect of T3 and T4 on TSH and TRH
    b. The effects of endorphins on growth hormone
    c. The effects of Progesterone secretion on GnRH
    d. The effect of oxytocin on uterine contractions

11) **Adrenocorticotropic Hormone binds to a GPCR receptor. This has the eventual effect of activating adenylate cyclase thus converting ATP to cAMP, triggering the signaling cascade. Blood serum levels of which of the following will most likely increase?**

    a. Calcium
    b. Norepinephrine
    c. Glucose
    d. Potassium

12) **In breast cancer, progesterone binds to progesterone receptors on the signaling cell, thus stimulating genes associated with cell growth and proliferation. This is an example of which type of signaling?**

    a. Juxtacrine signaling
    b. Paracrine signaling
    c. Autocrine signaling
    d. Endocrine signaling

13) A 22-year old woman with Lupus is prescribed corticosteroids to manage her condition. Prolonged use would put her at risk for developing which of the following conditions?

    a. Type 2 Diabetes
    b. Rheumatoid Arthritis (inflammation of the joints)
    c. Asthma
    d. Type 1 Diabetes

14) All of the following are pathways within the endocrine system EXCEPT:

    a. Hypothalamus → Pituitary → Adrenal Glands
    b. Hypothalamus → Pituitary → Kidneys
    c. Hypothalamus → Pituitary → Gonads (Testes/Ovaries)
    d. Hypothalamus → Pituitary → Thyroid

15) Researchers performed an adrenalectomy on a tiger. Six hours after the operation they injected the tiger with radio-labeled aldosterone. The researcher will most likely detect radioactivity in which of the following organs?

    a. Hypothalamus
    b. Kidney
    c. Adrenal cortex
    d. Pancreas

16) Individuals suffering from a degenerative disease affecting which of the following tissues is most like to also develop symptoms of anemia?

    a. Spleen
    b. Hypothalamus
    c. Kidney
    d. Thyroid

17) Circadian rhythms are established by which of the following organs of the endocrine system?

    a. Pancreas
    b. Thyroid
    c. Adrenal glands
    d. Pineal gland

18) Cells that metabolize and synthesize steroid hormones from cholesterol have an expanded smooth endoplasmic reticulum to house the required enzymes needed. Which of the following organs is likely to exhibit an expanded smooth endoplasmic reticulum?

    a. Pancreas
    b. Thyroid
    c. Adrenal glands
    d. Hypothalamus

19) A glucagonoma is a rare tumor of the pancreas that results in the overproduction of the hormone, glucagon. It is likely to appear in which of the following cells of the pancreas, and be associated with which symptoms?

a. alpha cells; weight gain and type 1 diabetes
b. beta cells; weight gain and type 2 diabetes
c. alpha cells; weight loss and type 2 diabetes
d. beta cells; weight loss and type 1 diabetes

20) **Prostaglandins are a group of lipid molecules that are produced at sites of tissue damage or infection. They affect processes such as inflammation, blood flow, and the formation of blood clots. Are prostaglandins endocrine hormones?**

a. Yes, because they are produced elsewhere in the body and travel through the bloodstream and bind to cell surface receptors on their target tissue
b. Yes, they function in much the same ways as other steroid hormones, traveling through the cell membrane and forming a hormone receptor complex within the cytosol
c. No, because endocrine hormones do not affect blood flow
d. No, because they are not produced at a specific site, but rather at multiple sites throughout the human body

Answers

1) **Answer: A**

   Explanation: Hyperpituitarism means that the pituitary gland is secreting excess hormones (in this case growth hormone). An excess in growth hormone can cause one of two conditions, gigantism or acromegaly. This narrows down the answer choices to A and C. Depending on what age an individual develops the adenoma will determine which condition arises. If the disease mechanism begins in childhood, prior to the fusion of the epiphyseal growth plates, gigantism will result. If the disease occurs in adulthood, after the fusion of the epiphyseal growth plates, acromegaly will result.

2) **Answer: B**

   Explanation: The hypothalamus secretes CRH which stimulates the anterior pituitary to begin secreting ACTH. An excess in ACTH secretion would cause the adrenal glands to secrete excess cortisol. Normally, when cortisol levels are high enough, the excess cortisol acts as a negative feedback regulator on the hypothalamus and pituitary gland to reduce the levels of CRH and ACTH. In Cushing's syndrome, this negative feedback system is defective.

3) **Answer: C**

   Explanation: Steroid hormones (choices A, B, and D), can pass through the cell membrane and bind to receptors within the cell to form a hormone-receptor complex. Peptide hormones on the other hand (Choice C), bind to receptors on the cell surface. G-Protein Coupled Receptors are an example of a cell surface receptor.

4) **Answer: A**

   Explanation: Somatostatin is produced by the delta islet cells of the pancreas. Therefore somatostatinomas can only occur in the pancreas.

5) **Answer: D**

   Explanation: Adrenocorticotropin hormone and corticotropin releasing factor are both secreted by the anterior pituitary. Epinephrine and norepinephrine are secreted by the adrenal medulla. Follicle stimulated hormone and luteinizing hormone are secreted by the anterior pituitary in response to Gonadotropin releasing hormone. Cortisol and aldosterone are secreted by the adrenal cortex, and are in short supply in Addison's disease.

6) **Answer: C**

> **Explanation:** Individuals with Addison's disease would exhibit low levels of glucocorticoids, and mineralocorticoids (like aldosterone). When left untreated, someone with Addison's disease can enter what is known as Addisonian crisis. Insufficient levels of glucocorticoids would lead to low levels of blood glucose (hypoglycemia). Aldosterone is secreted by the adrenal cortex in response to low blood pressure, and stimulates the reuptake of sodium and the excretion of potassium. Low levels of aldosterone will therefore lead to low blood pressure and low serum potassium (hypokalemia).

7) **Answer: D**

> **Explanation:** Calcitonin is secreted by the parafollicular cells of the thyroid gland, and are responsible for reducing blood calcium levels. Calcitonin inhibits bone removal by osteoclasts and promotes bone formation by the osteoblasts. Calcitriol is the name for the activated form of Vitamin D. Parathyroid hormone has the opposite effect of calcitonin, and serves to raise blood calcium levels. Vitamin E is a fat-soluble compound with antioxidant properties.

8) **Answer: B**

> **Explanation:** The thyroid produces thyroxine and triiodothyronine. Both hormones are involved in regulating the body's basal metabolic rate. The parathyroid produces parathyroid hormone, which is involved in regulating calcium levels in the blood, mainly by increasing the serum levels when they are too low. Parathyroid hormone stimulates osteoclast activity in the bone, promoting bone breakdown. Hyperparathyroidism, an excess production of parathyroid hormone, would lead to reduced bone density and osteoporosis in the long term.

9) **Answer: A**

> **Explanation:** The posterior pituitary is responsible for the secretion of two direct hormones: vasopressin, also known as antidiuretic hormone (ADH), and oxytocin. Prolactin is secreted by the anterior pituitary. Aldosterone is secreted by the adrenal glands. Progesterone and Estrogen are secreted by the ovaries in response to Follicle stimulating hormone and Luteinizing hormone.

10) **Answer: D**

> **Explanation:** Oxytocin is responsible for signaling and inducing contraction of the womb during labor. Oxytocin also promotes the production of prostaglandins which further increases the contractions. Uterine contractions stimulate more oxytocin to be secreted, which in turn stimulates the uterus to contract with greater intensity and frequency. Oxytocin is also responsible for the positive feedback mechanism involved in the milk-ejection reflex in the breast.

11) **Answer: C**

Explanation: Calcium levels are influenced by calcitonin and parathyroid hormone. ACTH stimulates the production of mineralocorticoids but to a lesser extent than the renin-angiotensin-aldosterone system. Mineralocorticoids, like aldosterone, promote the retention of sodium, but the excretion of potassium. Adrenocorticotropic hormone stimulates the production of cortisol and corticosteroids by the adrenal cortex. Glucocorticoids will activate gluconeogenesis and raised blood serum levels of glucose (choice C).

12) **Answer: C**

Explanation: In this situation, the breast cancer cells, as the signaling cells, are secreting progesterone. The progesterone binds to receptors on the surface of the breast cancer cell, inducing proliferation of the cancer. Since the signaling cell secretes a signaling molecule that binds to receptors on the surface of the same cell, this is an example of autocrine signaling.

13) **Answer: A**

Explanation: Exogenous corticosteroids mimic the effects of hormones produced by the body's own adrenal glands. Since corticosteroids inhibit the inflammatory response, these medications are commonly prescribed to control inflammation caused by conditions such as lupus and rheumatoid arthritis. Glucocorticoids, a type of corticosteroids, activate gluconeogenesis, raising blood glucose levels. Long term use would lead to consistently high blood glucose and can therefore lead to insulin resistance, and eventually type 2 diabetes.

14) **Answer: B**

Explanation: The interaction between the hypothalamus and anterior pituitary can be categorized into three major axes: The Hypothalamus-Pituitary-Adrenal Axis (HPA), the Hypothalamus-Pituitary-Gonadal Axis (HPG), and the Hypothalamus-Pituitary-Thyroid Axis (HPT). The anterior pituitary does not secrete any hormones that act on the kidneys. However, the posterior pituitary secretes antidiuretic hormone which does act upon the collecting duct within the nephron of the kidneys.

15) **Answer: B**

Explanation: In an adrenalectomy, the adrenal glands are removed, thus eliminating choice C. Since, Aldosterone acts on the distal convoluted tubule and collecting duct of the nephron, the researchers will most likely detect the radio-labeled aldosterone in the kidneys (Choice B). Aldosterone does not play a major role on the pancreas or in the hypothalamus (choices A and D).

16) Answer: C

Explanation: Anemia is a condition characterized by a deficiency of red blood cells. The kidneys are responsible for secreting the hormone erythropoietin, which acts on the bone marrow to stimulate the production of red blood cells. Individuals suffering from chronic kidney disease, a degenerative condition, often suffer from anemia.

17) Answer: D

Explanation: The pineal gland is responsible for secreting melatonin. Melatonin, an amphipathic molecule derived from tryptophan, is responsible for regulating the sleep cycle.

18) Answer: C

Explanation: Of the four tissue types listed above, only the adrenal glands secrete steroid hormones (cortisol, aldosterone, cortical sex hormones). Thyroid hormones are classified as amine hormones. Hormones secreted from the pancreas like Insulin, glucagon, and somatostatin, are all peptide hormones. The hormones secreted by the hypothalamus are peptide hormones as well.

19) Answer: C

Explanation: Glucagon is secreted by the alpha cells of the pancreas. Excess glucagon would have the effect of increasing blood glucose levels and prevent the uptake of glucose by somatic cells. Type 1 diabetes is an autoimmune condition in which the beta islet cells of the pancreas are destroyed by the body's own immune system. Type 2 diabetes frequently results from the body's inability to balance glucagon and insulin levels. Lastly, glucagon plays a role in appetite suppression. Therefore, excess glucagon would lead to weight loss.

20) Answer: D

Explanation: Endocrine hormones are produced by specific glands and travel to their target site through the bloodstream (choice A). The question stem reveals that Prostaglandins are produced at the sites of tissue damage. Even though Prostaglandins are considered to be lipid molecules, they differ from endocrine hormones in that they are not produced at a specific site (choice B). Furthermore, we have seen that endocrine hormones can affect blood flow by altering blood pressure (choice C). Therefore the answer is choice D.

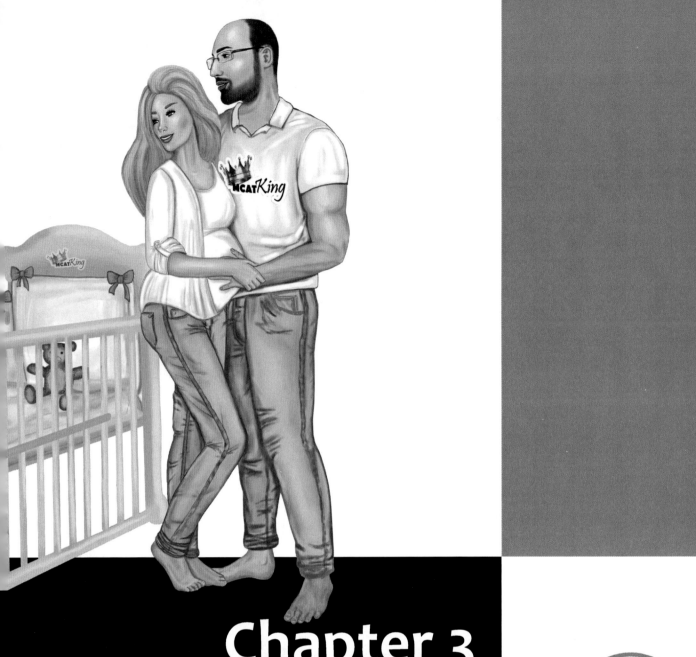

Chapter 3
Reproductive System

Chapter 3
The Reproductive System

Ah the reproductive system. If you are one of the "experienced" ones (wink wink), this chapter may simply be a review for you. But if not, let us explore our sexuality through the discussion of our reproductive organs, genitals, and the very mechanisms that make life possible.

The male and female reproductive systems are responsible for our pleeeeasuree and for allowing humans to sexually reproduce. During sexual reproduction, the male's **sperm** binds to the female's **egg** to produce a **zygote** and ultimately a newborn baby. The male and female reproductive systems also play a role in developing the primary and secondary sex characteristics of the male and female. Let us dive into and further discuss each sex's reproductive system individually.

Male Reproductive System

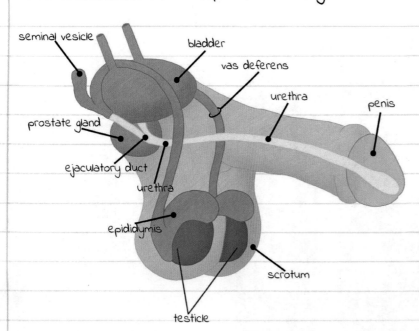

**Figure 3.1:
Anatomy of the Male
Reproductive System**

The primary function of the male reproductive system is to produce **sperm** to be ejaculated as a component of **semen** from the penis. Thus, it may be best to describe the anatomy of the male reproductive system by following the creation and path of sperm through it (**Figure 3.1**).

Sperm is made in the **seminiferous tubules** found in the **testes**. The testes are located in the sac-like structure found outside the male's body called the **scrotum**. From the testes, the sperm travels to the **epididymis** where it is stored and matured. When ejaculation occurs, the sperm travels up and through the **vas deferens**. The vas deferens ends at the **ejaculatory duct**, which also connects to the **seminal vesicle, prostate**, and **bulbourethral gland** (**Cowper's gland**). The latter three glands secrete a fluid, which when mixed with sperm from the vas deferens, forms semen. From the ejaculatory duct, the semen travels through the **urethra** and out of the penis. Urine also travels through the ejaculatory duct and urethra. During ejaculation, however, the sphincter for the urinary bladder closes to prevent urine from mixing with the semen.

Spermatogenesis

So how is sperm made? When males are born, they do not have any sperm. Instead, they have primordial germ cells ready to be differentiated. As a male undergoes puberty, **Leydig cells,** found in the interstitium between tubules, are stimulated by **luteinizing hormone (LH)** to release **testosterone.** Testosterone then stimulates the differentiation of germ cells into sperm in the seminiferous tubules. From puberty until death, men will continuously make sperm.

Spermatogenesis, as the name suggests, is the process that produces mature sperm (**Figure 3.2**). Spermatogenesis begins with **spermatogonium,** an undifferentiated germ cell. When puberty occurs and the spermatogonium is ready to enter meiosis, the spermatogonium becomes a **primary spermatocyte (2n).** The primary spermatocyte (2n) undergoes meiosis I and becomes a **secondary spermatocyte (n).** Meiosis II occurs and the secondary spermatocyte (n) becomes a **spermatid (n).**

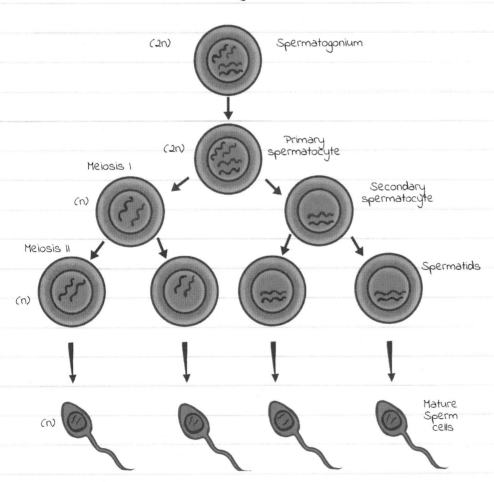

Figure 3.2: Spermatogenesis. Spermatogenesis begins with a germ cell, called Spermatogonium, and produces sperm that contain half of the parent's genetic information.

The letter "n" refers to the genetic information of one parent. So when you see "2n", a cell has the genetic information of both parents for a specific chromosome. Let us use chromosome 18 as an example. A healthy human

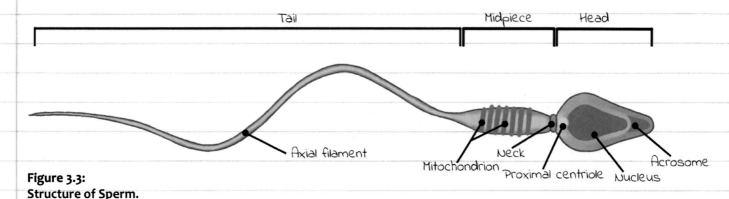

Figure 3.3:
Structure of Sperm.

IN-TEXT QUESTION:

Drug X is a new drug on the market to treat male infertility. However in some males, the drug decreases the anchoring strength of the microtubule to the kinetochore of chromosomes during prometaphase of spermatogenesis. During which phase of meiosis, meiosis I or meiosis II, is there an increased likelihood of the male's offspring acquiring Trisomy 21 if the drug's side effect were to present itself during that phase?

being has somatic cells having 2n for chromosome 18; meaning, each somatic cell for chromosome 18 consists of genetic information from the mother of the human being and father of the human being. When a cell has genetic information of both parents, it is considered diploid; when a cell has genetic information of only one parent per chromosome, it is considered haploid. Meiosis produces a haploid set of chromosomes represented by the letter "n." This is necessary for germ cell differentiation because the sperm ultimately combines with a haploid egg to produce a diploid zygote.

After meiosis, the spermatid matures by losing its cytoplasm and gaining a head, tail, and midpiece to become **sperm (Figure 3.3)**. During this process, **Sertoli cells** that line the seminiferous tubules nurture the spermatocytes and spermatids.

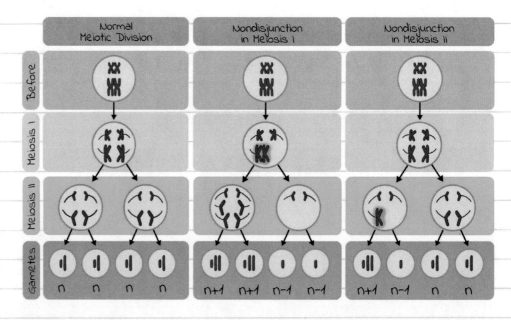

Figure 3.4:
Meiosis and Nondisjunction. In cases where nondisjunction occurs, the distribution of chromosomes within the gametes depends on whether it occurs in Meiosis I or Meiosis II. If it occurs in Meiosis I, two of the four gametes will contain n+1 chromosomes, whereas the other two would contain n-1 chromosomes. If it occurs in Meiosis II, two of the gametes would have the normal number of n chromosomes. Of the other two gametes, one will be n+1 and the other n-1.

Answer:

Meiosis I. If the drug's side effects were to present itself at Meiosis I, then the microtubule would not properly connect to the kinetochore of the homologous chromosomes for Chromosome 21. Thus during anaphase 1, when the homologous chromosomes are to separate, one secondary spermatocyte will have 2n, or homologous chromosomes, for chromosome 21 while the other secondary spermatocyte will have no chromosomes for chromosome 21. When meiosis II occurs, the homologous chromosomes in the 2n secondary spermatocyte will split into sister chromatids. There are now two spermatids that have sister chromatids for chromosome 21. If any of these two spermatids mature to sperm and fertilize an egg that is haploid (containing one chromatid) for chromosome 21, the zygote will be trisomic for chromosome 21. Compare this situation with the drug's side effects presenting itself in Meiosis II. In the latter situation, only one spermatid becomes trisomic for chromosome 21 (Figure 3.4).

Chapter 3 The Reproductive System

Female Reproductive System

A primary function of the female reproductive system is to produce a haploid **egg** to be fertilized by a sperm. If fertilization occurs and a **zygote** (2n) is created, the female reproductive system nurtures and develops the zygote into a fetus. If fertilization does not occur, then the cycle renews and releases another egg. There are a couple of parts of the female anatomy (**Figure 3.5**) that one should know to help visualize the reproductive system as we describe it: the **ovaries, fallopian tubes, uterus,** and **endometrium.**

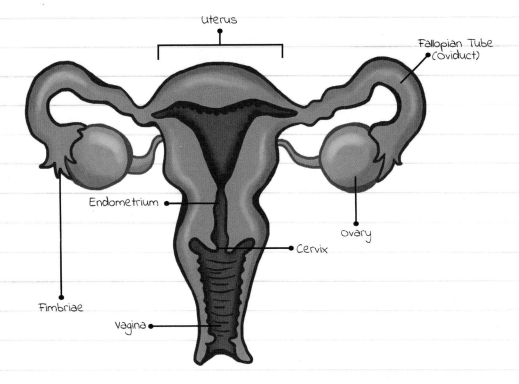

Figure 3.5:
Female Reproductive System.

Oogenesis

Unlike males, who continue producing sperm from puberty onward, a female produces all of her potential eggs before she is born. Female fetus germ cells undergo mitosis and convert into immature egg cells called **oogonia** (2n). Oogonia (2n) then transforms into **primary oocytes** (2n) that begin meiosis I but are halted at prophase I (**Figure 3.6**). Nearly all the female's eggs have reached this point prior to birth. The eggs are arrested at prophase I until puberty is reached, and the female begins menarche, or her first period, beginning the **menstrual cycle.**

On average, females start their menstrual cycle at around age 12 (ranges from 8-15). From this point until **menopause**, one primary oocyte (2n) comes out of arrest every month and completes meiosis I to form a **secondary oocyte** (n) and a **polar body**. Meiosis I generally produces two fully formed haploid cells that undergo meiosis II. In oogenesis, however, unequal distribution of the cytoplasm occurs during cytokinesis. Most of the cytoplasm is given to the secondary oocyte while the polar body

Figure 3.6:
Oogenesis. Notice how there is half as much genetic information in the cell that becomes the mature ovum (n) compared to the oogonium (2n).

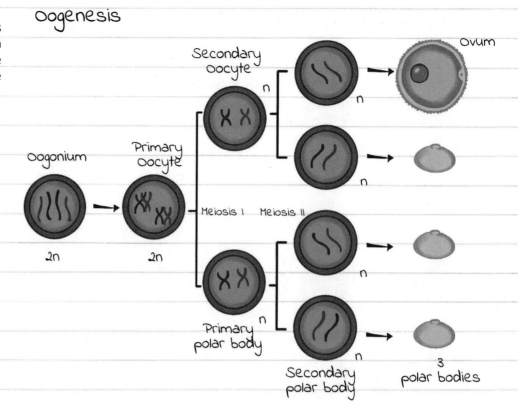

Oogenesis

Figure 3.7:
Oogenesis in the Ovary. The creation of the secondary oocyte from the oogonia occurs in the ovary. The secondary oocyte gets shuttled into the fallopian tube during ovulation. If sperm meets with the secondary oocyte, the secondary oocyte becomes a mature ovum.

is given much less. Consequently, the polar body is unable to be used for fertilization and thus undergoes apoptosis. The secondary oocyte (n) starts meiosis II, but is halted at metaphase II.

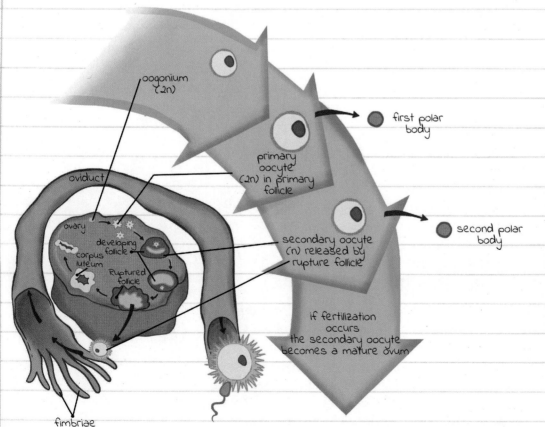

Ovulation occurs when the secondary oocyte (arrested at metaphase II) is released into the fallopian tube (Figure 3.7). The secondary oocyte waits in the fallopian tube until it makes surface contact with sperm. Once contact is made, the secondary oocyte completes meiosis II and releases another polar body. The egg is now a mature **ovum** (n); sperm can now completely penetrate and form a **zygote** (2n).

Chapter 3 The Reproductive System

Ovarian and Menstrual Cycle

The **ovarian cycle** and **menstrual cycle** occur simultaneously (**Figure 3.8**). The ovarian cycle pertains to the preparation of endocrine tissues and the release of eggs. The menstrual cycle pertains to the preparation, maintenance, and disintegration of the uterine lining.

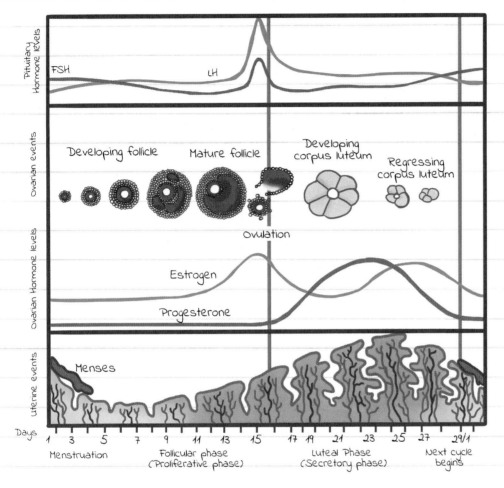

Figure 3.8:
Menstrual and Ovarian Cycle.
Notice the LH surge that occurs at ovulation!

IN-TEXT QUESTION:
As we have learned, only one sperm can penetrate an egg at a time. Using this knowledge, how is a mother able to birth twins, both identical and fraternal?

First, **gonadotropin-releasing hormone (GnRH)** causes the anterior pituitary to release **follicular stimulating hormone (FSH)** and **luteinizing hormone (LH)**. FSH stimulates the growth and maturation of the **follicle** that houses the oocyte. In the ovarian cycle, this phase is called the **follicular phase**, due to the fact that the follicle is developing. The oocyte in the follicle produces **estrogen**, which normally inhibits the release of FSH and LH from the anterior pituitary. When estrogen reaches a certain threshold, the negative feedback on LH turns off and causes a surge in LH. The LH surge causes the primary oocyte to turn into the secondary oocyte, followed by ovulation, during which the secondary oocyte (arrested at metaphase II) bursts out of the follicle and into the fallopian tube. In the ovarian cycle, ovulation marks the **ovulatory phase**. Following the LH surge and ovulation marks the beginning of the **luteal phase**.

The LH surge also stimulates the outer cells of the remaining follicle, turns the cells into the **corpus luteum**, and maintains it. The corpus luteum produces estrogen, causing the thickening of the endometrium. The corpus

Answer:
Identical twins are formed when one sperm penetrates one egg and forms an embryo that eventually splits into two. Since both embryos are derived from the same egg and sperm, they have the same genetic information. The embryos will ultimately develop into twins that look "identical" due to their similar genetic information. Fraternal twins are formed from the fertilization of two separate eggs. This is possible when a woman ovulates two eggs at the same time. Hyper-ovulation is not the norm but can happen. When it does, two sperm can fertilize the two eggs and form two separate embryos. The embryos will develop into fraternal twins that do not look as similar as identical twins would since two separate sperm, that vary slightly in genetic information, are penetrating two separate eggs, that also vary in genetic information.

luteum also secretes **progesterone** which maintains the thickness of the endometrium. If no fertilization occurs, LH levels fall, the corpus luteum dies and becomes the **corpus albicans**, estrogen and progesterone levels fall, and the endometrium sheds. This concludes the luteal phase of the ovarian cycle. The shedding of the endometrium is what causes menstruation (bleeding) in women. This entire cycle, from the development of the follicle to the shedding of the endometrium, takes roughly 28 days. Once menstruation has stopped, the cycle begins anew with FSH and LH levels rising again.

The process described above can be split into 3 phases in the menstrual cycle: **menstrual phase, proliferative phase,** and **secretory phase** (Figure 3.9). The menstrual phase begins during the shedding of endometrium. The proliferative phase occurs when estrogen causes the endometrium to thicken. The secretory phase starts when progesterone is secreted from the corpus luteum to maintain the thickness of the endometrium. The secretory phase ends when fertilization fails to occur and the endometrium sheds, marking the beginning of the menstrual phase once more.

Figure 3.9:
Menstrual and Ovarian Cycle Overlap!

Cycle	Pre - Ovulation		Ovulation	Post - Ovulation
Ovarian Cycle	Follicular Phase			Luteral Phase
Uterine Cycle	Menstrual Phase	Proliferative		Secretory

Pregnancy

If sperm is able to meet and penetrate an egg, typically in the fallopian tube, then **fertilization** can occur (**Figure 3.10**). The sperm's **acrosome** has enzymes that allow it to penetrate through the outer layer of the egg called the **zona pellucida**. This causes a **cortical reaction**, which prevents other sperm from also fertilizing the same egg. The egg undergoes meiosis II, becomes an ovum, and releases another polar body. The nucleus of the sperm (haploid) is now able to bind with the nuclei of the egg (haploid), resulting in fertilization and the formation of a diploid zygote.

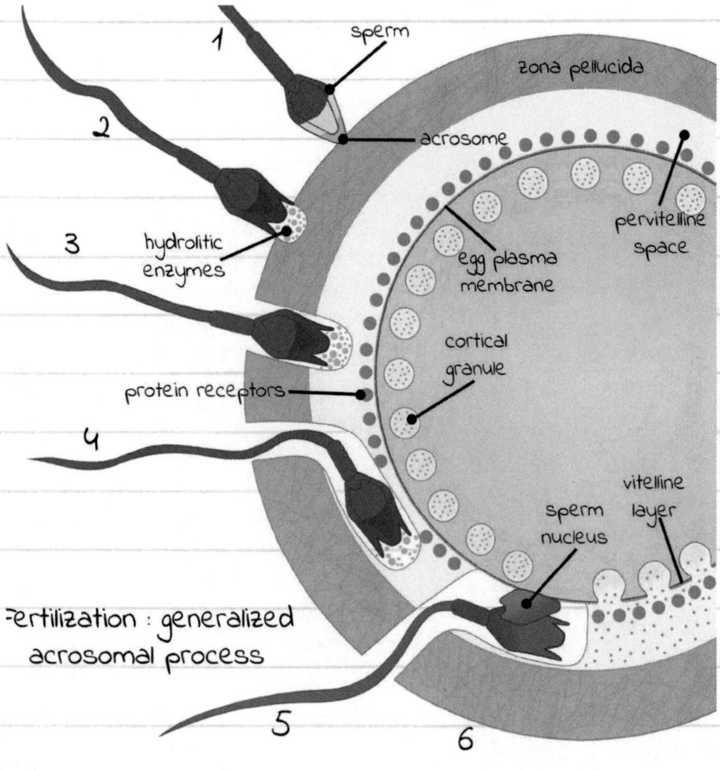

Fertilization : generalized acrosomal process

Figure 3.10:
Acrosomal Process.
1) Sperm makes contact with the egg.
2) Sperm's acrosome reacts with the zona pellucida of the egg.
3) The acrosome reacts with the perivitelline space.
4) Plasma membranes of the sperm and egg fuse.
5) Sperm's nucleus enters the egg.
6) The cortical granules of the egg fuse with the egg's plasma membrane and causes it to be impenetrable to another sperm.

Embryogenesis

Embryogenesis can be broken down into 4 steps (**Figure 3.11**):

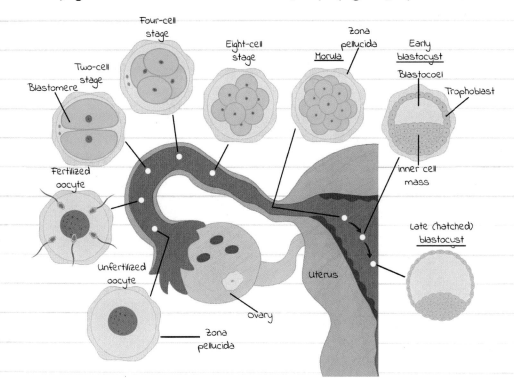

Figure 3.11:
Embryogenesis. Cleavage of the zygote forms the morula. The morula becomes the blastocyst, which implants itself into the uterine wall.

1. **Cleavage:** the zygote undergoes numerous mitotic divisions (and no cell growth) in a process called cleavage. Cleavage of the zygote produces a solid ball called a **morula**.

2. **Blastula/ Blastocyst** formation: the inside of the morula hollows out into a **blastula**. The hollow space is called the **blastocoel**. A mass of cells form inside the blastula called the **inner cell mass**. The presence of the inner cell mass marks the creation of the **blastocyst**. The blastocyst implants itself into the uterus.

   a) The implanted blastocyst releases **human chorionic gonadotropin (HCG)**, which mimics LH by maintaining the corpus luteum (as mentioned earlier in the chapter). By maintaining the corpus luteum, estrogen and progesterone secretion is maintained. HCG is the hormone tested for when determining if a woman is pregnant.

   b) The cells of the outer blastocyst combine with the uterine tissue and ultimately give rise to the **placenta**. Thereafter, the placenta takes over the job of secreting progesterone and estrogen. The inner cells, containing the blastocoel and inner cell mass, continue on with embryogenesis.

3. **Gastrulation:** cells from the inner cell mass move inward toward the **primitive streak** and to form the mesoderm. At the end of gastrulation, a **gastrula** has formed with the germ layers ectoderm, mesoderm, and endoderm present (**Figure 3.12**).

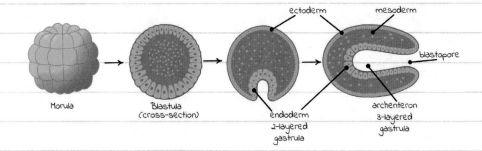

4. **Neurulation:** The ectoderm folds into a **neural tube** in a process called **neurulation**. The neural tube ultimately becomes the brain and spinal cord (the central nervous system). The **neural crest cells** surround the neural tube, and ultimately become the peripheral nervous system (**Figure 3.13**).

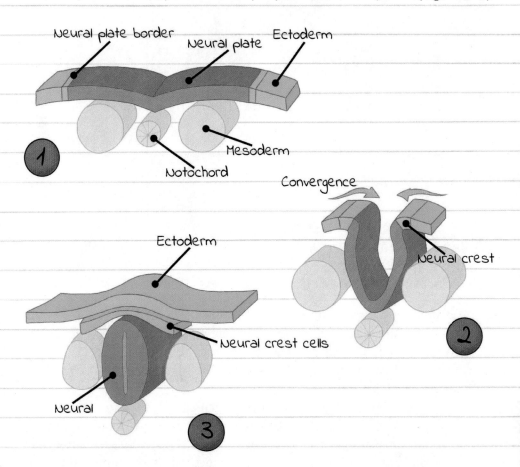

Figure 3.13:
Neurulation.

Germ Layers

The germ layers are covered in much more depth in *MCAT BIOLOGY I* on page 100. Let us briefly go over each layer and the organs they amount to.

1. **Endoderm:** the endoderm forms the innermost layer of the body. These organs include the digestive tract, lungs, pancreas, and liver.

2. **Mesoderm:** the mesoderm becomes muscle, blood and bone tissues, kidney, gonads, bladder, and the heart.

3. **Ectoderm:** the ectoderm becomes the skin, brain, spinal cord, and mouth.

Stem Cells

Stem cells are also extensively covered in *MCAT BIOLOGY I* on page 99. It is important, however, to summarize stem cells again as they relate to the reproductive system. There are three major types of stem cells:

- **Totipotent stem cells**: these cells can become any cell. Cells formed from cleavage are totipotent.

- **Pluripotent stem cells**: pluripotent stem cells can become one of the three germ layers and are found in the inner cell mass of the blastocyst. Pluripotent cells cannot differentiate into the placenta.

- **Multipotent stem cells**: multipotent stem cells are found in organs that are able to regenerate such as the skin, liver, and blood cells. Multipotent stem cells can only regenerate for the specific organ they are a part of. For example, skin multipotent cells regenerate skin cells, not liver cells.

Questions

1) **What is the correct order in which sperm is created and ejaculated?**
   a. Seminal Vesicles → Epididymis → Vas Deferens → Ejaculatory Duct → Urethra → Penis
   b. Testes → Epididymis → Vas Deferens → Ejaculatory Duct → Urethra → Penis
   c. Scrotum → Ejaculatory Duct → Urethra → Epididymis → Vas Deferens → Penis
   d. Scrotum → Ejaculatory Duct → Vas Deferens → Epididymis → Urethra → Penis

2) **Meiosis I in spermatogenesis produces which of the following?**
   a. Primary spermatocyte (2n)
   b. Primary spermatocyte (n)
   c. Secondary spermatocyte (2n)
   d. Secondary spermatocyte (n)

3) **Which of the following is correct in regards to spermatogenesis and oogenesis?**
   a. Spermatogenesis produces four sperm; oogenesis produces four eggs
   b. Spermatogenesis produces four sperm; oogenesis produces two eggs
   c. Spermatogenesis produces four sperm; oogenesis produces one egg
   d. Spermatogenesis produces two sperm; oogenesis produces one egg

4) **Women produce _____ while men produce _____:**
   a. Eggs continuously until the end of their lives; sperm continuously until the end of their lives.
   b. All of their potential eggs before birth; sperm continuously until the end of their lives.
   c. All of their potential eggs before birth; all of their potential sperm before birth.
   d. Eggs continuously until the end of their lives; all of their potential sperm before birth.

5) **Which type of cell makes contact with sperm?**
   a. Secondary oocyte halted at metaphase II
   b. Primary oocyte halted at prophase I
   c. Mature ovum
   d. Secondary oocyte halted at prophase II

6) **Where does fertilization usually occur?**
   a. Vagina
   b. Cervix

c. Fallopian Tube

d. Ovary

7) **A pregnancy is maintained due to the hormones that are secreted. Which of the following events may lead to a miscarriage?**

    a. Decrease in LH production

    b. Increase in progesterone

    c. Decrease in oxytocin

    d. Increase in estrogen

8) **Ovulation directly follows which of the events below?**

    a. Decrease in FSH

    b. Release of the egg into the fallopian tube

    c. A surge in LH

    d. A decrease in Estrogen

9) **The relationship of which two hormones is responsible for ovulation?**

    a. Estrogen and LH- negative feedback

    b. Estrogen and LH- positive feedback

    c. Estrogen and FSH- negative feedback

    d. Estrogen and FSH- positive feedback

10) **Which of the following structures maintain estrogen levels during the majority of a pregnancy?**

    a. Placenta

    b. Ovaries

    c. Corpus luteum

    d. Uterus

11) **A woman visits the doctor to test her fertility after multiple attempts to get pregnant. It is found that she is able to ovulate, but her estrogen levels are low throughout the secretory phase. Why would low estrogen levels throughout the secretory phase add difficulty to the woman's desire to get pregnant?**

    a. Low estrogen levels during the secretory phase would cause the egg to be defective

    b. Low estrogen levels during the secretory phase would make implantation of the blastocyst into the endometrium difficult

    c. Low estrogen levels during the secretory phase would prevent maturation of the follicle

    d. Low estrogen levels during the secretory phase would inhibit GnRH

12) **The zona pellucida is a critical player for the oocyte. What is its primary function?**

    a. To secrete estrogen

    b. To serve as a protective barrier for the oocyte

    c. To aid in sperm binding and the cortical reaction

    d. To secrete hormones in conjunction with the corpus luteum.

13) Which of the following meiotic stages is the longest?

    a. Metaphase I in males
    b. Metaphase II in females
    c. Prophase I in males
    d. Prophase I in females

14) A middle-aged woman thought she entered menopause because she had missed a couple of menstrual cycles. Then one day she got her period. Which of the following is true?

    a. Fertility was a possibility during the cycle of her period.
    b. Fertility was not a possibility during the cycle of her period
    c. She will not get her period again
    d. None of the above

Answers

1) **Answer: B**

   Explanation: Remember the acronym "SEVEN-UP" for the path through which sperm is created and ejaculated. SEVEN-UP stands for: Seminiferous tubules → Epididymis → Vas Deferens → Ejaculatory Duct → NOTHING → Urethra → Penis. The seminiferous tubules are located within the testes, making **B** the correct answer.

2) **Answer: D**

   Explanation: A primary spermatocyte (2n) undergoes meiosis I and becomes a secondary spermatocyte (n). The secondary spermatocyte (n) undergoes meiosis II and becomes a spermatid (n). An easy way to think about it is to associate the word "primary" with "Meiosis I" and the word "secondary" with "Meiosis II".

3) **Answer: C**

   Explanation: Spermatogenesis produces four sperm; oogenesis produces one egg. In spermatogenesis, meiosis I produces two secondary spermatocytes. Meiosis II follows and produces two spermatids. In oogenesis, meiosis I produces a secondary oocyte and a polar body. Meiosis II follows, producing an ovum and another polar body. Remember, polar bodies cannot be fertilized. Thus, spermatogenesis produces four sperm while oogenesis produces one egg.

4) **Answer: B**

   Explanation: Women create all of their potential eggs, known as oogonia, before birth. The oogonia transform into primary oocytes and begin meiosis I but are halted at prophase I until puberty. Once puberty arrives, one primary oocyte completes meiosis I, becomes a secondary oocyte, begins meiosis II, and halts at metaphase II until fertilization.

5) **Answer: A**

   Explanation: Prior to birth, all of the female's oogonia (2n) transform into primary oocytes (2n) and begin meiosis I, but are halted at prophase I, making **B** incorrect. When a female reaches puberty and begins her menstrual cycle, one primary oocyte completes meiosis I and becomes a secondary oocyte. The secondary oocyte begins meiosis II but halts at metaphase II. The secondary oocyte will complete meiosis II and become a mature ovum once it makes contact with sperm. This makes **C** and **D** incorrect, leaving **A** as the correct answer.

6) **Answer: C**

> **Explanation:** An egg is released into the fallopian tube from the ovary during ovulation. Sperm typically travels up the vagina, through the cervix, past the endometrium, and into the fallopian tube to fertilize the egg.

7) **Answer: A**

> **Explanation:** LH from the anterior pituitary maintains the corpus luteum. The corpus luteum is responsible for producing progesterone which is necessary for maintaining the thickness of the endometrium, which houses the developing embryo. Without proper levels of LH, and ultimately progesterone, the endometrium will not be able to carry the developing embryo.

8) **Answer: C**

> **Explanation:** A characteristic component of ovulation is the LH surge that precedes it. This is a high yield concept that is commonly tested. Reference **Figure 3.7**.

9) **Answer: B**

> **Explanation:** As estrogen levels increase, LH production is typically inhibited. This is a negative feedback loop. Once estrogen crosses a certain threshold, the negative feedback loop is turned off and a surge in LH occurs. Thus, the increase in estrogen causes an increase in LH; this is the definition of a positive feedback loop.

10) **Answer: A**

> **Explanation:** Before pregnancy and the initial days of a pregnancy, the corpus luteum is responsible for secreting estrogen and progesterone. Once the placenta is formed, the placenta takes the role of secreting estrogen and progesterone.

11) **Answer: B**

> **Explanation:** Low estrogen levels during the secretory phase would prevent the thickening of the endometrium. The endometrium is the site of implantation for the blastocyst. If the endometrium is not thick enough for implantation, the blastocyst will not be able to implant itself and pregnancy would be halted.

12) **Answer: C**

> **Explanation:** The zona pellucida is the outer covering of the secondary oocyte. During fertilization, the acrosome of the sperm binds specifically to the zona pellucida of the secondary oocyte to initiate the cortical reaction that prevents other sperm from fertilizing the egg and allow the sperm to pass on its genetic material.

13) Answer: D

> **Explanation:** This phase occurs from birth until maturation. Therefore, the egg can be stuck in this phase for 10-13 years.

14) Answer: A

> **Explanation:** The woman having her period was indicative of her undergoing a full menstrual cycle, including ovulation. In theory, though she may be showing signs of entering menopause, the woman could have conceived during that cycle since she ovulated (release an egg).

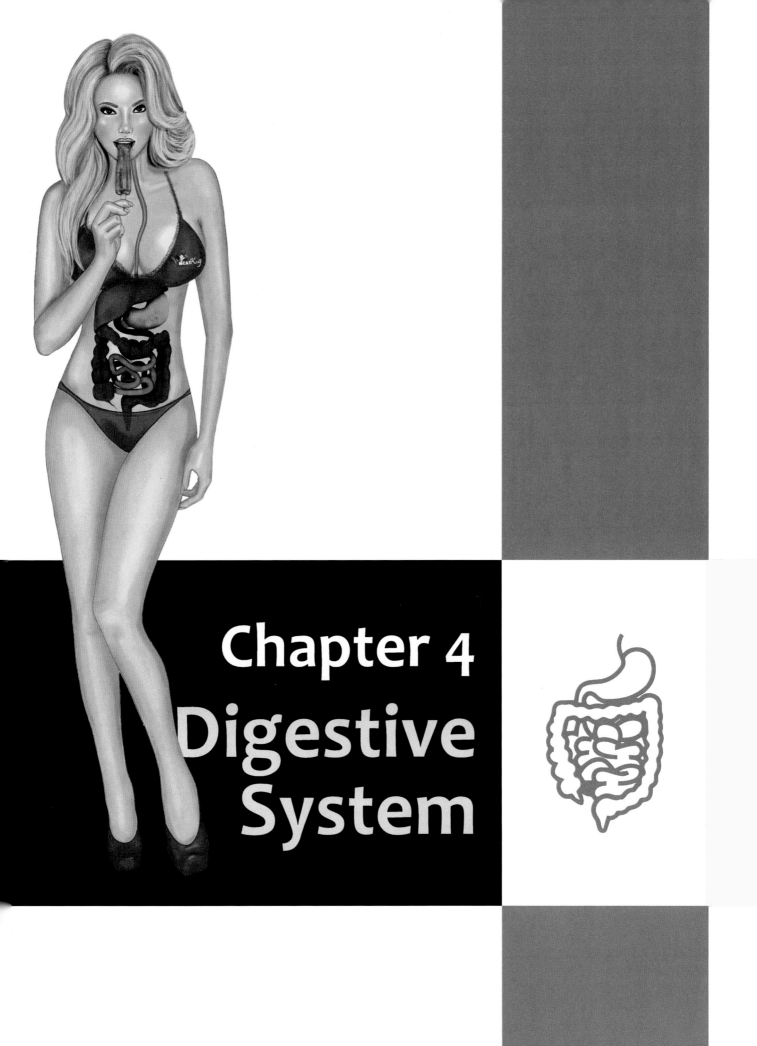

Chapter 4
Digestive System

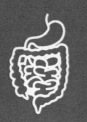

Chapter 4

Digestive System

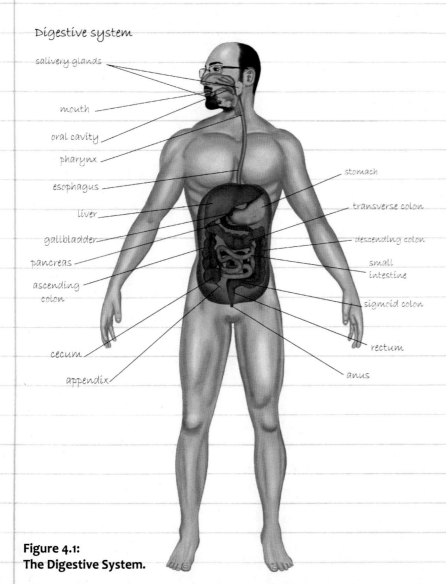

Digestive system

- salivery glands
- mouth
- oral cavity
- pharynx
- esophagus
- liver
- gallbladder
- pancreas
- ascending colon
- cecum
- appendix
- stomach
- transverse colon
- descending colon
- small intestine
- sigmoid colon
- rectum
- anus

Figure 4.1:
The Digestive System.

The digestive system: The organ system that allows us to enjoy our delicious meals and take in all of its healthy and unhealthy particles. Our digestive system functions to break down our food and absorb its nutrients to be used as cellular building blocks and as a source of energy. These nutrients include carbohydrates, proteins, fats, fiber, minerals, vitamins, and water. Without our digestive system, we would be eating food simply for its deliciousness. Let us begin exploring the digestive system by first discussing its structure as displayed by our sexy stripper.

Structure and Function

The first component of the digestive system to understand is the **gastrointestinal tract (Figure 4.1)**. The gastrointestinal system is a long tube composed of **muscle** and **epithelium** that moves nutrients from the external environment through the body. The function of the gastrointestinal tract is to digest, or breakdown, the food that we eat in order to absorb its nutrients.

Where does the digestive system begin? Think about your last meal. Where did it go first? Your **mouth!** People generally think of the stomach first, but the oral cavity is the first structure that begins digesting food.

There are two types of digestion, chemical and mechanical, both of which occur in the mouth. With respect to the mouth, **mechanical digestion** refers to the chewing of food. Mechanical digestion results in an increase in the food's surface area that is available to be chemically digested. **Chemical digestion** refers to the use of enzymes to break down polymers of macromolecules so that they can be readily metabolized. The **salivary glands** of the mouth secrete **salivary amylase** that cleaves alpha-1,4 glycosidic bonds in long chain carbohydrates, such as starch. Our tongue then turns our digested food into a small round ball, called a **bolus**, and moves it into the **pharynx**.

The **pharynx** leads to two pathways: the **larynx** and the **esophagus**. The larynx is part of our respiratory system and contains our vocal cords. The bolus must travel down the esophagus to be properly digested and absorbed. What happens when food travels down our larynx? The food blocks our air passageway and we choke! Our body reacts by coughing to push out the blockage. Fortunately, we have an **epiglottis** that blocks the larynx when we swallow (most of the time!), allowing direct passage of the bolus into the esophagus.

Interestingly, the entrance to the esophagus consists of skeletal muscle, whereas the lower parts consist of smooth muscle. This is why swallowing is a voluntary process in the oral phase, but is involuntary once we reach the pharynx and esophagus. The smooth muscle propels food down into the stomach and through the rest of the GI tract in a process called **peristalsis**. As we will discuss later, smooth muscle is under involuntary control; thus, peristalsis is too! Peristalsis are waves of contraction that pass from section to section of the GI tract. The circular muscles of the GI tube contract and this action pushes the food forward. Different regions in the GI tract will include other types of contraction. For example, while peristalsis propels the food forward, there is another type of contraction that mixes the food we have eaten called **segmentation contractions**. Segmentation contraction is the alternating contraction and relaxation of the outer longitudinal muscle in the wall of the digestive tract. Why is mixing necessary? For better digestion! Mixing enables the wide variety of digestive enzymes to act on all of the food (**Figure 4.3**).

Figure 4.2:
Salivary glands. The salivary glands secrete enzymes that aid in the chemical digestion of food.

IN-TEXT QUESTION:
Since salivary amylases can break down carbohydrates, why can't sugars be directly absorbed by the cells of the mouth?

Answer:
There are two major bonds to be broken in starch: alpha-1,4 glycosidic bonds in amylose and alpha-1,6 glycosidic bonds in amylopectin. Salivary amylase only cleaves the former, and polysaccharides need to be completely broken down into monosaccharides before they can be taken up by the cell. Furthermore, cells in the mouth don't have the proper transport mechanisms to absorb monosaccharides. Such mechanisms are only found in the cells of the small intestine, which we will get to later!

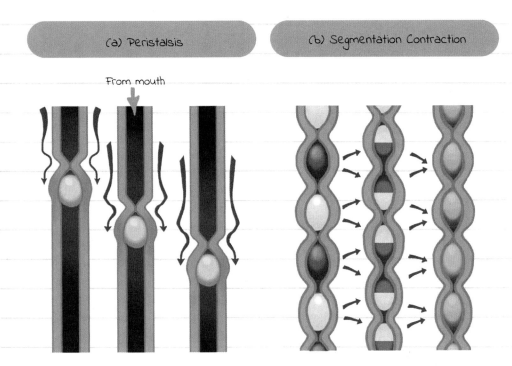

(a) Peristalsis

(b) Segmentation Contraction

From mouth

Figure 4.3:
Peristalsis vs. Segmentation Contractions.
a) Peristalsis propels food forward. Some mixing may occur.
b) In segmentation contractions, food is moved forward then backwards. This movement mixes the food and breaks it down mechanically.

From the esophagus, food is passed through the esophageal sphincter. Sphincters are a ring of muscle that guard the passage of food or waste into the next cavity. The opening of the esophageal sphincter allows the bolus to leave the esophagus and move onto the **stomach!**

Stomach

Once the bolus is in the stomach, we enter the **gastric phase** of digestion. The stomach can be broken up into five parts as shown in **Figure 4.4:** the **cardia, fundus, body, antrum**, and **pylorus**. The cardia is where the esophagus connects to the stomach. The stomach stores food, digests food, and destroys foreign bacteria due to its very acidic environment.

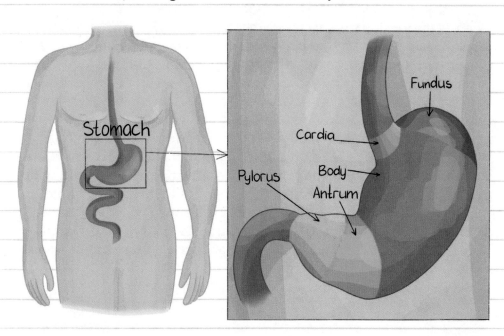

**Figure 4.4:
The Stomach.**

The stomach contains cells that release secretions directly onto its epithelial surface and into the bloodstream. There are four types of secretory cells in the stomach that you must know: **G-cells, parietal cells, chief cells**, and **goblet cells**.

G-cells, a type of **enteroendocrine cells,** are stimulated via stomach distension, proteins in the stomach, and the vagus nerve of the parasympathetic nervous system, to secrete **gastrin. Enteroendocrine cells** are a type of gastrointestinal cell that secretes hormones. Gastrin is a hormone that promotes the secretion of **HCl** from **parietal cells**. Since gastrin is a hormone, it is secreted into the bloodstream to act on the parietal cells. It is *not* directly secreted into the lumen of the stomach.

Parietal cells are specialized cells in the stomach that release **gastric acid** composed of **HCl**, giving the stomach a pH of 2. The acid denatures proteins, destroys foreign invaders, and cleaves **pepsinogen** into **pepsin**. Pepsin digests proteins. Parietal cells also release an **intrinsic factor,** a glycoprotein, that is critical for **vitamin B12** absorption.

Chief cells are specialized cells in the stomach that are responsible for secreting **pepsinogen**. Pepsinogen is the inactivated form of pepsin. Pepsinogen is cleaved into pepsin by the hydrogen ions of HCl.

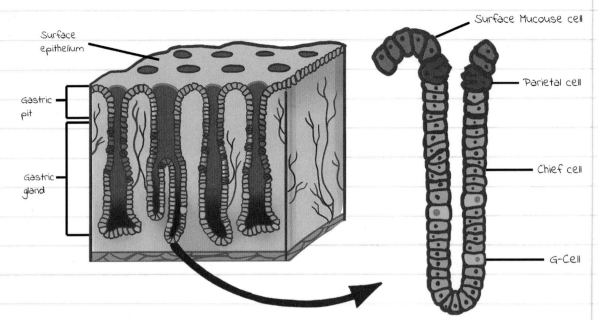

Figure 4.5:
Cells of the Stomach.

Goblet cells, also known as **mucosal cells**, are responsible for creating a thick layer of mucus that protects the lining of the stomach from the acidic (due to HCl) and proteolytic (due to the presence of pepsin) environment.

The combination of these secretions, our digested food, and mechanical churning by the stomach creates a mixture called **chyme**.

After hanging out in the stomach for a while, the chyme moves through the **pyloric sphincter** and into the small intestine. This begins the **intestinal phase**.

Figure 4.6:
Villi of the Small Intestine.

Small Intestine

Throughout the epithelia of the entire small intestine are finger-like projections called **villi**. The villi are surrounded by intestinal cells called **enterocytes**. On the enterocytes are smaller finger-like projections called **microvilli**. To get a better idea of the layout, take a look at the **Figure 4.6**!

The microvilli forms a brush border that consists of enzymes that break down carbohydrates, proteins, and nucleic acids. Together, the villi and microvilli serve to increase the surface area of the lumen, thereby increasing overall digestion. **Goblet cells**, that secrete mucus, are also present in the small intestine.

The small intestine has three parts shown in **Figure 4.7**: the **duodenum, jejunum,** and **ileum**. Chyme first enters the duodenum and is met by **bicarbonate**, a secretion of the **pancreas**, that neutralizes the acidic chyme to a pH of 6 in the small intestine. Interestingly enough, the pancreas plays a much larger role in the digestion of food than simply

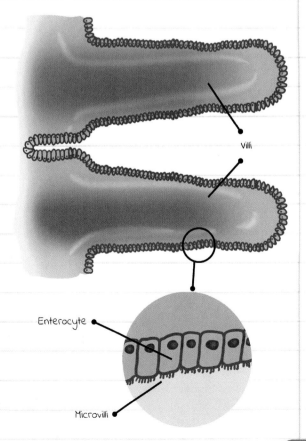

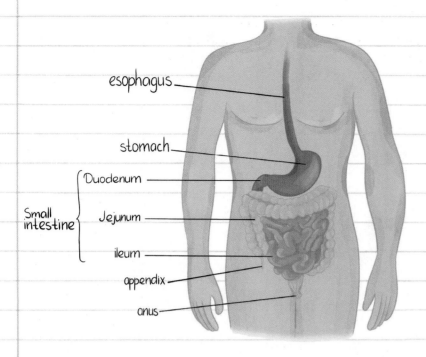

esophagus

stomach

Duodenum

Small intestine { Jejunum

ileum

appendix

anus

Figure 4.7:
Parts of the Small Intestine.
The small intestine begins at the duodenum, continues to the jejunum, and ends at the ileum.

IN-TEXT QUESTION:
Secretin is a hormone that acts on the pancreas to release certain enzymes. Is secretin released into the lumen of the duodenum or the lumen of the pancreas?

Answer:
Neither! It is a hormone, meaning it must be released into the bloodstream.

secreting bicarbonate in the small intestine! We know that the endocrine function (secreting directly into the bloodstream) of the pancreas is to secrete insulin and glucagon into the bloodstream during periods of feeding and fasting, respectively. With respect to digestion, the pancreas also functions as an **exocrine gland** (secreting onto epithelial surface) by secreting **trypsin, chymotrypsin, carboxypeptidase, pancreatic amylase, ribonuclease, deoxyribonuclease,** and **lipase** into the small intestine via the **pancreatic duct (Figure 4.8)**. These are digestive enzymes that break down long polymers of a macromolecule into its monomers. However, all of these enzymes are first secreted as inactive precursors called **zymogens**. Let us take a look at how these enzymes work for each macromolecule!

1. **Proteins:** When **trypsin** is secreted into the small intestine, it is activated by **enterokinase** on the brush border of the villi. Activated trypsin then activates the rest of the digestive enzymes released by the pancreas, including **chymotrypsin** and **carboxypeptidase**. Trypsin, chymotrypsin, and carboxypeptidase function to break down proteins into polypeptides. These polypeptides are then broken down further by other brush border digestive enzymes into amino acids to be absorbed.

2. **Carbohydrates:** **Pancreatic amylase** functions in the same way as salivary amylase but is much more powerful. In conjunction with brush border enzymes, pancreatic amylase is able to break down polysaccharides into monosaccharides that can be absorbed in the small intestine.

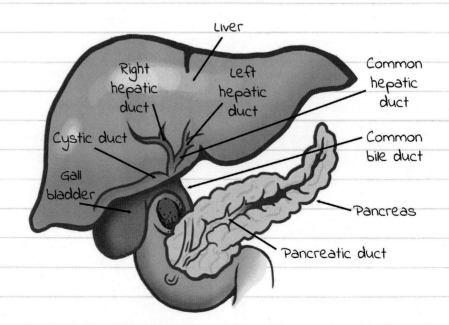

Figure 4.8:
The Pancreas and Liver. The pancreas is able to secrete into the duodenum via the pancreatic duct. The liver and gallbladder are able to secrete into the duodenum via the common bile duct.

Chapter 4 Digestive System

3. **Nucleotides: Ribonuclease** and **Deoxyribonuclease** break down RNA and DNA polynucleotides, respectively, into nucleotides (monomers). These nucleotides are further digested by phosphatases and nucleosidases to produce nitrogenous bases, pentose sugars, and phosphate ions that are absorbed into the small intestine.

4. **Fats** and **Cholesterol:** The digestion of fats and cholesterol in the small intestine is a little more complicated than the digestion of other molecules. **Lipase** breaks down fats, specifically triglycerides, into glycerol and fatty acids. Fats and cholesterol are nonpolar, but the lumen of the small intestine is aqueous. In this environment, fat and cholesterol molecules aggregate and form clumps. Due to the low surface area for lipase to work, lipase is unable to effectively attack the triglycerides. How does our body combat this issue? **Bile,** baby! The **liver** produces bile and stores it in the **gallbladder.** When it's time, the gallbladder sends bile through the **common bile duct** into the small intestine (**Figure 4.8**). In a process known as **emulsification,** bile breaks up fat aggregates into smaller pieces on which lipase can work more effectively. But how does bile emulsify fats? The answer lies in the active ingredient of bile, called **bile acid.** Bile acid is **amphipathic,** meaning that it contains both a hydrophobic and a hydrophilic portion. When bile acid is added, its hydrophobic portion binds to the fat aggregate while its hydrophilic portion faces out towards the aqueous solution. This breaks up the fat aggregate back into **triglycerides.** Lipase reacts with the triglycerides to produce **fatty acids** and **glycerol.** The bile acid then surrounds the fatty acids, glycerol, and cholesterol to create **micelles** that can be transferred into enterocytes. **Figure 4.9** shows the emulsification of fat:

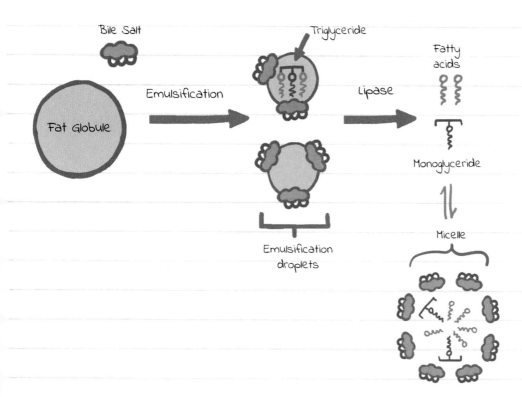

Figure 4.9:
Emulsification of Fats.

Now that we have covered how carbohydrates, proteins, fats, and nucleic acids are broken down, let us talk about how and where they are absorbed. While most of the digestion process occurs in the duodenum, most of the absorption occurs in the jejunum and ileum. Each macromolecule is uniquely absorbed into the body. Let's take a look!

Proteins: After proteins have been broken down into shorter polypeptides or amino acids they are transferred into an enterocyte using a **cotransport system**. Amino acids cannot simply diffuse into the enterocyte because the membrane of the enterocyte is nonpolar. Remember! ONLY nonpolar molecules can easily diffuse across a membrane. Amino acids are not considered nonpolar molecules; some do, however, have nonpolar side chains. In the cotransport mechanism, sodium is pumped via a **Na⁺/K⁺ ATPase pump** into the basolateral side (side of the cell that adjoins underlying tissue) of the enterocyte (**Figure 4.10**). This ultimately creates a strong concentration gradient for sodium to want to enter back into the enterocyte. Sodium binds to a transporter in the membrane facing the lumen of the small intestine, opening a binding site for an amino acid on the transporter. Using the energy from the concentration gradient of sodium, the amino acid is moved into the enterocyte via the transporter. The smaller polypeptides (dipeptides and tripeptides) enter in a similar manner to amino acids, but instead use a hydrogen ion cotransporter. Any dipeptides and tripeptides that enter the enterocyte are enzymatically broken down into amino acids. All the amino acids in the enterocyte are then absorbed into the blood. While in circulation, the amino acids are taken up by tissues. Those amino acids that are not taken up by tissues are transported to the liver.

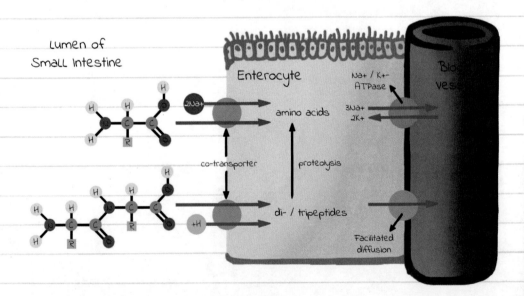

Figure 4.10:
Enterocyte Cotransport System.

Carbohydrates: Once complex sugars have been broken down into monomers, it is ready to be absorbed into the enterocyte. Glucose and galactose enter via the same sodium cotransporter mechanism that amino acids use. Fructose enters using another type of transporter and is converted into glucose in the enterocyte. From the enterocyte, these sugars are absorbed into the blood and transported to the liver.

Nucleic Acids: The nitrogenous bases, pentose sugars, and phosphate ions are absorbed into the enterocyte, into the blood, and sent to the liver.

Fats and **Cholesterol:** Micelles are able to easily diffuse across the membrane of an enterocyte. Why? Remember! Nonpolar, or hydrophobic, molecules can move through a nonpolar membrane! The bile acids that surround the glycerol, fatty acids, and cholesterol of a micelle are made of hydrophobic tails. This allows a micelle to pass through the nonpolar membrane of the enterocyte. Once inside, fatty acids and glycerol are converted back into triglycerides. The triglycerides are sent to the golgi body, where they are clumped together with cholesterol, phospholipids, and proteins to form a **chylomicron.** Chylomicrons do not get directly absorbed into the blood but are instead absorbed into a lacteal. A lacteal is a finger like extension of the lymphatic system in the villi (Figure 4.11). These fat aggregates travel through the lymphatic system until the lymphatic system drains into the thoracic duct, a large vein of the neck, at which point the fat has entered blood circulation. The chylomicron's hydrophobic interior, made of triglycerides and cholesterol, and hydrophilic exterior, made of phospholipids and proteins, allow it to transport fat effectively through the blood. Chylomicrons are a form of **lipoprotein**, which, as the name suggests, is a combination of lipids and proteins.

Figure 4.11:
Lacteals. Lacteals are finger-like projections of the lymphatic system under the villi that absorb chylomicrons.

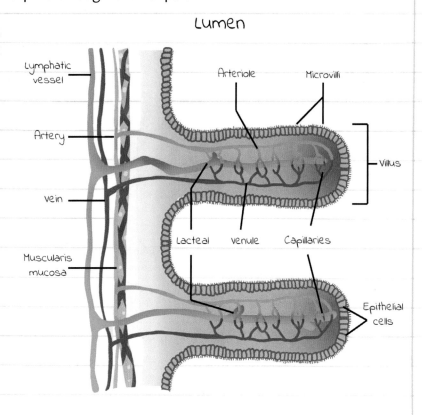

Figure 4.12:
Summary of Fat Absorption. Fat globules are emulsified by bile and turned into micelles. Micelles enter the enterocyte and its products are repackaged at the Golgi. Chylomicrons are formed and are shuttled into the lacteals (part of the lymphatic system).

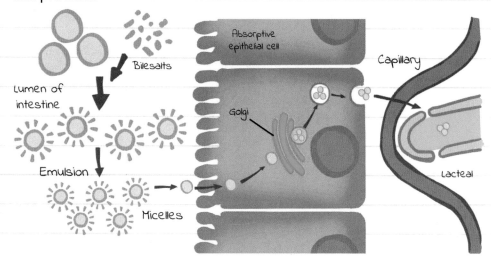

Once chylomicrons enter the blood, they travel through arteries, then to capillaries, where they face **lipoprotein lipase**. Lipoprotein lipase functions in the same way as our intestinal lipase: by breaking triglycerides into fatty acids and glycerol. The thin and porous walls of the capillaries allow the products of chylomicrons to enter nearly all types of tissue to be used for energy, in particular muscle and adipose tissue. In fact, the function of adipose cells is to store fat. The brain and red blood cells **do not absorb fats**. Why? Fats cannot enter the brain because they are NOT able to cross the blood brain barrier. Fats do not enter red blood cells because red blood cells do not contain the mitochondria needed to perform the beta oxidation of fats. Beta oxidation is the breakdown of fatty acids into acetyl-CoA. Remember acetyl CoA from our Biology Book I? That's right! Acetyl CoA enters the citric acid cycle, binds with oxaloacetate, and helps produce ATP for the cell. Those chylomicrons that are not taken up by tissue are directed to the liver.

As you may have noticed, all of our digested molecules must pass through the liver after absorption. The liver is where many of these molecules are either stored, metabolized, or sent throughout the body. We will cover the liver in much greater detail later on in this chapter. For now, let us continue down the gastrointestinal tract. We, along with the waste products now ready to leave the ileum of the small intestine, shall now enter the large intestine.

Large Intestine

The large intestine has six regions shown in **Figure 4.13.** The entrance of the large intestine has a valve, called the **ileocecal valve,** through which chyme enters.

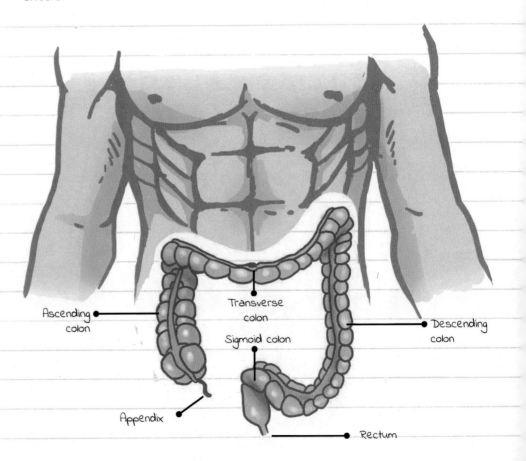

Figure 4.13:
Large Intestine. Waste travels through the large intestine as follows: Appendix, Ascending Colon, Transverse Colon, Descending Colon, Sigmoid Colon, and Rectum.

Chapter 4 Digestive System

Waste products move forward via specialized movement called **mass movement.** This movement pushes the waste toward the rectum, causing the defecation reflex, or the feeling of needing to poop! Involuntary smooth muscle sphincters allow the feces to move through the rectum to the anus. At this point, defecation is at our voluntary control.

You might wonder, are there other functions in the large intestine besides defecation? The large intestine is responsible for absorbing water and electrolytes, as well as retaining nutrients from food before it is sent out to the rectum. The colon also contains bacteria, known as **flora**, that help in the production of vitamin B1 (thiamin), B2 (riboflavin), B12, and K.

With feces leaving our body, we are done with the digestive system! What happened to all the nutrients that got absorbed? Right! It went to the liver! In the next section, we will look at all the functions of one of the most important organs of our body: the liver!

The Liver

We mentioned earlier that the liver produces bile that is ultimately stored in the gallbladder and secreted into the small intestine. In addition to this, the liver functions in the following ways:

1. Metabolization of ingested macromolecules: All of the following enter the liver from the abdomen via the **hepatic portal vein** except for fats. Chylomicrons enter the liver by having the lymphatic system empty into blood which ultimately travels to the liver.

   a) **Proteins:** Amino acids enter the liver and get deaminated. Deamination is the removal of nitrogen connected to three functional groups, hydrogens, or a combination of the three. Ammonia is released and enters into the **Urea cycle.** The remaining carbon chain is used as substrates for the **Krebs cycle, gluconeogenesis,** and/or **ketogenesis.** These processes are covered more extensively in the Biology I book!

   b) **Carbohydrates:** Glucose absorbed in the small intestine is shipped to the liver to be stored and/or released. Glucose is converted into glycogen in a process called **glycogenesis.** **Glycogen** is a polysaccharide and serves as a storage of glucose. When glucose is needed by the body, glycogen is hydrolyzed and glucose is released. The liver can also perform **gluconeogenesis** to create glucose from non-sugars. This glucose and/or the stored glucose can be released from the liver and be used to create energy via **glycolysis.**

   c) **Lipids:** We mentioned earlier that chylomicrons drain into a large vein of the neck, enter into blood circulation, and are taken up by tissues. Those chylomicrons that are not taken up by tissues are directed to the liver. The liver reprocesses its products (triglycerides, cholesterol, phospholipids, etc.) into another lipoprotein called **low density lipoprotein (LDL).** These lipoproteins have a very low protein density relative to its lipid concentration. LDL is sent out from the liver to the rest of the body. In capillaries, LDL has the opportunity to once again be acted upon by lipoprotein lipase and enter into adipose tissue. Note: Low density lipoproteins are considered the "bad" cholesterol because they carry cholesterol away from the liver and toward the blood vessels. LDLs can stick to the walls of the blood vessels and cause them to clog up! Conversely, high density lipoprotein (HDL) is created and released by the liver to bring cholesterol from the blood vessels back to the liver, thereby stopping cholesterol from clogging these vessels. This is why HDL is considered "good" cholesterol!

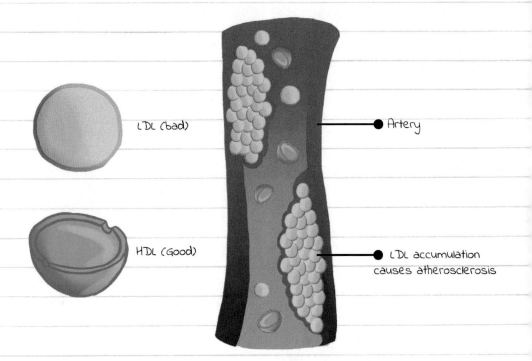

Figure 4.14:
LDL vs. HDL.

A few hours after a meal, insulin levels drop and glucagon levels increase to provide us energy. The increase of glucagon stimulates the release of fatty acids from adipocytes into the bloodstream, where they are transferred throughout the body using **albumin** as a transporter. The fatty acids are absorbed by different tissues to produce energy via **B-oxidation**. Remember! The brain and red blood cells cannot absorb fatty acids and use it for energy. Thus, the liver absorbs the unabsorbed fatty acids to create glucose via gluconeogenesis. The glucose is then sent to the brain and red blood cells to be used to make ATP.

2. Creation of important proteins: The liver synthesizes **albumin**. As mentioned earlier, albumin transports fatty acids in the blood throughout the body. Albumin helps maintain oncotic pressure in the blood. The liver also synthesizes **clotting factors** that are used during blood coagulation.

3. Storage: The liver can perform glycogenesis to store excess blood glucose as glycogen. When blood sugars are low, this glycogen can be used to normalize glucose levels. The liver is also known to store vitamins A, D, E, K, and B12.

4. Detoxification: The liver metabolizes the alcohol and drugs we ingest. When we ingest too much of these substances, we can overwork the liver and cause it to fail.

5. Immune functions: The liver has **Kupffer cells** that destroy improper **erythrocytes** (red blood cells) in conjunction with the spleen. Kupffer cells also kill bacteria brought from the small intestine.

Messaging of the Digestive System

We have discussed how food is digested and absorbed up through the end of the small intestine. But how do the parts of the digestive system communicate with each other and with the rest of the body to function as a unit?

Leptin and **Ghrelin** are two hormones that mediate hunger. Leptin is secreted by fat cells in adipose tissue and acts on the hypothalamus. Leptin is known as the satiety hormone because it inhibits hunger; its primary purpose is to regulate energy use so that the body does not feel hungry when it is not necessary. Ghrelin is released from enteroendocrine cells of the stomach and acts on the hypothalamus and anterior pituitary gland to increase hunger. Ghrelin also prepares the body for food intake by increasing gastric motility and gastric acid secretion.

The **enteric (intestinal) nervous system** consists of neurons that are part of the autonomic nervous system; these neurons surround the organs of the digestive system. The enteric nervous system controls peristalsis, hormone secretion, blood flow, and chemical secretions. Before food enters the stomach, the brain signals the release of gastrin- the vagus nerve of the brain communicates with the enteric nervous system to act on G-cells of the stomach to secrete gastrin. Gastrin then stimulates the release of HCl from parietal cells. Gastrin is also released when the stomach becomes fuller and distends.

As chyme leaves the stomach and enters the small intestine, a series of other hormones are sent from the small intestine to other digestive organs. Let us take a look at these hormones down below:

1. **Secretin**: the HCl in the chyme that enters the small intestine triggers the small intestine to secrete **secretin.** Secretin acts on the pancreas to secrete bicarbonate and other pancreatic enzymes that aid in digestion of food in the small intestine (**Figure 4.15**).

IN-TEXT QUESTION:
Which branch of the autonomic nervous system would promote activity of the enteric nervous system?

Answer:
The sympathetic nervous system generally inhibits the activity of the GI tract in order to prepare for "fighting or flighting," while the parasympathetic nervous system stimulates the enteric nervous system, thereby promoting "resting and digesting."

Figure 4.15:
Communication from the Small Intestine via Secretin and CCK.

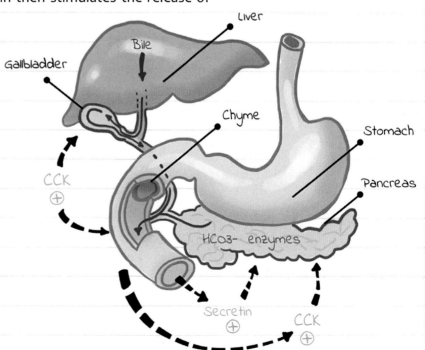

2. **Gastric inhibitory polypeptide (GIP)**: the fat and protein in chyme that enters the small intestine, triggers the small intestine to secrete **gastric inhibitory polypeptide**. Gastric inhibitory polypeptide decreases acid secretion and motor activity in the stomach. Why? By decreasing the motor activity of the stomach, the small intestine can work on digesting and absorbing a certain amount of food at a given time. Without decreasing the stomach motor activity, chyme will be continuously pushed into the small intestine at a rate too fast for it to be digested and absorbed. In addition, by slowing down the movement of food, GIP induces insulin secretion and allows tissues to prepare for transport and metabolism of the nutrients from the GI tract.

3. **Cholecystokinin (CCK)**: the fat in chyme that enters the small intestine triggers the small intestine to secrete **CCK**. CCK functions the same way as gastric inhibitory polypeptide by stimulating enzyme secretion from the pancreas and decreasing motor activity in the stomach. In addition, CCK causes gallbladder contraction, promoting the secretion of bile into the small intestine (**Figure 4.15**).

Enzyme	Produced In	Site of Release	Function
Carbohydrate Digestion:			
Salivary Amylase	Salivary glands	Mouth	Breaks down complex carbohydrates, like starch, into maltose
Pancreatic amylase	Pancreas	Small Intestine	Breaks down polysaccharides into disaccharides and trisaccharides, such as starch into maltose
Protein Digestion:			
Pepsin	Gastric Glands	Stomach	Breaks down proteins into peptides
Trypsin	Pancreas	Small intestine	Breaks down proteins into peptides
Chymotrypsin	Pancreas	Small intestine	Breaks down proteins into peptides
Carboxypeptidase	Pancreas	Small intestine	Breaks down peptides into smaller peptides and amino acids
Enterokinase	Small intestine	Mucosa of small intestine	Converts trypsinogen (inactive form) into trypsin (active form)
Nucleic Acid Digestion:			
Nuclease	Pancreas	Small intestine	Break downs nucleic acids (RNA and DNA) into nucleotides
Fat Digestion:			
Lipase	Pancreas	Small Intestine	Breaks down triglycerides into glycerol and fatty acids

Figure 4.16: Digestive Enzymes

Hormone	Origin	Stimulus	Target	Function
Gastrin	G-cells within gastric glands and the duodenum	Presence of proteins; stomach distention during a meal; stimulation of the vagus nerve	Parietal cells within gastric glands	Stimulates the secretion of HCl from parietal cells
Secretin	Small intestine (duodenum)	Presence of HCl in chyme	Pancreas	Stimulates the secretion of bicarbonate and pancreatic enzymes that aid in digestion
CCK (Cholecystokinin)	Small intestine (duodenum)	Presence of fat in chyme	Pancreas, gallbladder	Stimulates the pancreas to release digestive enzymes; decreases motor activity in the stomach; stimulates gallbladder to eject bile
GIP (Glucose-dependent insulinotropic peptide)	Small intestine (duodenum)	Presence of fat and proteins in chyme	Stomach, pancreas	Decreases secretion of acid and motor activity in the stomach; stimulates pancreas to release insulin
Leptin	Fat cells in adipose tissue	Depends directly on the levels of adiposity	Hypothalamus	Suppresses appetite; control energy metabolism
Ghrelin	Enteroendo-crine cells of the stomach	Stimulation of the vagus nerve	Hypothalamus and anterior pituitary	Stimulates appetite; increases gastric motility and gastric acid secretion

Figure 4.17: Digestive Hormones

Questions

1) **Which of these is not a function of HCl in the stomach?**

    a. It activates pepsinogen.
    b. It destroys pathogens.
    c. It cleaves alpha-1,4 glycosidic bonds.
    d. It denatures proteins into peptides.

2) **Which of the following is not a location of chemical digestion in the GI tract?**

    a. Mouth
    b. Stomach
    c. Large Intestine
    d. Small Intestine

3) **Which of the following is a true statement about parietal cells?**

    a. They secrete gastrin to promote the release of HCl in the stomach.
    b. They secrete gastric acid which lowers the pH of the stomach.
    c. They secrete pepsinogen which later gets cleaved into pepsin.
    d. They create a thick layer of mucus to protect the lining of the stomach from the acid lumen.

4) **The small intestine plays a role in all of the following *except*:**

    a. Neutralizing chyme in the duodenum using bicarbonate.
    b. Absorbing water and electrolytes.
    c. Increasing the surface area of epithelium to assist in nutrient breakdown.
    d. Breaking down proteins into polypeptides using trypsin and chymotrypsin.

5) **Which of the following statements about the pancreas is true?**

    1. It is activated by gastric inhibitory polypeptide
    2. It secretes inactive enzymes into the small intestine
    3. Its endocrine function enables digestion in the small intestine
    a. I only
    b. II only
    c. I and II
    d. II and III

6) **A mutation in which someone cannot produce pancreatic amylase will result in difficulty in digesting which of the following nutrients?**

    a. Glucose
    b. Lipids
    c. Fructose
    d. Starch

7) **All of the following are true about bile *except*:**

    a. It breaks down triglycerides into glycerol and fatty acids

b. It contains molecules that have both hydrophobic and hydrophilic regions
c. It emulsifies fat aggregates into smaller particles
d. It creates micelles to transfer fatty acids into the enterocytes

8) **How do amino acids enter the enterocytes?**

a. They are small enough to diffuse through the membrane
b. Nonpolar amino acids can diffuse through the membrane while polar and charged amino acids enter through protein channels
c. They enter via a cotransport mechanism in which Na^+ is pumped into the basolateral side of the enterocyte
d. They enter via a cotransport mechanism in which H^+ is pumped into the basolateral side of the enterocyte

9) **Once complex carbohydrates have been broken down into glucose, glucose:**

a. Is immediately sent into the bloodstream to be distributed to the body
b. Enters enterocytes through a sodium cotransport mechanism
c. Passes into the enterocytes via simple diffusion
d. Enters enterocytes via facilitated diffusion

10) **Why are fats transported through the lymph rather than through the bloodstream?**

a. Their hydrophobicity prevents transport through blood
b. Chylomicrons are too big to fit into blood vessels
c. To prevent large spikes in the fat levels of the blood to maintain arterial health
d. All of the above

11) **Fats can enter all of the following cell types *except*:**

a. White blood cells
b. Muscle cells
c. Red blood cells
d. Skin cells

12) **What is the purpose of the bacterial flora that exists in the large intestine?**

a. Increase surface area to aid in nutrient absorption
b. Break apart fat globules into smaller micelles
c. Aid in the production of vitamins
d. Synthesize enzymes to assist in nutrient breakdown

13) **All of the following enter the liver via the hepatic portal vein *except*:**

a. Amino acids
b. Lipids
c. Carbohydrates
d. All of the above nutrients enter the liver via the hepatic portal vein

14) What type of reaction do amino acids undergo in the liver?

    a. Decarboxylation
    b. Oxidation-reduction
    c. Acid-catalyzed hydrolysis
    d. Deamination

15) All of the following are exit pathways for amino acids after processing in the liver *except:*

    a. Glycogenolysis
    b. Gluconeogenesis
    c. Ketogenesis
    d. Krebs cycle

16) Which of the following is the difference between low density lipoproteins (LDL) and high density lipoproteins (HDL)?

    a. LDLs carry cholesterol away from the liver and toward the blood vessels while HDLs carry cholesterol away from the blood vessels and toward the liver
    b. HDLs carry cholesterol away from the liver and toward the blood vessels while LDLs carry cholesterol away from the blood vessels and toward the liver
    c. HDLs can stick to the walls of blood vessels causing them to clog up while LDLs do not
    d. HDLs raise blood cholesterol while LDLs lower blood cholesterol

17) Which of the following is a function of the liver?

    a. Secrete digestive enzymes into the small intestine
    b. Signal the entrance of chyme into the small intestine via CCK secretion
    c. Synthesis of proteins that assist in the transport of fatty acids
    d. Storage of complex amino acids by combining them into larger polypeptides

18) Which of the following choices represent the source and the target of Leptin?

    a. Enteroendocrine cells; anterior pituitary
    b. Adipose tissue; hypothalamus
    c. Enteroendocrine cells; hypothalamus
    d. Adipose tissue; anterior pituitary

19) All of the following are functions of cholecystokinin (CCK) *except:*

    a. Stimulate enzyme secretion from the pancreas
    b. Decrease motor activity in the stomach
    c. Promote gallbladder contraction
    d. Increase motor activity in the small intestine

20) Why is it necessary for gastric inhibitory polypeptide (GIP) to decrease motor activity of the stomach upon the entrance of chyme into the small intestine?

    a. To induce glucagon secretion which allows tissues to prepare for transport and metabolism of the nutrients from the GI tract.

b. To limit the rate of chyme entrance into the small intestine
c. To prevent backflow of food from the stomach into the esophagus
d. To create a more hospitable environment for enzyme secretion

21) **Suppose your friend Sarah has a mutation for which she produces an inactive salivary amylase. What type of bond would her body have difficulty in breaking down?**

    a. Ester
    b. Ether
    c. Amide
    d. Amine

22) **Suppose your friend Michael has a defective glucose transporter. This would result in the upregulation of all of the following processes *except*:**

    a. Glycogenesis
    b. Glycogenolysis
    c. Gluconeogenesis
    d. Ketogenesis

23) **An individual with an overactive ghrelin response would exhibit which of the following?**

    a. Constitutively high serum glucagon levels to facilitate glycogenesis
    b. Lower levels of gastric inhibitory polypeptide to decrease motor activity in the stomach preventing excess flow into the small intestine
    c. Constitutively high serum insulin levels to facilitate glucose transport into the cells
    d. Overactive alpha cells of the pancreas to induce excess insulin release

24) **What happens with weak signaling of the vagus nerve?**

    a. Not enough norepinephrine is released to act on G cells to secrete gastrin
    b. The rate of peristalsis would quicken due to deficits in inhibition by the vagus nerve
    c. The pH of the stomach would increase
    d. The pancreas would over secrete digestive enzymes

Answers

1) **Answer: C**

   Explanation: HCl has three main functions in the stomach - to destroy foreign invaders, to assist in acidic proteolysis of pepsinogen, and to denature proteins into smaller peptides. This eliminates A, B and D. C is the only choice that is not a function of HCl - rather, salivary amylase cleaves alpha-1,4 glycosidic bonds, making C the correct answer.

2) **Answer: C**

   Explanation: Salivary amylase in the mouth begins the breakdown of starch by cleaving alpha-1,4 glycosidic bonds, eliminating A. Once pepsinogen gets cleaved into pepsin, pepsin breaks down proteins into smaller polypeptides by cleaving peptide bonds, eliminating B. Trypsin, chymotrypsin, carboxypeptidase, pancreatic amylase, ribonuclease, deoxyribonuclease, and lipase are all released into the small intestine to break down carbohydrates, proteins, and fats eliminating D. The large intestine is mainly responsible for absorbing water and electrolytes, making C the correct answer.

3) **Answer: B**

   Explanation: G cells secrete gastrin, eliminating A. Chief cells secrete pepsinogen, eliminating C. Goblet cells create the mucus layer to protect the stomach lining, eliminating D. Parietal cells secrete gastric acid containing HCl which, being an acid, lowers the pH of the stomach, making B the correct answer.

4) **Answer: B**

   Explanation: The pancreas secretes bicarbonate into the small intestine to neutralize chyme, eliminating A. The villi and microvilli in the small intestine serve to increase the surface area of the lumen, thereby increasing overall digestion and eliminating C. The pancreas uses trypsin and chymotrypsin to break down proteins into polypeptides.

5) **Answer: B**

   Explanation: Gastric inhibitory polypeptide acts on the small intestine, making choice I false and eliminating A and C. The pancreas secretes digestive enzymes in the form of zymogens, which are inactive precursors to the actual enzyme, making choice II true. The pancreas is both an endocrine and an exocrine gland, but in this case, it is its exocrine function that enables digestion, as it secretes enzymes through ducts rather than through the bloodstream, making choice III false and eliminating D, leaving B as the correct answer.

6) **Answer: D**

   Explanation: Glucose and fructose are already monosaccharides, meaning they do not need to be broken down any further to be taken up by enterocytes, eliminating A and C. Lipids are broken down by lipase with the help of bile leaving it unaffected by deficits in pancreatic amylase, eliminating B. Pancreatic amylase acts on long polysaccharides like starch to break them down into smaller sugars, making D the correct answer.

7) **Answer: A**

   Explanation: The active ingredient of bile - bile acid - is amphipathic, meaning has a hydrophobic and a hydrophilic portion, eliminating B. Its hydrophobic region binds to these fatty acids while the hydrophilic region faces the aqueous exterior, which breaks up fat aggregates into individual triglycerides, making them accessible to lipases and eliminating C. After triglycerides are broken down into fatty acids and glycerol, bile acid encapsulates them along with cholesterol to form micelles which can be taken up by the epithelium, eliminating D. Lipases break down triglycerides into glycerol and fatty acids, not bile, making A the correct answer. What is important to note here is that bile is not an enzyme - it is an emulsifier, similar to how soap breaks up dirt and grease on your hands into smaller particles.

8) **Answer: C**

   Explanation: Amino acids, even those with nonpolar side chains, are generally polar due to a deprotonated carboxyl group and a protonated amino group at physiological pH. Therefore, they cannot diffuse through the nonpolar cell membrane, eliminating A and B. It is the buildup of sodium ions on the basolateral side of the erythrocytes that binds a transporter creating a binding site for amino acids allowing them to enter the cell - not a buildup of hydrogen protons. This eliminates D and makes C the correct answer.

9) **Answer: B**

   Explanation: Glucose is too big and polar to enter enterocytes and there are no carrier proteins or channels big enough to facilitate its diffusion, eliminating C and D. Free glucose in the lumen of the small intestine needs to first be taken up by enterocytes before being sent to the bloodstream, eliminating A. Like amino acids, glucose enters the enterocytes by means of a sodium concentration gradient in which sodium and glucose both enter the cell, making B the correct answer.

10) **Answer: D**

   Explanation: Since fats are hydrophobic, when placed in an aqueous environment, they will clump together, making transport more difficult and making A correct. Chylomicrons are large lipoproteins containing triglycerides, cholesterol, phospholipids and proteins, making them too big to pass through blood vessels all at once making B correct. This is enough to get the answer, but C is also true because large spikes in fat levels can be detrimental to arterial health, making D the correct answer.

11) **Answer: C**

Explanation: Fats do not enter red blood cells because red blood cells do not have a mitochondria to perform the beta oxidation of fats, which is the breakdown of fatty acids into acetyl-CoA that can enter the citric acid cycle, bind with oxaloacetate, and produce ATP for the cell. All other cell types other than neurons can take up fats and perform beta oxidation, making C the correct answer.

12) **Answer: C**

Explanation: Villi and microvilli increase the surface area in the small intestine to aid nutrient absorption, making A incorrect. Bile is responsible for breaking apart fat globules into smaller micelles, making B incorrect. No digestive enzymes are synthesized in the large intestine, making D incorrect. Bacterial flora help in the production of vitamins B1, B2, B12, and K, making C the correct answer.

13) **Answer: B**

Explanation: Lipids enter the bloodstream from the lymph at the thoracic duct near the neck in the form of chylomicrons, which later reaches the liver through said bloodstream. Both amino acids and carbohydrates directly enter the liver via the hepatic portal vein, making B the correct answer.

14) **Answer: D**

Explanation: Decarboxylation of amino acids would lead to a buildup of carbon dioxide in the blood and thus lowering blood pH, eliminating A. Acid-catalyzed hydrolysis breaks polypeptides into individual amino acids but is not involved in subsequent reactions, and there is no redox reaction of amino acids in the liver, eliminating B and C. Amino acids are determined to release ammonia which can then enter the Urea cycle, making D the correct answer.

15) **Answer: A**

Explanation: Amino acids are determined to release ammonia which can then enter the Urea cycle. The remaining carbon chain can be converted into pyruvate, which can enter gluconeogenesis to form glucose, or undergo oxidation to acetyl-CoA which can enter the Krebs cycle, eliminating B and D. Acetyl CoA can also form ketone bodies via ketogenesis, eliminating C. Glycogenolysis entails the breakdown of glycogen into glucose, without involvement of pyruvate or amino acid derivatives, making A false and thus the correct answer.

16) Answer: A

> **Explanation:** LDLs can stick to the walls of arteries causing them to clog up, not HDLs, eliminating C. LDLs carry cholesterol from the liver and toward the blood vessels, raising blood cholesterol and eliminating B and C making A the correct answer.

17) Answer: C

> **Explanation:** The liver does secrete bile into the small intestine, but bile is not an enzyme, eliminating A. The small intestine itself secretes CCK to the pancreas in response to chyme entrance, eliminating B. The liver deaminates amino acids and delivers them to other metabolic pathways, not by reforming them into polypeptides eliminating D. The liver synthesizes albumin, a protein that transports fatty acids throughout the body, making C the correct answer.

18) Answer: B

> **Explanation:** Leptin is secreted by fat cells in adipose tissue and acts on the hypothalamus to inhibit hunger, making B the correct answer and all the other answer choices incorrect. It is ghrelin that is secreted by enteroendocrine cells and targets the anterior pituitary along with the hypothalamus.

19) Answer: D

> **Explanation:** In response to chyme entrance into the small intestine, CCK is secreted by the small intestine. CCK causes the pancreas to release digestive enzymes into the small intestine, it causes the gallbladder to contract to secrete bile, and it reduces motor activity in the stomach, eliminating A, B and C. CCK does not increase motor activity in the small intestine as too much motor activity would cause the digestate to pass through before adequate breakdown and absorption, making D the correct answer.

20) Answer: B

> **Explanation:** Glucagon is only secreted when blood glucose is low, which is not true shortly after a meal, eliminating A. The esophageal sphincter is what is responsible for preventing backflow of food from the stomach into the esophagus, eliminating C. D is irrelevant and thus incorrect. GIP decreases the motor activity of the stomach to limit the rate of chyme entrance into the small intestine to allow for adequate breakdown and absorption of nutrients, making B the correct answer.

21) Answer: B

> **Explanation:** Salivary amylase breaks alpha-1,4 glycosidic bonds which are ether in nature, making B the correct answer. Amide bonds connect amino acids in polypeptides, and ester bonds connect glycerol to fatty acids, eliminating A and C. No macromolecule contains amine as a unitary bond, eliminating D.

22) Answer: A

Explanation: A defective glucose transporter would result in limited glucose uptake into cells. In order to continue producing ATP, cells would undergo processes to produce glucose internally, such as glycogenolysis to breakdown glycogen into glucose and gluconeogenesis to produce glucose from pyruvate, eliminating B and C. Cells would also look to other pathways to produce energy, such as ketogenesis, eliminating D. Glycogenesis is the only process which would not be upregulated as the source of glucose for the cells is limited, making A the correct answer.

23) Answer: C

Explanation: Ghrelin increases hunger and subsequently an overactive ghrelin response would result in increased food intake. This would lead to high serum glucose, which would result in an upregulation of insulin levels, not glucagon, eliminating A, and insulin is released by the beta cells of the pancreas, not the alpha cells, eliminating D. Increased intake would lead to increased GIP to decrease motor activity in the stomach upon chyme entrance into the small intestine, as now it is more important than ever to limit the rate of chyme entrance to allow for adequate breakdown and absorption of nutrients, eliminating B. Increased intake and subsequently increased serum glucose would signal the release of insulin to facilitate the uptake of excess glucose into cells, making C the correct answer.

24) Answer: C

Explanation: The vagus nerve releases acetylcholine as its neurotransmitter as do all neurons in the parasympathetic nervous system, eliminating A. The rate of peristalsis would slow down due to deficits in excitation by the vagus nerve, eliminating B. Since the vagus nerve activates pancreas exocrine function, weaker signaling would diminish the secretion of enzymes, not promote it, eliminating D. The vagus nerve acts on G cells to secrete gastrin which promotes the secretion of HCl from parietal cells, reducing the pH of the stomach. Weak signaling of the vagus nerve would result in an increase in the pH of the stomach, making C the correct answer.

Chapter 5
Cardiovascular System

Chapter 5
Cardiovascular System

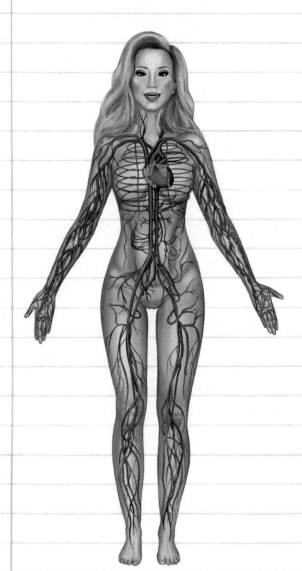

We assume your dream is to become a doctor and to help the world. When treating patients, knowledge alone is insufficient. Good doctors need to have empathy — especially *big* hearts!

Aside from giving us empathy, our heart's main purpose is to ensure that the rest of the tissues in the body get the nutrients and oxygen that they need to function. The heart is no quitter. It beats an average of 115,000 beats per day! In this chapter, we will review the structure and function of the cardiovascular system as well as its main component, the heart!

Functions of the Cardiovascular System

An important function of the cardiovascular system is the transport of vital molecules throughout the body including nutrients, gases, and hormones. The cardiovascular system also transports waste from the tissues to eventually be expelled from the body. You can think of it's blood vessels as an intricate system of highways and roads.

The main components that make up the cardiovascular system are the heart and the blood vessels. Additionally, the cardiovascular system includes the blood which contains plasma and blood cells. Before focusing on the entire circulatory system, let us focus on the **heart**. The heart is the engine, the unbelievably durable machine, that keeps blood flowing.

Structure of the heart

The heart itself is made up of **myocardium**, a fancy term for heart muscle, that enables its pumping function. The heart is also encased in a tough membrane sac called the **pericardium**, which encloses the pericardial cavity. The pericardial cavity contains a thin layer of clear **pericardial fluid** that lubricates the external surface of the heart. The heart is divided by a wall called the **septum** that splits the heart in half. Each half contains two chambers: an **atrium** and a **ventricle** (**Figure 5.1**). Blood enters the heart through the atrium and leaves the heart through the ventricle. But how exactly does blood move throughout the body?

Blood flow

The basic flow of blood throughout the body goes as follows: deoxygenated blood from the tissues enters into the right side of the heart. From the heart, the blood is sent to the lungs to get oxygenated. The left side of the heart then receives the newly oxygenated blood from the lungs and pumps it to the tissues of the body. Before we take a deeper look at the flow of blood, we must go over a couple of key points.

Although we label the blood coming to the right side of the heart as "deoxygenated," this term is somewhat misleading. The blood does contain some oxygen, but the concentration is much lower than that of the newly oxygenated blood that is returned from the lungs. In addition, you may remember being taught that **arteries** carry oxygenated blood and **veins** carry deoxygenated blood. While this is true most of the time, there are notable exceptions! There are arteries that carry deoxygenated blood and veins that carry oxygenated blood. A more encompassing definition that is *always* true is that arteries carry blood **AWAY** from the heart while veins carry blood **TOWARD** the heart. For this reason, the deoxygenated blood carried to the lungs from the heart travels along arteries and is returned to the heart, freshly oxygenated, through veins.

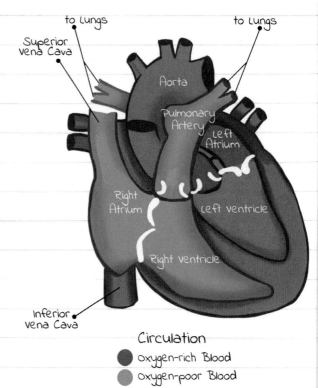

Figure 5.1:
Anatomy of the Heart.

Notice in **Figure 5.2** that the blood that flows to the lungs goes through the pulmonary artery, despite being deoxygenated.

Let us begin our trip through the cardiovascular system at the right side of the heart. Blood flows into the heart through the right atrium. It continues from the right atrium to the right ventricle and then to the lungs via the **pulmonary artery.** After refilling on oxygen gas (and expelling gaseous waste — carbon dioxide) in the lungs, the blood travels through the **pulmonary veins** to the left atrium. The vessels we just discussed, the pulmonary arteries and veins, make up the **pulmonary circulation (Figure 5.2)**.

From the left atrium, the blood is pumped into the left ventricle. Blood from the left ventricle is then pumped into a large artery called the **aorta.** The aorta branches into arteries and smaller arteries, called **arterioles**, which ultimately lead to a network of **capillaries**. Blood exchange of fluid, gases, nutrients, and waste to the tissues and cells occur at these capillaries.

After the exchange at the capillaries occurs, the blood enters the venous portion of circulation in order to return to the heart. As the blood gets closer and closer to the heart, the small venules join together to form larger veins, eventually reaching the two major veins that lead to the heart. Veins from the upper part of the body form the **superior vena cava**. The veins from the lower part of the body form the **inferior vena cava**. These terms are easy to remember: superior means top and inferior means bottom.

Both venae cavae will empty into the right atrium where the cycle begins once more. The circulation that brings blood from the left side of the heart to the tissues and back to the right side of the heart, providing blood and nutrients to cells throughout the body, is called the **systemic circulation** (**Figure 5.2**).

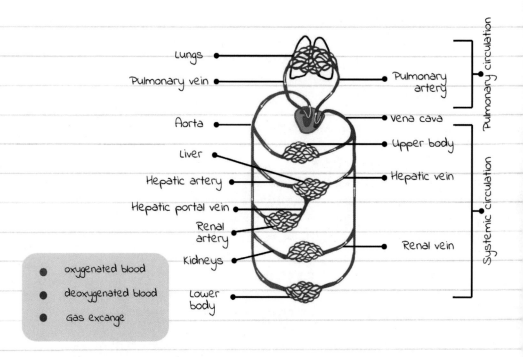

Figure 5.2:
Pulmonary and Systemic Circulation. Blood exiting the right side of the heart (in blue) goes to the lungs to be oxygenated. Blood exiting the left side of the heart (in red) goes to the body tissues to provide oxygen and nutrients.

Before continuing, let's discuss one more type of vein: **portal veins**.

The blood leaving the digestive tract goes to the liver via the **hepatic portal vein** (**Figure 5.2**). Critical thinking question: why is it that the digestive tract has a portal system that directly takes the blood to the liver rather than to the heart like all veins? The liver detoxifies foreign substances that may be in the blood. The blood from the digestive tract is sent to the liver to ensure detoxification is performed before the blood is sent back to the systemic circulation.

Valves

Now that we've completed our journey and properly transported oxygen to the tissues of the body, it's time to go back to the heart. How does the heart allow blood flow harmoniously in one direction? How is it that oxygenated blood and blood carrying waste don't mix? The answer lies in another structural component of the heart: the **valves** (**Figure 5.3**). The valves prevent the backflow of blood to ensure that oxygenated blood and waste-filled blood do not mix. One set of valves is located between the atria and ventricles. These are called the **atrioventricular valves**. The other set, called the **semilunar valves,** are located between the ventricles and the arteries. Thanks to these valves, blood only flows in one direction and does not flow backward.

The two atrioventricular (AV) valves are not structurally the same. The AV valve separating the right atrium and the right ventricle has three cusps (three flaps) and is appropriately named the **tricuspid valve**. The valve separating the left atrium and left ventricle has two cusps (two flaps) and is appropriately named the **bicuspid valve**. Another name commonly used to refer to the bicuspid valve is the **mitral valve**.

There are two different kinds of semilunar valves as well. One of these valves, the **aortic valve**, is located between the left ventricle and the aorta. The other, the **pulmonary valve**, lies between the right ventricle and the pulmonary trunk. Notice how these are all easy to remember because the names include their location! Each of these valves has three leaflets that snap closed when blood tries to flow backward.

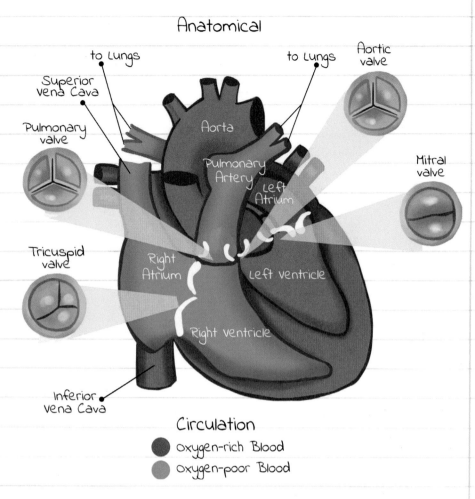

Figure 5.3:
Heart Valves. Remember, the tricuspid valve and mitral valve are known as the atrioventricular valves. Notice also that the mitral valve has only two flaps.

Now that we have reviewed the overall heart and blood flow, let us get into the functioning unit of the heart: cardiac muscle cells.

Cardiac Muscle Cells

The unique feature of cardiac muscle cells is that they can contract without stimulation from the nervous system. How can that be? Didn't we just spend hours discussing the nervous system, depolarizations, and action potentials? Where does the signal to contract come from? There are special cells in the heart called **autorhythmic cells**, also called **pacemakers**, that generate an action potential without external stimulation from the nervous system and stimulate cardiac muscle contraction. The autonomic nervous system does however innervate the heart and control the speed and strength at which the heart contracts.

Cardiac muscle cells differ from skeletal muscle cells (discussed to greater extent in the chapter on muscles). The main distinguishing property of cardiac muscle cells is that **intercalated disks** connect the cardiac muscle cells to each other. The intercalated disks contain **gap junctions** through which signals can quickly pass from one heart cell to another (**Figure 5.4**). This allows the heart to function as a single contractile unit.

Figure 5.4:
Cardiac Muscle Cell. Electrical signals pass from one cardiac muscle cell to another via gap junctions across intercalated discs. Cardiac muscle cells are held together at the intercalated discs by desmosomes within a cardiac muscle fiber.

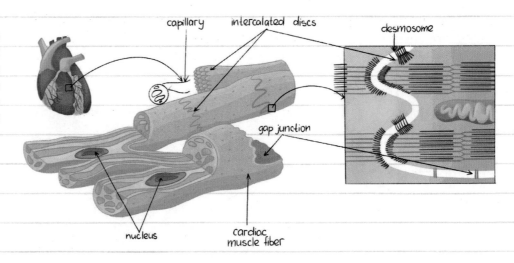

Contraction Initiation

Contraction of cardiac cells is called **excitation contraction coupling.** The difference from other muscle cells is that the action potential comes from autorhythmic cells rather than the nervous system. As you read, follow the diagram to visualize the process (**Figure 5.5**).

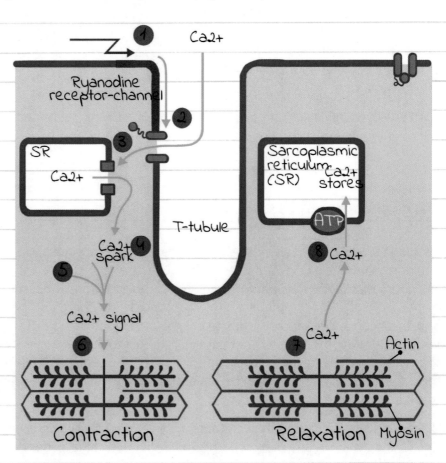

Figure 5.5:
Cardiac Muscle Cell Contraction Initiation.

1) Action potential enters cell,
2) Voltage gated channels open and Ca+ enters,
3) Ca^{2+} stimulates Ca release through RhR receptors,
4) Release cause Ca+ spike,
5) Intracellular Ca+ levels increase,
6) Ca binds to troponin to stimulate contraction,
7) When Ca^{2+} releases from troponin relaxation takes place,
8) Ca+ is pumped back into SR for storage

An action potential from a pacemaker cell initiates depolarization in a contractile cell. As a result, voltage-gated calcium channels open and calcium travels into the cell. This influx in calcium causes further calcium release from the sarcoplasmic reticulum through special channels called **ryanodine receptor channels** (sometimes abbreviated **RyR**). This process is called **calcium-induced calcium release**. The calcium released from the **sarcoplasmic reticulum** is the cell's major source of calcium for muscle contraction. The extracellular calcium mainly acts to initiate the calcium release from the sarcoplasmic reticulum. The calcium in the cytoplasm then binds to **troponin** on **actin** and initiates contraction. Once calcium releases from troponin, the muscle cells relax and calcium is actively pumped back into the sarcoplasmic reticulum where it is stored for the next round. We will cover how the binding of calcium to troponin causes a contraction in the musculoskeletal system chapter.

The Heart as a Pump

The heart is able to function so efficiently because the contraction of the cells occurs in an organized, coordinated fashion. How does this happen? Above, we discussed that an autorhythmic cell initiates an action potential on a contractile cell. Depolarization begins to spread across all the contractile cells via gap junctions and enables the heart to act as a functional unit. Contraction follows, first through the atria and then the ventricles. Let's take a closer look.

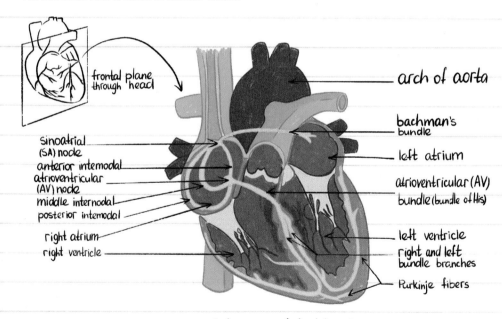

Anterior view of frontal section

Figure 5.6:
Depolarization of the Heart.

In the heart, depolarization begins in a special structure located in the wall of the right atrium called the **sinoatrial node,** or SA node (**Figure 5.6**). The sinoatrial node is a cluster of **pacemaker cells,** referred to earlier as autorhythmic cells, that are located in the wall of the right atrium. The depolarization spreads through a network of fibers called the **internodal pathway** that connects the sinoatrial node to another node called the **atrioventricular node** (the AV node). The atrioventricular node is located on the bottom of the right atrium close to the septum. It slows down the current from the SA node before the signal is allowed to pass down to the ventricles. Why is this delay necessary? The delay ensures that the atria fully contracts before the ventricles are stimulated. Otherwise, not all of the blood would be expelled from the atria. This would not be efficient. The other way that the heart is slowed down is through action by the **vagus nerve**, which is part of the parasympathetic nervous system. Recall from the nervous system chapter that the parasympathetic nervous system is part of the autonomic nervous system and functions in the "rest and digest" response.

From the atrioventricular node, the signal moves to the **atrioventricular bundle**, also called the **bundle of His**. The bundle of His is located in the ventricular septum and separates into left and right bundle branches. The branches conduct the electrical signal to lower parts of the ventricles. Further down the branches, the fibers of the atrioventricular bundle divide into **Purkinje fibers** that spread out among the entirety of the ventricle and cause its contraction.

Let us summarize the signaling of a muscle contraction that we just discussed. The SA node depolarizes, causing the electrical signal to move through the internodal pathway to the AV node. There, the depolarization spreads across the atria, slowing along the way because of the AV node. Depolarization moves more rapidly through the atrioventricular bundle downward to the apex of the heart, where signals are sent through purkinje fibers to cause depolarization of the ventricles.

Electroactivity in the heart and how to read electrocardiograms

Those of you who have volunteered in emergency rooms (or watched Grey's Anatomy) are familiar with the concept of an EKG. For the purpose of the MCAT, you should be able to follow an electrocardiogram through one cycle (**Figure 5.7**).

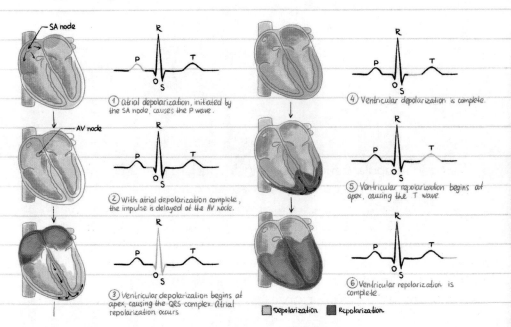

Figure 5.7:
Electrocardiogram (EKG)

Chapter 5 Cardiovascular System   Copyright © 2019 MCAT King

An EKG graph shows us a change in voltage over time in the heart.

The two parts of the electrocardiogram are waves and segments. The major waves in an electrocardiogram are the **P wave**, the **QRS complex**, and the **T wave**. The P wave corresponds to the first depolarization of the atria. This is the depolarization from the SA node to the AV node. Overall, the P wave corresponds to atrial depolarization. Then, conduction will slow down due to the AV node cells. The QRS complex corresponds to ventricular depolarization. The T wave corresponds to the repolarization of the ventricles. You should understand that the EKG is not one depolarization, but the sum of the depolarizations that occur in many muscle cells.

Cardiac Cycle

There are two phases in a heart cycle. The first is called **diastole**: the phase in which the cardiac muscle relaxes. During diastole, the chamber fills with blood. The second phase is called **systole**, the time during which the muscle is contracting and blood is being ejected from the chamber (**Figure 5.8**).

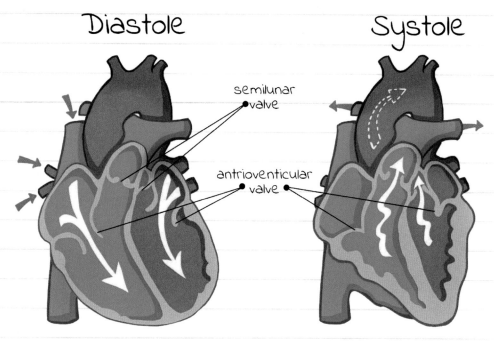

Figure 5.8:
Phases of the Cardiac Cycle:
Diastole vs. Systole

We begin the cycle with the atria in diastole. The atria are filling with blood from the veins just as the ventricles have completed a contraction. The ventricles relax and the AV valves (between the atria and ventricles) open, allowing blood to flow from the atria into the ventricles.

Not all of the blood flows into the ventricles, however. The last 20 percent is pumped in by the contraction of the atria. This contraction brings us into atrial systole which is initiated by the depolarization wave that spreads across the atria, like we discussed above.

Remember, as the atria contract, the depolarization wave spreads to the AV node. The depolarization then travels down to the purkinje fibers. The increasing volume of blood and pressure within the ventricle causes blood to push against the underside of the atrioventricular valves, forcing them to close so that the blood cannot flow back into the atria. This closing of the atrioventricular valves is responsible for the first heart sound, called S1. This closure creates the first "lub" sound that we normally associate with the heart beat.

With both the AV and semilunar valves closed, the blood is trapped in the ventricle.

Ventricular systole begins at the apex of the heart, located at the lowest portion of the heart. As the ventricles contract, they generate enough pressure to open the semilunar valves and push the blood into the arteries. This pressure is the driving force for the flow of blood.

While the ventricles contract, the atria begin to relax, causing the atrial pressure to drop below the pressure in the veins. Therefore, since we mentioned that fluids go from higher to lower pressure, the blood flows into the atria from the veins once more. At the end of the ventricular contraction, the ventricles begin to relax and the pressure decreases. Eventually the pressure in the ventricles becomes lower than pressure in the arteries and blood begins to flow backward into the ventricles. This backward flow forces the semilunar valves to close. The closing of the semilunar valves is responsible for the second heart sound, called S2. This closure creates the second "dub" sound that we normally associate with the heart beat. Since there is a decrease in pressure in the ventricle, blood from the atria (high pressure) moves into the ventricles.

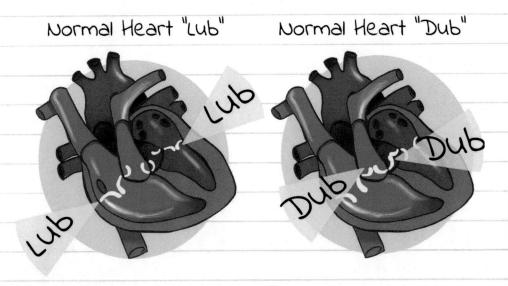

Figure 5.9:
Closing of the Heart Valves. The "lub" sound is caused by the closing of the atrioventricular valves. The "dub" sound is caused by the closing of the semilunar valves.

Pressure Volume Curves

The MCAT may sometimes show you a **pressure-volume graph** to test your understanding of the cardiac cycle (**Figure 5.10**).

In the curve, volume is the x-axis and pressure is the y-axis. Look at the diagram which represents one cardiac cycle of the left ventricle.

At Point D, the left atrial pressure exceeds left ventricular pressure. This causes the mitral valve to open and blood to flow into the left ventricle until Point A is reached.

At Point A, left ventricular diastole has ended and the left ventricle now has greater pressure than the left atria. This causes the mitral valve to close: think of pushing a door on the side you are supposed to pull.

From Point A to Point B, the ventricle goes through **isovolumetric contraction**. During this phase, the pressure increases but the volume of blood in the ventricle stays the same. Think about it as tightening your grip on a small foam ball before you squish it. Your hand represents the ventricle and the ball represents the blood. When you tighten your hand slightly without squishing the ball, the pressure inside your hand increases but the volume of the ball has not changed.

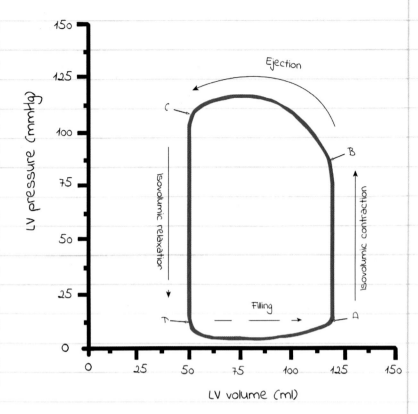

Figure 5.10:
The Pressure-Volume Graph of the Left Ventricle

At Point B, the left ventricular pressure exceeds aortic pressure and causes the aortic valve to open. Blood ejects from the left ventricle into the aorta from Point B to C.

At Point C, the aortic pressure exceeds the left ventricular pressure and causes the aortic valve to close. This stage is called **end systolic pressure**.

From Point C to Point D is called **isovolumic relaxation**: the volume of blood in the left ventricle is constant but the pressure is decreasing. The volume of blood is constant because no more blood is being added to or ejected from the ventricle; the pressure is decreasing because the volume of the ventricle is slowly increasing.

At Point D, ventricular diastolic filling begins again.

There is still blood remaining in the ventricles at the end of each contraction. Why does the ventricle not completely empty itself every cycle? The heart acts like a reserve, ensuring that there is still blood available in case the ventricle needs to send out more blood via an extra forceful contraction. Although typically, the heart does not fully contract.

The **stroke volume** is the amount of blood pumped by the ventricle during a single contraction. It can be measured using the following formula:

$$EDV - ESV = Stroke\ Volume$$

Where **EDV (end Diastolic Volume)** is the volume of blood in the ventricle before contraction, and the **ESV (end systolic volume)** is the volume of blood in the ventricle after contraction.

Cardiac output is the volume of blood pumped by one ventricle in a given period of time (volume/time). We can calculate the cardiac output by multiplying the **heart rate** (beats/time) and the **stroke volume** (volume/beat).

Although the heart does not rely on the nervous system to initiate contraction due to pacemaker cells, heart rate can still be influenced by autonomic neurons and hormones. As we mentioned in the chapter discussing the nervous system, the sympathetic and parasympathetic divisions of the autonomic nervous system have opposite effects. We described the parasympathetic system as the rest and digest system. Therefore, it makes sense that the parasympathetic system slows the rate of the heart. The MCAT wants you to memorize the name of the parasympathetic nerve that innervates the heart: the **vagus nerve.** The sympathetic system is responsible for the fight or flight response. Consequently, the sympathetic nervous system increases heart rate.

The Blood Vessels

The three main types of blood vessels are **arteries, veins,** and **capillaries.** Arteries and veins are generally composed of 3 different layers (**Figure 5.11**).

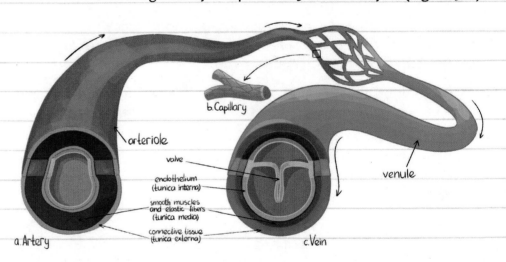

Figure 5.11: Blood Vessels.

The innermost layer is called the **endothelium,** or **tunica interna.** The endothelium is a relatively thin layer made of epithelial cells. Directly surrounding the endothelium are smooth muscle and elastic fibers. This layer, known as the **tunica media,** is thicker in arteries compared to veins. Why is that so? Arteries regulate blood pressure by using their smooth muscle to constrict and dilate themselves. In addition, the large amount of elastic fibers help to withstand the pressure exerted by blood against the arterial wall as the blood exits the heart. The outermost layer of arteries and veins is called the **tunica externa,** composed of connective tissue. This layer is thicker in veins to prevent the collapse of the blood vessel, since blood pressure is much lower in veins compared to arteries. Veins are also more superficially located and so this layer is thicker as a means of protection.

Blood moves from arteries into smaller blood vessels called **arterioles.** Arterioles further branch out into **metarterioles.** From the **metarterioles,** the blood proceeds into **capillary beds**. There is a drop in blood pressure as blood reaches the capillaries, so arteries closer to the capillary bed do not need to be as elastic as the first arteries that encounter blood from the heart.

Fluid exchange occurs at the capillaries and the blood continues its journey to the **venules**. Blood flows from venules to **veins** as it makes its way closer to the heart. The largest of these veins, **vena cavae**, empties into the right atrium. Since veins lack the thickness of tunica media, the diameter of veins is larger than the diameter of arteries. What does that mean in terms of volume? That's right, the volume within the veins will be larger, which is why veins hold more than half of the blood in the circulatory system. While the volume of blood carried by vessels increases from arteries to veins, the pressure of blood within these vessels decreases (**Figure 5.12**).

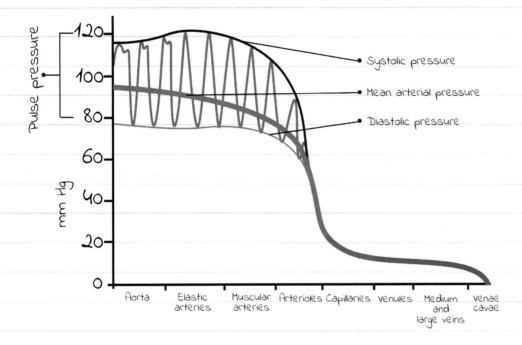

Figure 5.12:
Blood pressure throughout various blood vessels.

The capillaries are the smallest vessels in the cardiovascular system and are the site of gas and nutrient exchange. The capillaries' diameter is extremely small and is barely larger than the size of a red blood cell. As a consequence, blood cells are forced to flow in a single file line. Capillaries have absolutely no smooth muscle or connective tissue. Instead, capillaries only contain a one-cell-thick endothelium. This feature is desirable because gases and nutrients are able to pass through and between the cells of the endothelium.

It is not good to be too permeable, however, and one consequence of the one-cell-thick endothelium may be that the capillaries can leak. To fix this, the capillaries are associated with special cells known as **pericytes**, which surround the capillaries and "tighten" things up, minimizing the amount of leaking that could occur.

Different tissues have different metabolic needs. The capillary density and capillary type of a certain tissue is related to the metabolic activity and needs of that tissue's cells. There are different types of capillaries we will discuss (**Figure 5.13**).

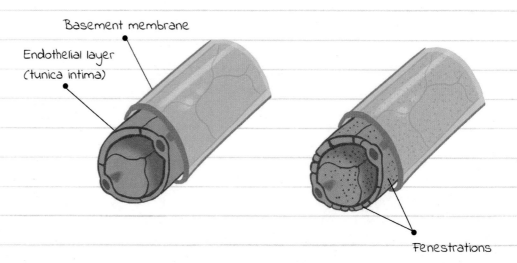

Continuous   Fenestrated

Basement membrane

Endothelial layer
(tunica intima)

Fenestrations

1. **Continuous capillaries**: these are the most abundant capillaries in the body. These capillaries have very small perforations and thus allow only small molecules to pass through. They can be found in muscles, neural tissue, and connective tissue. The famous blood-brain barrier is formed from continuous capillaries.

2. **Fenestrated capillaries**: the name of these capillaries comes from their large pores. Fenestra means window. The large pores allow a large volume of fluid to pass between the plasma and the interstitial fluid. Fenestrated capillaries are commonly found in the kidney and intestine.

How does exchange occur? Most of the exchange actually involves the diffusion of solutes and gasses through the endothelium of capillaries. The rate depends on the concentration gradient between the plasma and interstitial fluid.

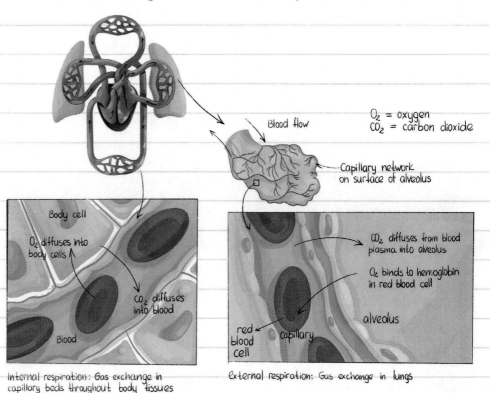

Blood flow

O_2 = oxygen
CO_2 = carbon dioxide

Capillary network on surface of alveolus

Body cell

O_2 diffuses into body cells

CO_2 diffuses into blood

Blood

Internal respiration: Gas exchange in capillary beds throughout body tissues

CO_2 diffuses from blood plasma into alveolus

O_2 binds to hemoglobin in red blood cell

alveolus

red blood cell   capillary

External respiration: Gas exchange in lungs

Figure 5.14:
Diffusion of Gases Across Capillaries.

Bigger molecules that are incapable of diffusing across will be transported via a mechanism called **transcytosis,** in which a vesicle carries the macromolecule from one side of the cell to another via a membrane-bound vessel. Another form of exchange is called **bulk flow.** Bulk flow is the mass movement of molecule-containing fluids in and out of capillary beds (**Figure 5.14**).

The Physics of Blood Flow

For the next couple of pages we will discuss a very important topic that will bring together your knowledge of biology and physics. We will discuss pressure, volume flow, and resistance within the context of the circulatory system.

Blood is not an ideal fluid, but for the MCAT we can assume that it acts as one unless told otherwise. A fluid's pressure is due to the force the fluid exerts on the container that holds it. According to Boyle's law, pressure and volume are inversely proportional. Fluids are also incompressible, meaning a change in pressure does not change the density of the fluid (mass/ volume). Thus, as the ventricles of the heart contract, the pressure inside the ventricles increases. Since blood is incompressible, the blood is forced out of the ventricle into the vessel. This pressure that drives blood forward through the vessels is called **driving pressure.** Pressure changes also occur in the vessels. Through neural stimulation and hormonal action, arteries can either dilate to decrease pressure or contract to increase pressure, depending on the needs of the body.

From fluid mechanics, we know that fluids (both gases and liquids) flow from an area of high pressure to an area of low pressure. How does this apply to the human body? In humans, the blood pressure is highest leaving the heart due to forceful contractions of the ventricles. The blood continues traveling to lower areas of pressure as it gets further away from the heart. How so? Resistance by vessels to blood flow decreases blood pressure! Resistance in fluid dynamics is analogous to friction in mechanics. The blood encounters friction as it flows through blood vessels and this friction results in a loss of energy and a decrease in pressure. In other words, the flow of the blood is inversely proportional to the resistance. The resistance is primarily influenced by three factors:

1. The radius of the tube
2. The length of the tube
3. the viscosity of the fluid

The above factors and their relationship to resistance can be represented mathematically according to **Poiseuille's Law.**

$$\frac{\text{Volume}}{\text{Flowrate}} = \mathcal{F} = \frac{P_1 - P_2}{R} = \frac{\pi(\text{Pressure difference})(\text{radius})^4}{8(\text{viscosity})(\text{length})}$$

$$Q = \frac{\Delta P \, \pi \, r^4}{8 \, \eta \, l}$$

$$\frac{\text{Resistance}}{\text{to Flow}} \quad R = \frac{8\eta L}{\pi r^4}$$

Where Q = Volume Flow Rate, ΔP = pressure, r = radius, η = viscosity, and *l* = length of the tube

Notice that the resistance is most heavily influenced by the radius. Resistance is inversely proportional to the 4th power of the radius! Thus a slight change in radius can cause a significant change in resistance, which in turn causes a significant change in pressure. That is why the body exerts control over resistance by dilating or contracting blood vessels.

Two measurements that you should know and be able to differentiate in regard to blood flow are **flow rate** and **the velocity of flow**. The two are easy to confuse. The flow rate is the volume of blood that passes a given point in the system per unit time. In contrast, the velocity of flow is the distance that a fixed volume of blood travels per unit time. To clarify, think of traffic. Imagine you are standing at the corner of a street watching the cars pass by. Flow rate would be analogous to how many cars pass you in a minute. Velocity of flow would be analogous to how long it takes an individual car to go past you.

Flow rate and velocity of flow both depend on area. As the equation above shows, flow rate is directly proportional to the 4th power of the radius. Thus, a slight increase in radius can cause a significant increase in flow rate. This makes sense with our traffic analogy-- the more lanes in a highway, the more cars are able to pass per unit time. In terms of velocity of flow, the larger the area, the smaller the velocity of flow. This should seem familiar, as we've encountered this relationship before in fluid mechanics with the **continuity equation**.

Recall that the continuity equation states that $A_1v_1 = A_2v_2$, where A is the cross sectional area and v is the velocity. With this formula, it is clear that as the area increases, the velocity decreases; conversely, as the area decreases, the velocity increases. Let's apply this to blood vessels. The cross sectional area of a vein is larger than the cross sectional area of an artery; thus, blood flow through the veins is slower than blood flow through the arteries. How does this apply to capillaries? The cross sectional area of a single capillary is much smaller than that of a vein or an artery. Therefore, the velocity must be faster in capillaries than in the larger blood vessels, correct? WRONG! The cross sectional area of a single capillary may seem smaller than the area of the aorta, but the total cross-sectional area of all capillaries summed together is greater than the cross sectional area of the aorta. Consequently, the flow of blood is the slowest through the capillaries. This is beneficial to us because the capillaries are the site of fluid exchange. In order for exchange to be thorough, we want fluid flow through capillaries to be slow so that all necessary materials can pass in and out of the capillaries.

Now that we understand the mechanics of blood flow throughout the body, how does blood exchange occur at the capillaries? Blood exchange at the capillaries occurs due to two types of pressure: hydrostatic pressure and osmotic pressure. Hydrostatic pressure is the pressure exerted by the fluid in an enclosed space; in regards to capillaries, hydrostatic pressure is the pressure exerted by the blood against the capillary wall and is responsible for fluid wanting to leave the capillary. On the other hand, osmotic pressure of the capillary is responsible for fluid wanting to be pulled into the capillary. Osmotic pressure is determined by the solute-to-water concentration in the blood compared to solute-to-water concentration in the interstitial fluid. If there is an osmotic pressure gradient and solutes are unable to pass through the membrane, water is pulled towards the direction of higher solute-to-water concentration. Take a look at **Figure 5.15.** When the pressure exerted by the blood against the internal capillary wall (hydrostatic pressure) is greater than the pressure of the fluid trying to enter the capillary (osmotic pressure), fluid leaves the capillary. Fluid enters the capillaries when the opposite is true.

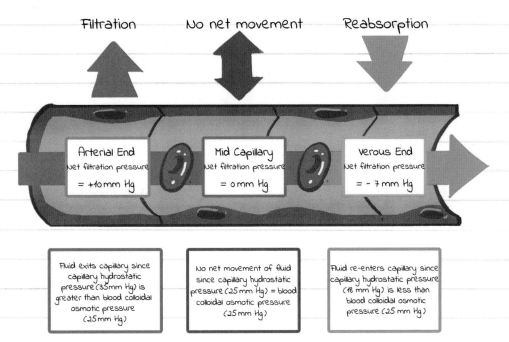

Figure 5.15:
Filtration through a Capillary.

Blood Pressure Regulation

All of the complicated structures and processes discussed above have one simple, yet critical, function: supply the brain and vital organs with proper blood flow.

By regulating blood pressure, our body is able to make sure adequate amounts of blood reaches various parts of the body in a timely manner. One way to regulate blood pressure is through the **baroreceptor reflex**. How does the body know whether adequate blood flow is being sent? There are special stretch-sensitive sensory receptors called **baroreceptors** located in the carotid arteries and the aorta. These receptors monitor the pressure of blood flowing to the brain and to the rest of the body.

The receptors regularly fire action potentials as blood flows past them, but the frequency of the firing changes depending on the change in blood pressure. An increase in blood pressure increases the frequency of the firing of the receptor, while a decrease in blood pressure decreases the firing rate of the receptor.

Figure 5.16:
Blood Pressure Regulation.

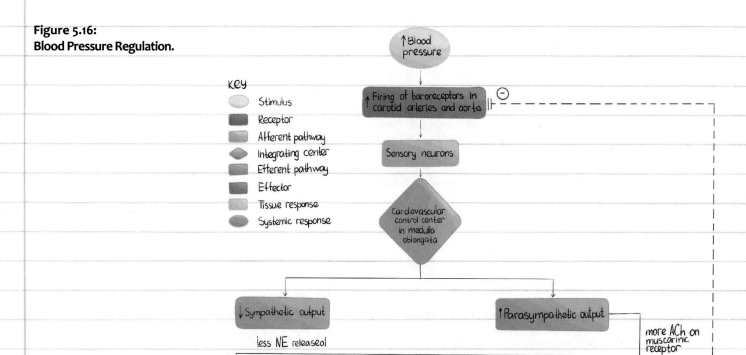

Figure 5.16 walks us through the process in which blood pressure is lowered via baroreceptors. What you should take away from this image is that an increase in detected blood pressure tells the brain to decrease sympathetic output and increase parasympathetic output. This causes vasodilation of blood vessels, decreased force of contraction of the heart, and a decrease in heart rate. Due to there being less resistance in the vessels and a lower volume of blood being pumped from the heart, the overall pressure in the blood vessels drops.

Another way to regulate blood pressure is through the **renin angiotensin pathway.** A drop in blood pressure initiates the release of the enzyme **renin** from the kidneys, which converts **angiotensinogen** (produced in the liver) to **angiotensin I.** Then, an enzyme called **angiotensin-converting enzyme** (ACE) converts angiotensin I to **angiotensin II.** Angiotensin II binds to receptors in blood vessels and causes them to constrict, resulting in an increase in blood pressure. Additionally, angiotensin II induces the release of **aldosterone,** from the adrenal cortex, which causes the retention of sodium and water at the kidney. Specifically, more sodium ions are taken up in the distal convoluted tubule and collecting duct, at the expense of potassium being excreted. As more sodium is absorbed, water follows via osmosis. The reuptake of water increases blood volume, and thereby blood pressure.

Thermoregulation

On top of everything that we have discussed thus far, the cardiovascular system also plays a role in **thermoregulation**, which is how the body attempts to maintain a stable temperature despite the temperature of the environment.

We all know what it feels like to be sweating on a hot day, but we will discuss the function of sweating in the context of the circulatory system (Figure 5.17). The blood vessels that lead to capillaries in our skin dilate (become wider) so that more blood flow reaches the skin and heat can be released into the environment. This is called **vasodilation**. On a cold day, we want to keep the precious heat that we have in our body. So, the blood vessels that lead to capillaries in our skin constrict to lessen the amount of blood that reaches the skin, preventing the release of heat into the environment. This is called **vasoconstriction.**

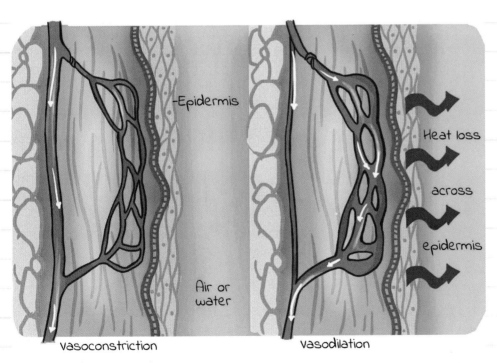

vasoconstriction   vasodilation

Blood

The blood running through our body has four main components to it: **plasma, red blood cells, white blood cells,** and **platelets (Figure 5.18). Plasma** is the fluid component of the blood. All the cellular components of the blood are

IN-TEXT QUESTION:
If arteries can constrict in response to systemic changes in the body, why don't materials from the blood then squeeze out of the arteries into the surrounding tissue?

Answer:
Exchange of material only occurs in the capillaries — the arterial walls are too thick and muscular for any form of exchange.

Figure 5.17:
Thermoregulation by the Circulatory System. Blood vessels near the epidermis dilate so that more blood can reach close to the skin. As more blood flows near the surface of the skin, energy is released as heat. The heat is then expelled via sweat.

Components of Blood

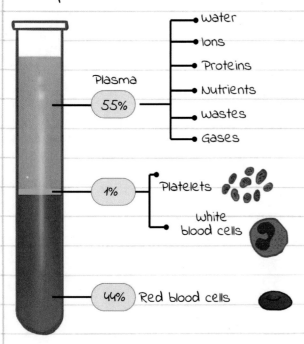

Plasma
55%
- water
- Ions
- Proteins
- Nutrients
- Wastes
- Gases

1% — Platelets

White blood cells

44% — Red blood cells

Figure 5.18:
Components of Blood.

suspended within the plasma. The plasma is also composed of proteins and ions. The most prevalent plasma proteins are the **albumins**, which are made by the liver and secreted into the blood. They help to transport nonpolar substances through the polar blood, since nonpolar substances cannot dissolve well in the blood on their own.

Production of Blood Cells

All of the cells of the blood that we will soon discuss are derived from a single cell. This parent cell is called the **pluripotent hematopoietic stem cell**, a cell that is found in the **bone marrow**. Remember from biology book 1, we mentioned that pluripotent stem cells are cells that can become any cell of the embryo. Blood cells are produced in the bone marrow in a process called **hematopoiesis**.

Blood Cells

There are three main blood cell types:

1. **Red blood cells:** these cells are also called **erythrocytes**. Their production is regulated by a hormone called **erythropoietin**. Red blood cells' main function is to transport oxygen from the lungs to the tissues and carbon dioxide from the tissues to the lungs. They carry hemoglobin molecules in order to transport oxygen (**Figure 5.19**).

Hemoglobin Molecule

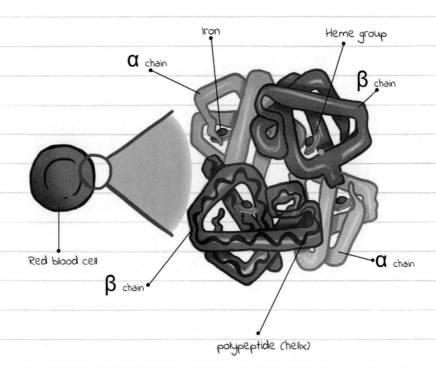

Iron

Heme group

α chain

β chain

Red blood cell

β chain

α chain

polypeptide (helix)

Figure 5.19:
Hemoglobin Molecule.
Hemoglobin contains four subunits: 2 alpha and 2 beta subunits. Each subunit has a heme group that has an iron atom that reversibly binds to an oxygen molecule.

When oxygen levels are low, **erythropoietin** is released by the kidneys in response so that more oxygen carriers are available to be transported throughout the body. **Erythropoietin** increases the production of red blood cells.

Mature red blood cells do not contain a nucleus or mitochondria. What do you think the consequences are of not having mitochondria? What kind of metabolic process is the red blood cell reliant upon for energy production? That's right! Glycolysis. Without a mitochondria, the blood cell cannot produce energy via the citric acid cycle or oxidative phosphorylation. Why would it be beneficial for red blood cells to lack mitochondria?? Think about it, what is the blood cell's function? To carry oxygen for transport. What does the mitochondria use when making energy? OXYGEN. Do you really want your main oxygen transporter to be using the oxygen it is carrying for use in the body? Of course not, so it is better for the red blood cells to be reliant on glycolysis for energy

Red blood cells have a biconcave shape, in which they are the thinnest at their center. There is an important significance to the shape. For one, the cell's small size and biconcave shape improve gas exchange by increasing its surface area. Additionally, the lack of the nucleus provides the space for **hemoglobin**. The red blood cell not only carries oxygen, but also transports carbon dioxide to the lungs to be expelled.

2. **White blood cells**: these cells are also called **leukocytes**. The five types of mature blood cells (which will be discussed more in depth in the immune system) are **lymphocytes, monocytes, neutrophils,**

Figure 5.20: Cell Tree.

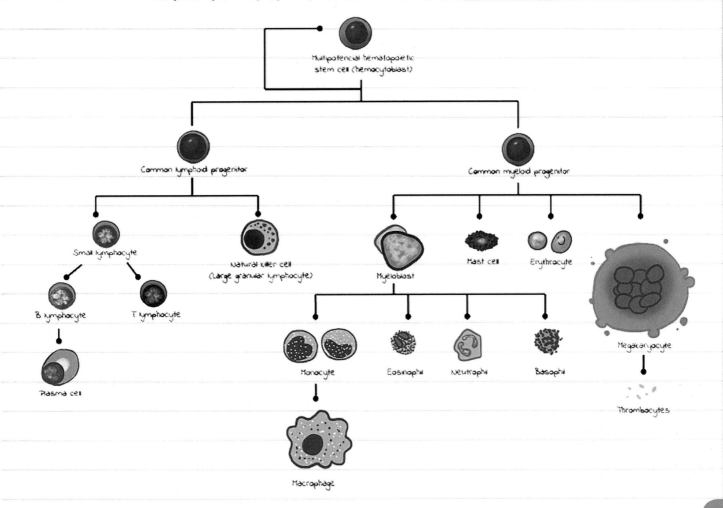

eosinophils, and basophils. Lymphocytes are involved in acquired immunity. There are two types of lymphocytes: T-lymphocytes and B-lymphocytes. Monocytes are cells that eventually leave the circulation to develop into macrophages that engulf pathogens and destroy them. Neutrophils also engulf and destroy pathogens. Eosinophils secrete toxic proteins and free radicals to destroy pathogens. Basophils secrete histamine to assist with inflammation (**Figure 5.20**).

3. **Platelets**: these cells are also called **thrombocytes**. Platelets are cell fragments that have split from a larger parent cell called a **megakaryocyte**. Platelets play a role in blood clots in a process called **coagulation**. They use a molecule called **fibrinogen** to mediate blood clot formation. To understand the role that platelets play in blood clotting, let us discuss what happens when a blood vessel is damaged (**Figure 5.21**).

First, the damaged vessel immediately constricts due to paracrines (hormones) released by the endothelium, resulting in the decrease of blood flow and pressure within the vessel. This is important as we do not want more blood flow when the vessel lining is damaged. In the second step, platelets normally floating in the blood detect the ruptured area and the exposed connective tissue and collagenous fibers. The platelets stick to **collagen** and activate. As a result of their activation, the platelets release cytokines around the injury, resulting in further vasoconstriction and the recruitment and activation of more platelets. As more platelets adhere to the collagen and endothelial lining, they seal the exposed area and form a **platelet plug.** The third and final step is the **coagulation cascade**. This is a series of enzymatic reactions that result in the conversion of **fibrinogen** to **fibrin**. The main enzyme responsible for this conversion is **thrombin.** Fibrinogen is converted to fibrin because fibrinogen is a water soluble protein whereas fibrin is not. The fibrin threads strengthen and support the platelet plug to ensure no further blood is lost. This reinforced plug is now called a **clot**. Slowly but surely, the vessel repairs itself and the clot is eventually dissolved by a protein called **plasmin.**

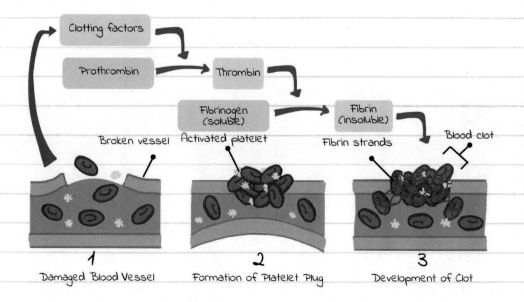

Figure 5.21:
Blood Clot Formation.

1
Damaged Blood Vessel

2
Formation of Platelet Plug

3
Development of Clot

Blood Antigens

Red blood cells express proteins on their surface. These proteins are called **antigens.** An antigen is a specific target, typically a protein, to which the immune system reacts to using **antibodies**. Antibodies are antigen-specific binding proteins that aid in the recognition and/or destruction of cells and pathogens (described more in the Immune System Chapter). The two antigens relevant for blood groups are the **ABO antigens** and the **Rh factor.**

The **ABO system** contains three alleles that determine the antigens present on each cell. This display of antigens ultimately determines one's blood type. Two of these alleles, A and B, are co-dominant, while the O allele is recessive. If someone has one A allele and one O allele, then that person has A antigens on their blood cells and consequently has type A blood. Likewise, if someone has one B allele and one O allele, then that person has B antigens on their blood cells and consequently has type B blood. The A and B alleles are codominant, meaning that a person with both alleles will express both A and B surface antigens, and their blood type would be AB. The O allele is the recessive allele to both the A and B alleles. People with blood type O do not express either A or B antigens and are considered to have type "O" blood.

Our blood type matters and has medical implications. If someone needs a blood transfusion, the blood type of the donor needs to match the blood type of the recipient. People with blood type O are considered **universal donors** since they do not have any of the A or B antigens. People with blood type AB are **universal recipients** because they have both antigens, so they do not have antibodies against A or B antigens, and can receive blood from anyone.

It is important to understand why type O blood is the universal donor and why type AB blood is the universal recipient. Rejection of infused blood occurs when the recipient has antibodies against the foreign blood. Type O blood does not have the A antigen or the B antigen. Therefore, it cannot be attacked by the production of antibodies from another person's body, and is the **universal donor** because it can be given to any recipient, regardless of their blood type. Type AB blood, on the other hand, contains both the A antigen and the B antigen. Therefore, their body does not make antibodies for these antigens because these antigens are not considered foreign to the person. Since the person does not produce either antibody, they can accept any type of blood without the possibility of rejection.

To clarify a point regarding antibodies: they are created in response to an antigen, and they specifically target that antigen. You cannot expect to have antibodies against a foreign invader you've never been exposed to.

Rh factor (Rhesus D) is also a surface protein that is expressed on red blood cells. Rh positive or Rh negative refers to the presence or absence of a specific allele called D. The presence or absence of D can also be indicated with a plus or minus subscript on the ABO blood type. Rh-positive follows autosomal dominant inheritance, so one positive allele is enough for the Rh protein to be expressed and be present on the red blood cell surface. The Rh factor is very important in maternal-fetal medicine. During childbirth, women are exposed to a small amount of fetal blood. If a woman is Rh negative and her fetus is Rh positive, she will become sensitized to the Rh factor, and her immune system will begin making antibodies against it. For the first child this is not an issue because the mother is exposed to the fetus's blood during childbirth. However, if the woman has another child, it may be an issue depending on the fetus's Rh factor. The woman now has antibodies against the Rh positive allele; so if the second child is Rh positive, the child's blood cells will be attacked by the mother's immune system while the child is growing inside the mother. Doctors combat this problem in a multitude of ways; one of which is through prescribing a medication that prevents the mother from producing antibodies against the Rh factor (**Figure 5.22**).

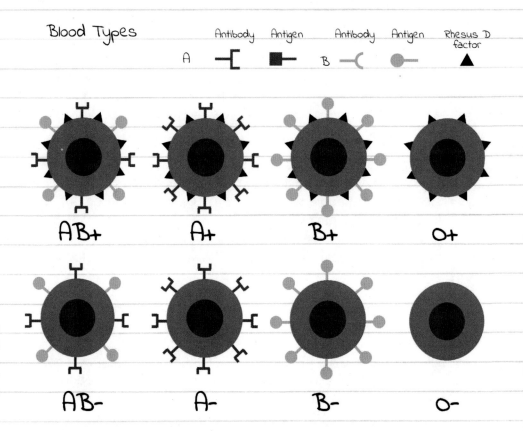

Figure 5.22:
Blood Type. Blood Types are determined by the antigen(s) that the cell displays on its membrane. Notice at the top right how antibodies are specific to a type of antigen.

Questions

1) **Which of the following represents the correct flow of blood through the heart?**
   a. Right atrium → bicuspid valve → right ventricle → pulmonary circulation → left atrium → tricuspid valve → left atrium → aortic valve → aorta
   b. Right atrium → mitral valve → right ventricle → pulmonary circulation → left atrium → bicuspid valve → left atrium → aortic valve → aorta
   c. Right atrium → tricuspid valve → right ventricle → pulmonary circulation → left atrium → bicuspid valve → left atrium → aortic valve → aorta
   d. Right atrium → semilunar valve → right ventricle → pulmonary circulation → left atrium → mitral valve → left atrium → aortic valve → aorta

2) **How are action potentials generated in the heart?**
   a. The vagus nerve projecting from the medulla releases acetylcholine at the gap junctions in the sinoatrial node, causing the cells to reach threshold and eventually opening voltage-gated channels
   b. The bundle of His conducts ambient electrical signals and transfers them to the atrioventricular node, causing those cells to depolarize
   c. Passive diffusion of solutes from the circulation causes the influx of sodium and calcium ions, leading to a strong enough depolarization in the sinoatrial node to result in an action potential
   d. The sinoatrial node spontaneously depolarizes due to slow sodium leak channels

3) **Which of the following statements is true of the cardiac cycle?**
   a. During diastole, decreasing pressure in the atria causes the blood to empty into the ventricles from the atria
   b. During systole, decreasing pressure in the ventricles causes the blood to empty into the ventricles from the atria
   c. During diastole, decreasing pressure in the ventricles causes the blood to empty into the ventricles from the atria
   d. During systole, increasing pressure in the ventricles causes the blood to empty into the ventricles from the atria

4) **Why does the mitral valve close after left ventricular diastole?**
   a. Because the volume in the left atrium exceeds the volume in the left ventricle
   b. Because the pressure in the left atrium exceeds the pressure in the left ventricle
   c. Because the volume in the left ventricle exceeds the volume in the left atrium
   d. Because the pressure in the left ventricle exceeds the pressure in the left atrium

5) If three individuals all require the same cardiac output, which individual will require the highest heart rate?

    a. The individual who weighs the most
    b. The individual with the smallest heart by mass
    c. The individual with the lowest stroke volume
    d. The individual with the highest blood pH

6) Which is true of the relationship between the cardiac output of the right ventricle and that of the left ventricle?

    a. The cardiac output of the left ventricle is greater as it must pump blood out to the entire systemic circulation
    b. The cardiac output of the right ventricle is greater as it receives blood from the entire circulation
    c. The cardiac output of the left ventricle is greater as it passes blood into the aorta, which has the highest pressure of all the arteries
    d. The cardiac output of both ventricles is the same

7) Which of the following nerves can modulate heart rate?

    a. The trigeminal nerve
    b. The hypoglossal nerve
    c. The vagus nerve
    d. The cardiac nerve

8) Which of the following have the largest volume?

    a. Systemic arteries
    b. Systemic veins
    c. Systemic capillaries
    d. Vena Cavae

9) What is one difference between continuous capillaries and fenestrated capillaries?

    a. Continuous capillaries are found in the kidney and intestines while fenestrated capillaries are found in muscles, neural tissue, and connective tissue
    b. Fenestrated capillaries have larger pores
    c. Continuous capillaries allow a large volume of fluid to pass between the plasma and the interstitial fluid
    d. Fenestrated capillaries are responsible for the blood-brain barriers

10) The resistance of blood is influenced by all of the following except:

    a. The radius of the vessel
    b. The length of the vessel
    c. The density of the blood
    d. the viscosity of the blood

11) Where is the blood pressure the highest?

    a. The aorta
    b. The pulmonary artery

c. The jugular artery
d. The coronary artery

12) **What would be the most effective way for the body to decrease the resistance of blood?**

    a. By dilating blood vessels
    b. By adding more solutes to the blood
    c. By synthesizing adhesion molecules on the walls of endothelial cells
    d. By reducing the heart rate

13) **Jack sees a bear in the forest and starts running away from it. What would be the hemodynamic effect in his skeletal muscles?**

    a. Resistance would increase and blood flow rate would decrease
    b. Resistance would decrease and blood flow rate would increase
    c. Resistance would increase and blood flow rate would increase
    d. Resistance would decrease and blood flow rate would decrease

14) **Where in the capillary is the hydrostatic pressure the greatest?**

    a. The arteriole end
    b. The mid capillary
    c. The venous end
    d. None of the above

15) **Mary, an otherwise healthy woman, suddenly experiences a severe drop in her blood pressure. Which of the following would be a systematic response in her body?**

    a. Less norepinephrine released to postganglionic effectors
    b. An decrease in peripheral resistance
    c. An increase in cardiac output
    d. A decrease in heart rate

16) **Sally, who is also a healthy woman, suffers an anxiety attack and as a result, her blood pressure shoots through the roof. Which of the following would be a systematic response in her body?**

    a. Increased retention of sodium at the nephron
    b. Decrease in the firing rate of action potentials in the baroreceptors of the arteries
    c. Increased activity of angiotensin-converting enzyme
    d. Decreased synthesis of renin

17) **Which of the following will IMMEDIATELY raise blood pressure?**

    a. A deep wound that causes a large amount of blood loss, leading to the release of norepinephrine
    b. Eating a big mac with fries
    c. Running on the treadmill
    d. Urination

18) **Which of the following statements are true of erythrocytes?**

    1. They undergo oxidative phosphorylation to synthesize ATP

2. Their production is regulated by the hormone erythropoietin
3. Their nucleus has more compact than normal DNA to create space for hemoglobin
   a. I only
   b. II only
   c. I and II only
   d. I, II and III

19) **All of the following are true of white blood cells except:**

   a. Monocytes are cells that eventually leave the circulation to develop into macrophages that will engulf pathogens and destroy them
   b. Neutrophils assist platelets in cell adhesion and clotting
   c. Eosinophils secrete toxic proteins and free radicals to destroy pathogens
   d. Band basophils secrete histamine to assist with inflammation

20) **If a mother has AB+ blood type and a father has A- blood type, which of the following blood types are possible for their children?**

   1. They undergo oxidative phosphorylation to synthesize ATP
   2. Their production is regulated by the hormone erythropoietin
   3. Their nucleus has more compact than normal DNA to create space for hemoglobin
      a. I only
      b. II only
      c. I and II only
      d. I, II and III

Answers

1) **Answer: C**

   Explanation: Only answer choice C illustrates the correct flow of blood through the heart along with the correct valves at their respective junctures. All of the other choices are incorrect.

2) **Answer: D**

   Explanation: The vagus nerve does release acetylcholine to the heart, but only to modulate the rate of action potential conduction, not to generate them from the start, eliminating choice A. Choice B is completely true, but it is not responsible for the generation of action potentials, only their propagation, eliminating choice B. The sinoatrial node depolarizes as a result of the influx of cations that are already in the extracellular space of the heart, eliminating choice C and making choice D correct.

3) **Answer: C**

   Explanation: Fluids generally move from areas of higher pressure to areas of lower pressure, which eliminates choices A and D as those state that blood would flow in the opposite direction. Blood empties into the ventricles from the atria during diastole, not systole, eliminating B and making choice C correct.

4) **Answer: D**

   Explanation: The volume of fluid of the atria and ventricles do not play a role in valve openings as they are not responsible for producing forces, eliminating A and C. The mitral valve closes once the pressure in the left ventricle exceeds the pressure in the left atrium after being filled. If it were the opposite, then blood would never be able to enter the ventricle, eliminating B and making choice D correct.

5) **Answer: C**

   Explanation: Cardiac output is the product of two quantities: stroke volume and heart rate. Bodyweight, mass of heart, and pH have no direct effect on any of those quantities, eliminating choices A, B, and D. An individual with a low stroke volume would need to compensate with a higher heart rate to achieve the same cardiac output as the other individuals, making choice C correct.

6) **Answer: D**

   Explanation: The units of cardiac output are volume/time. Assuming heart rate is constant and total blood volume is constant, the cardiac output of all the chambers should be the same. If not, there would be a backlog of blood in one of the chambers, making choice D correct.

7) **Answer: C**

   Explanation: The trigeminal nerve (the fifth cranial nerve) is responsible for sensation in the face and motor functions such as biting and chewing, eliminating choice A. The hypoglossal nerve (the twelfth cranial nerve), innervates muscles of the tongue for motor function, eliminating choice B. The cardiac nerve supplies blood to the heart but is not involved in heart rate, eliminating D. Only the vagus nerve can modulate heart rate by release of acetylcholine, making C the correct answer.

8) **Answer: D**

   Explanation: The capillaries are the smallest of the blood vessels (only one red blood cell thick!) in order to assist in the transport of nutrients, eliminating choice C. Since veins lack the thickness of tunica media, the diameter of veins is larger than the diameter of arteries, eliminating choice A. However, the largest of the veins are the vena cava, as they receive the entirety of the systemic circulation, making choice D correct.

9) **Answer: B**

   Explanation: Continuous capillaries are found in muscles, neural tissue, and connective tissue while fenestrated capillaries are found in the kidney and intestines, eliminating choices A and D (fenestrated capillaries are not found in the brain). Continuous capillaries have very small perforations and thus allow only small molecules to pass through, eliminating choice C. Fenestrated capillaries have larger pores than continuous capillaries, making choice B correct.

10) **Answer: C**

    Explanation: According to Poiseuille's Law, the resistance of blood flow is primarily dependent on the radius of the vessel, the length of the vessel, and the viscosity of the blood, eliminating choices A, B and D and making choice C correct.

11) **Answer: A**

    Explanation: While choices B, C, and D refer to arteries that have a high pressure, the pressure is highest in the aorta as it requires enough driving force to push blood through the entire body, making A the correct answer.

12) **Answer: A**

    Explanation: Adding solutes, synthesizing adhesion molecules, and reducing heart rate have no effect on the resistance, eliminating choices B, C, and D. Remember, resistance is only dependent on radius, length, and viscosity. As per Poiseuille's Law, an increase in vessel radius through dilation would decrease resistance, making A the correct answer.

13) Answer: B

Explanation: We know that as part of a fight-or-flight response, vessels that vascularize skeletal muscles dilate in order to supply those regions with more blood. This dilation causes a decrease in resistance, eliminating choices A and C. We also know from Poiseuille's law that a small increase in the radius results in a large increase in blood flow rate, eliminating choice D and making choice B correct.

14) Answer: A

Explanation: The hydrostatic pressure is the result of fluid pushing against the walls of the capillaries. As fluid moves through the capillaries, some of it gets absorbed into the cells, decreasing the hydrostatic pressure in the capillaries. Thus, it is greatest in the arteriole end of the capillary, making A the correct choice.

15) Answer: C

Explanation: A drop in blood pressure would result in an increase in the sympathetic response and a subsequent increase in heart rate norepinephrine release to postganglionic effectors, eliminating choices A and D. Furthermore, it would be an increase in peripheral resistance that would stimulate an increase in blood pressure, not a decrease, eliminating choice C. An increase in cardiac output would be required to bring blood pressure back to stable levels, which would result from an increased heart rate, making C the correct answer.

16) Answer: D

Explanation: Increased reuptake of sodium in the nephron would result in a congruent reabsorption of water, increasing total blood volume and subsequently blood pressure, eliminating choice A. Increased blood pressure causes the arteries to stretch which would increase the firing rate of baroreceptors, not decrease, eliminating choice B. ACE activity is only induced in response to falling blood pressure not rising blood pressure, eliminating choice C. The opposite would occur in the renin-angiotensin system, in that renin synthesis would decrease to compensate for the increased blood pressure, making choice D correct.

17) Answer: C

Explanation: A deep wound would lead to a reduction in total blood volume which would, in turn, reduce blood pressure, eliminating choice A. Eating a large meal would result in the stimulation of the parasympathetic nervous system and an overall decrease in blood pressure, eliminating choice B. Choice C, like choice A, results in a loss of total blood volume, eliminating it. Exercising causes muscles to contract which increases heart rate, cardiac output, and subsequently blood pressure, making choice C correct.

18) Answer: B

Explanation: Erythrocytes do not contain mitochondria and therefore cannot undergo oxidative phosphorylation, making statement I false and eliminating choices A, C, and D. That alone would make B correct, but statement III is false because erythrocytes also do not have a nucleus. When oxygen levels are low, erythropoietin is released by the kidneys to increase the production of red blood cells, thus making statement II true.

19) Answer: B

Explanation: Neutrophils engulf and destroy pathogens, but they do not assist in cell adhesion and clotting, making choice B false and the correct answer. All of the other choices are true statements.

20) Answer: D

Explanation: Since the mother has an A and a B allele, if the father has 1 O allele, then an A, B, and AB blood type are all possible. Since the Rh-positive follows autosomal dominant inheritance, only one is needed for penetrance, making I and III possible. Assuming the mother has 1 Rh-negative allele, then II is also possible, making choice D correct.

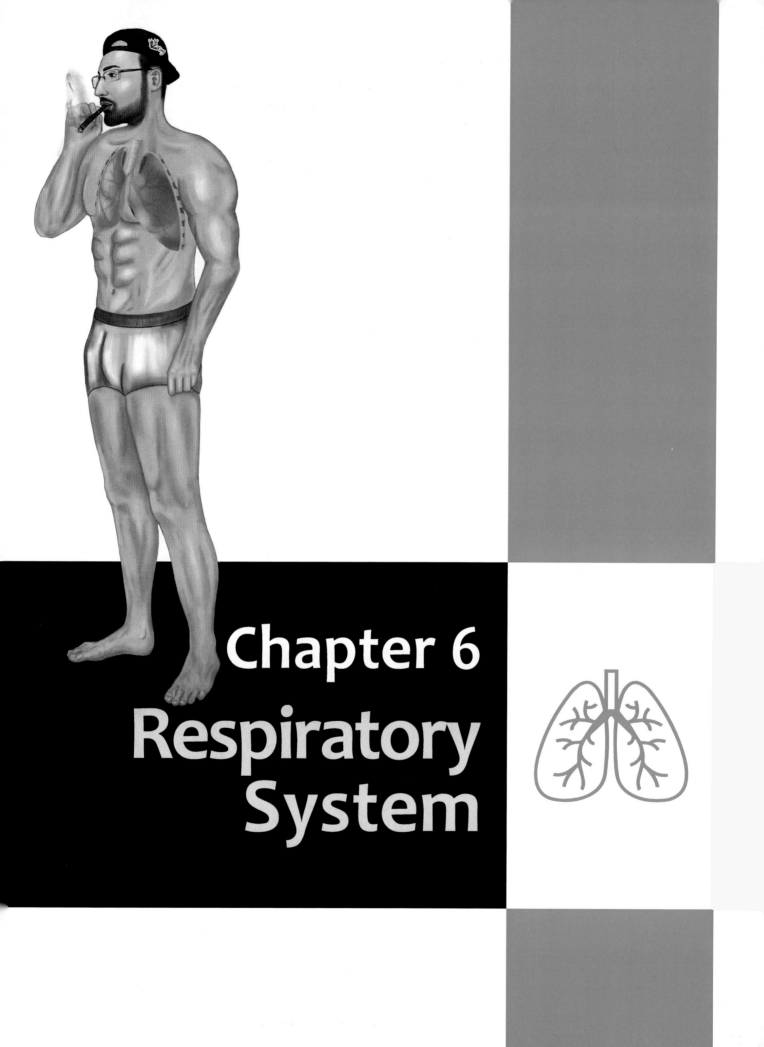

Chapter 6
Respiratory System

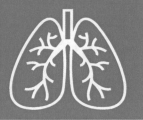

Chapter 6

The Respiratory System

The respiratory system helps us breathe, but also reminds us how terribly out of shape we are! If you stepped outside and went for a few laps, you may feel yourself huffing and puffing to get in as much oxygen as you can into your system! The respiratory system, however, is responsible for more than just breathing. In this chapter, we will explore this wonderful system and its role in keeping us alive!

There are 3 major functions of the respiratory system: **gas exchange, maintenance of pH**, and **protection from pathogens**.

The lungs are the major site of **gas exchange**. The tissues and cells of the body need oxygen to survive. Through inhalation, the body takes oxygen in. The oxygen then passes from the lungs to the blood where it can then be distributed to the body tissues. Additionally, the carbon dioxide that is produced via cell metabolism is carried from the tissues, through the blood, and finally to the lungs. Through exhalation, the carbon dioxide is then expelled from the body into the external environment.

The lungs play an important role in **maintaining pH balance**. The body pH must be tightly regulated; otherwise, a cascade of negative consequences will occur. The lungs are capable of regulating pH by influencing carbon dioxide concentrations through exhalation. In order to do this, the respiratory system works with the circulatory system to either increase or decrease the amount of dissolved carbon dioxide in the blood via the bicarbonate buffer system.

Finally, the lungs serve as a resource for **protection.** The respiratory system contains a few defenses that thwart pathogen invaders from harming us. For example, thick mucus that traps pathogens to be expelled by coughing. The protective ability of the respiratory system is covered more in depth in the Immune System chapter.

In this chapter, we will cover in depth the functions of the respiratory system. But first, let us dive into the structure of the respiratory system!

Anatomy of the Respiratory System

There are two levels of respiration. Here, we will discuss the **macro** level, detailing how gas moves from the atmosphere to the lungs and cells of our body. The **micro** level, cellular respiration, was already discussed in the biochemistry chapter of Book 1. It includes the citric acid cycle and oxidative phosphorylation.

The anatomy of the respiratory system can be divided into two different parts called **zones**. The first of these is the **conducting zone** and is composed of the structures that are not directly involved in gas exchange including the **nose, pharynx, larynx, trachea, bronchi,** and **bronchioles**. The other area is known as the **respiratory zone,** which is where gas exchange happens and includes the **alveolar ducts** and **alveoli**.

The respiratory system can be also divided into specific regions: **upper** and **lower respiratory tracts**. The **upper respiratory tract** includes the **mouth, nasal cavity, pharynx** and **larynx**. The **lower respiratory tract**, also known as the **thoracic portion**, includes the **trachea, bronchi,** and **bronchioles**. Alveoli, and therefore gas exchange, are located at the end of bronchioles (**Figure 6.1**).

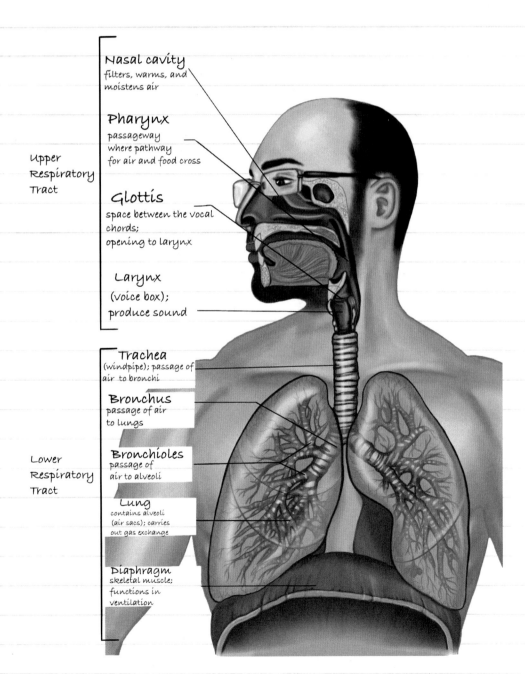

Nasal cavity
filters, warms, and moistens air

Pharynx
passageway where pathway for air and food cross

Glottis
space between the vocal chords; opening to larynx

Larynx
(voice box); produce sound

Upper Respiratory Tract

Trachea
(windpipe); passage of air to bronchi

Bronchus
passage of air to lungs

Bronchioles
passage of air to alveoli

Lung
contains alveoli (air sacs); carries out gas exchange

Diaphragm
skeletal muscle; functions in ventilation

Lower Respiratory Tract

Figure 6.1:
Upper and Lower Respiratory Tract.
The conducting zone includes the nasal/oral cavity, pharynx, larynx, trachea, bronchi, and bronchioles.

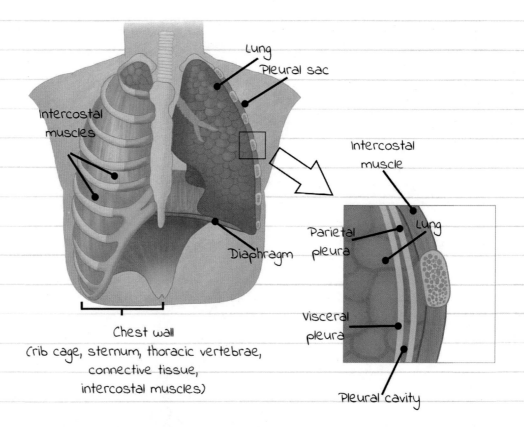

The lower respiratory system is located in the **thoracic cavity**. Since the lower respiratory system needs to be protected, it is surrounded by the **"thoracic cage"** aka the bones of the spine and rib cage. Underneath is a structure made of skeletal muscle, called the **diaphragm,** that divides the thoracic cavity from the abdominal cavity. Two sets of muscles run between the ribs called the **internal** and **external intercostal muscles**. Underneath the ribs and intercostal muscles, but above the lungs, is a membranous sac. Just as the heart is surrounded by the **pericardial sac,** the lungs are surrounded by **pleural sacs**, one for each lung (**Figure 6.2**).

Each pleural sac contains fluid called **pleural fluid**. Why do we need this fluid? We take thousands of breaths per day; about 23,000 per day. Every time we breathe, our lungs expand and shrink within the thoracic cage. Pleural fluid reduces the friction between the lungs and the walls of the thoracic cavity, and thus minimizes possible damage to the lungs. Now that we have covered the anatomy of the respiratory system, let us look at how air travels through it!

Air Flow

Air first enters through the mouth and/or the nose. Air then makes its way down the pharynx, larynx, and then the trachea. It is important to note that the pharynx is the last location where both food and air can reside in the same location. The pharynx splits into the larynx for air and **esophagus** for food. What helps our body separate the two into their correct compartments? The **epiglottis**! When we ingest food, the epiglottis covers the opening of the larynx so that food passes down the esophagus. When we breathe, the epiglottis no longer covers the opening of the larynx and allows air to pass through. This is why we are supposed to abstain from talking or laughing while we eat. When we do, we leave ourselves vulnerable to food passing through the wrong tube and choking! (**Figure 6.3**)

From the trachea, air enters into the **bronchi**. Each bronchus enters one lung. These bronchi branch off within the lungs into smaller and smaller branches called **bronchioles**. These bronchioles also branch into smaller branches called the respiratory bronchioles. Even though the diameter of these branches becomes progressively smaller, the overall surface area increases. Sound familiar? This is exactly what we saw in the circulatory system with the progression from arteries to arterioles to capillaries. There is a good lesson to learn here: wherever exchange of either oxygen or nutrients is important, it is most efficient to have as large of a **surface area** as possible.

Gas exchange occurs through a very important structure in the respiratory system: **alveoli**. Clusters of alveoli appear at the end of the respiratory bronchioles. Each alveolus is extremely small and is made up of a single layer of epithelium. There are two types of epithelial cells in the alveoli. **Type II alveolar cells** are thicker and secrete a very important chemical called **surfactant**. Surfactant aids the alveoli in expanding during inhalation by reducing the surface tension of the molecules in the fluid lining of the alveoli. We shall cover how this occurs in greater detail later on in the chapter. The other is **type I alveolar cells**. These are larger and occupy most of the alveolar surface area. They are extremely thin and allow gases to easily diffuse across.

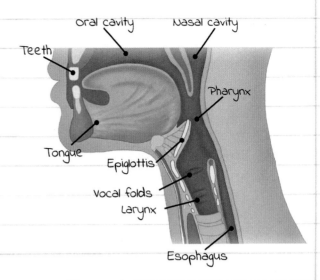

Figure 6.3:
Air flow. Air travels from the oral/nasal cavity to the pharynx, and then to the larynx. The epiglottis covers the larynx when we eat food.

Pressure Gradients and Breathing

How is it that we are able to force air from the environment into our body? Let's dive in:

The air that we breathe is not merely oxygen. The atmosphere is composed of a mixture of gases and water vapor. When discussing the mechanisms of respiration, we are concerned with only gas, specifically, its **pressure**. We know that according to **Dalton's law**, the total pressure of a mixture of gases is the sum of the pressures exerted by the individual gases that make up the mixture. The pressure exerted by an individual gas amongst a mixture of gases is called **partial pressure**. The partial pressure of an individual gas will depend on that gas's prevalence in the atmosphere.

Gases only flow from one area to another if there is a pressure gradient. A pressure gradient is a situation where there is an immense difference in

Answer:
Inhalation is always an active process. Inhalation uses the diaphragm and external intercostal muscles. The diaphragm contracts and straightens, which uses energy, so the chest wall expands outwards. The volume of intrapleural space increases causing the pressure to decrease. However, exhalation does not always require energy. In a relaxed state, the relaxation of the diaphragm and external intercostal muscles is enough to result in air being exhaled. However, in more active states like running, internal intercostal muscles and abdominal muscles can be contracted to actively decrease volume of the chest cavity.

pressure between two areas. Gases will flow from an area where there is a high pressure to an area of low pressure. For the purposes of respiration, we are concerned with oxygen; therefore, remember that oxygen will flow from an area of higher partial pressure to an area of lower partial pressure.

As the lungs inhale and exhale they expand and contract, resulting in a change in volume. **Boyle's law** discusses the relationship between volume and pressure that we need to understand for respiration. The pressure of a gas is the result of the gas particles colliding with the walls of the container. Therefore, as the container gets smaller, or volume decreases, there are more particle collisions with the walls. The more collisions, the higher the pressure. In short, a decrease in volume results in an increase in pressure. Volume and pressure are, thereby, inversely related to one another. During respiration, when the volume of the lung increases, the pressure in the lungs decreases. Since the pressure within the lungs has decreased, air flows from the environment (higher pressure) into the respiratory system (now lower pressure). The increase in the volume of the lungs due to the expansion of the chest cavity results in a lower pressure space within the respiratory system, compared to the external atmosphere. This is the mechanism behind inhalation. In contrast, in order to exhale we must make our lungs a higher pressure system than the atmosphere. When the volume within the lungs decreases, the alveolar pressure increases and air flows out of the lungs.

How does our body control the volume of the lungs?

During inhalation, the **diaphragm** will **contract**, shifting downward, resulting in an increase of thoracic volume. The contracted state of the diaphragm occurs when the diaphragm appears flattened, (as opposed to the dome shape of the relaxed diaphragm). **The external intercostal** and scalene muscles also contract, expanding the rib cage further. The lungs are attached to the wall of the chest cavity by the parietal, or outer, pleura. Therefore, as the diaphragm and rib muscles cause chest cavity volume to increase, the lungs also increase in volume. The pressure in the lungs consequently decreases, thereby allowing air to flow in from the environment.

The opposite course of events occurs during **exhalation**. As we exhale, the diaphragm and rib muscles relax. The relaxed state of the diaphragm results in the muscle taking on a "dome-shape." This results in a decrease in volume and simultaneous increase in pressure within the chest cavity and lungs. When the pressure in the alveoli is higher than the pressure in the atmosphere, the air flows out of the lungs and into the external environment. **Internal intercostal muscles**, which differ from the **external intercostal muscles**, contract during exhalation, pulling the ribcage further inward to decrease the volume of the chest cavity. Abdominal muscles are also used during exhalation, but mainly for forceful exhalation. To assist the lungs during forceful exhalation, abdominal muscles will contract to push the abdominal organs inwards and force the diaphragm further up. The volume of the lungs and chest cavity will decrease, the pressure will increase, and air will be pushed out the lungs (**Figure 6.4**).

Chapter 6 The Respiratory System

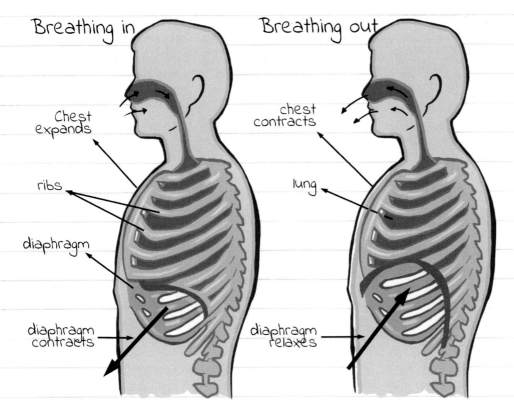

Breathing in

Chest expands

ribs

diaphragm

diaphragm contracts

Breathing out

chest contracts

lung

diaphragm relaxes

Figure 6.4:
Volume Control of the Thoracic Cavity During Inhalation and Exhalation. During Inhalation, the diaphragm contracts, expanding the thoracic cavity. This decreases the pressure in the lungs and causes air to flow into the lungs. The opposite series of events occurs during exhalation.

A set of specific terms are used to define the different volumes of air that exist within the lungs while we breathe (**Figure 6.5**). **Tidal volume** is the volume of air a person inhales during a normal breath. **Inspiratory reserve volume** refers to the extra volume in the lungs that is present after normal inhalation. For example, imagine you inhale a normal breath and at the end of the breath you try to inhale further, to take in as much extra air as you can. This additional volume of air is called the inspiratory reserve volume. **Expiratory reserve volume** is a similar concept to the inspiratory reserve volume, except the opposite. Imagine you exhale normally, and then at the end you force yourself to exhale as much as you can. The additional volume of air that you expel is called the expiratory reserve volume. **Residual volume**, unlike the other volumes we've discussed,

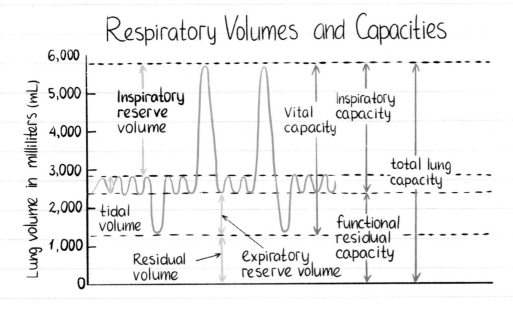

Respiratory Volumes and Capacities

Lung volume in milliliters (mL)

Inspiratory reserve volume

tidal volume

Residual volume

expiratory reserve volume

Vital capacity

Inspiratory capacity

total lung capacity

functional residual capacity

Figure 6.5:
Respiratory Volumes and Capacities.

cannot be directly measured. Why? Residual volume refers to the volume that is always in your lungs — no matter what. You can continually exhale until you turn blue: this residual volume of air always remains in the lungs and airway. Thus, the residual volume is the volume of air left after maximal exhalation.

Capacity is another term that is often used when discussing respiration. The capacity refers to the sum of specific lung volumes. **Vital capacity** is the sum of the inspiratory reserve volume, expiratory reserve volume, and tidal volume. This capacity represents the maximum volume of air that can voluntarily be inhaled or exhaled. **Total lung capacity** refers to the vital capacity plus the residual volume. **Inspiratory capacity** refers to the tidal volume plus inspiratory reserve volume. **Functional residual capacity** refers to the expiratory reserve volume plus the residual volume.

Lung Compliance and Elastance

Compliance refers to the ability of the lungs to expand and contract based on changes in pressure. This definition can be represented mathematically as the change in volume per unit pressure change. **Elastance** refers to the ability of the lungs to spring back against stretching in a process known as **elastic recoil**. Low lung compliance means that the lungs are stiff and thus have high elastance. People with illnesses that cause low lung compliance, such as pulmonary fibrosis, have trouble inhaling since their lungs have difficulty expanding. On the other hand, high lung compliance suggests that the lungs are too pliable and thus have low elastance. People with illnesses that cause high lung compliance, such as emphysema, have trouble exhaling due to their lung's inability to recoil back to its original shape.

The Role of Surfactant

Surfactant is a chemical that is composed of lipids and proteins. As mentioned before, it is secreted by the epithelial type II cells in the alveolar space. Its primary function is to reduce the surface tension present at the air/liquid interface in the lung. Well what does this exactly mean?

The alveoli are extremely small spherical structures lined with alveolar fluid. Like many fluids, alveolar fluid has surface tension which means that it is relatively difficult to break the intermolecular bonds that are present on the surface of the fluid. Without breaking the bonds of the fluid, we cannot expand the alveoli. Additionally, the intermolecular bonds of the alveolar fluid can cause alveolar collapse (as shown in **Figure 6.6**) and make it very difficult for us to breathe at all. Luckily, our savior, surfactant, comes to the rescue. Surfactant is a detergent that has both hydrophilic and hydrophobic components of its structure. The hydrophilic portions bind

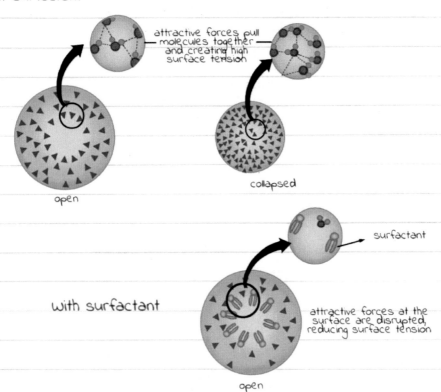

to the polar regions of the fluid molecules lining the alveoli. The binding of the hydrophilic portions to the alveolar fluid molecules breaks the intermolecular bonds between the individual fluid molecules. This weakens the surface tension of the fluid because the molecules are no longer as strongly associated with each other. Thus, surfactant **increases alveolar compliance**, allowing for it to expand, and **decreases alveolar elastance**, preventing its collapse, by **reducing surface tension**.

Resistance to Air Flow

Just like blood vessels resist blood flow, the respiratory system has resistance to air flow. The relationship is similar to **Poiseuille's Law** that we mentioned in the circulatory system chapter. The biggest factor of resistance is the radius:

$$\text{Volume Flowrate} = F = \frac{P_1 - P_2}{R} = \frac{\pi(\text{Pressure difference})(\text{radius})^4}{8(\text{viscosity})(\text{length})}$$

$$\text{Resistance to Flow} \quad R = \frac{8\eta L}{\pi r^4}$$

Figure 6.7:
Poiseuille's Law. Volume flow rate is inversely proportional to resistance.

The bronchi and bronchioles can influence resistance to air-flow by either constricting, via **bronchoconstriction**, or dilating, via **bronchodilation** (**Figure 6.8**). Why is control over our bronchi and bronchioles important?

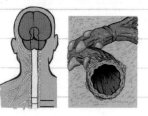

Sympathetic ANS

Bronchodilation

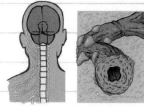

Parasympathetic ANS

Bronchoconstriction

As we reviewed in our discussion on the nervous system, during a fight or flight situation our body utilizes the sympathetic nervous system. One of the responses to sympathetic nervous system activation is bronchodilation. Why? Because in a fight or flight situation we want as much oxygen as possible to fuel our highly active bodies!

**Figure 6.8:
Bronchodilation vs.
Bronchoconstriction.**

Gas Exchange and Transport

You may remember Henry's law from General Chemistry. It states that the amount of gas that is dissolved in a liquid is directly proportional to the partial pressure of the gas.

So, the amount of gas that is dissolved in the blood depends on that gas's partial pressure. The higher the partial pressure, the more gas is dissolved in the blood. In terms of respiration, Henry's law allows us to predict how gases dissolve between the alveoli and blood stream. When we inhale, we take in a fresh supply of oxygen from the environment. At the alveoli, this fresh supply of oxygen is met with blood coming from tissues. Since the partial pressure of oxygen is greater in the alveoli than in the blood vessels at the alveoli, oxygen diffuses into the blood (**Figure 6.9**).

This blood from the lungs then travels to the tissues. When the blood reaches the capillaries of tissues, oxygen diffuses into the tissues because the partial pressure of oxygen in the blood is higher than it is in the tissues. Therefore, the oxygen diffuses down its pressure gradient and into the cells. The blood then returns to the lungs to get oxygenated again and the cycle begins anew (**Figure 6.10**).

For carbon dioxide, the same concepts apply but in reverse. Just think about whether you want your gas to diffuse in or out of the area of interest. At the tissues, the partial pressure of carbon dioxide is higher in the tissues than in the blood. As a result, carbon dioxide diffuses down its pressure gradient and into the blood. Then, at the capillaries of the pulmonary circulation, the partial pressure of carbon dioxide is higher in the blood than it is in the alveoli. Carbon dioxide diffuses out of the blood and into the alveoli where it is expelled via exhalation (**Figure 6.10**).

Bronchiole

Oxygen-deficient blood from the pulmonary artery

Oxygenated blood to the pulmonary vein

Alveolus

Capillaries

Alveolus wall

Capillary wall

Oxygen-deficient blood cell

Carbon dioxide

Oxygen

Oxygenated blood cell

**Figure 6.9:
Diffusion of Oxygen at the Lungs.**

There are ways that the above processes can go wrong. Let us discuss pulmonary diseases to see how.

Chapter 6 The Respiratory System.

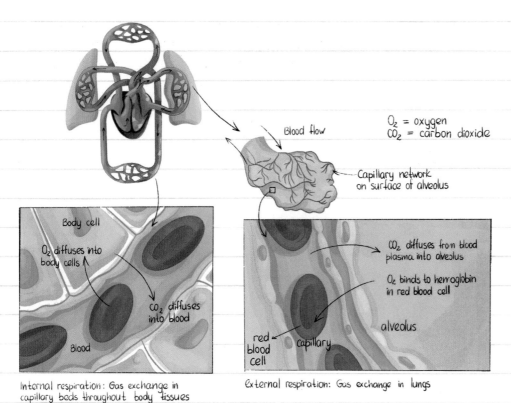

Figure 6.10:
Gas Exchange at the Lungs and the Tissues. Since after inhalation there is greater partial pressure of oxygen in the lungs than in the blood, oxygen diffuses out of the lungs and into the blood. Blood travels to the tissues where there is greater partial pressure in the blood than there is in the tissues. Oxygen diffuses out of the blood and into the tissues. Carbon dioxide follows the same principle but in a different order.

Labels in figure:
O_2 = oxygen
CO_2 = carbon dioxide
Blood flow
Capillary network on surface of alveolus
Body cell
O_2 diffuses into body cells
CO_2 diffuses into blood
Blood
Internal respiration: Gas exchange in capillary beds throughout body tissues
CO_2 diffuses from blood plasma into alveolus
O_2 binds to hemoglobin in red blood cell
alveolus
red blood cell
capillary
External respiration: Gas exchange in lungs

Emphysema: people with emphysema have over-inflated and damaged alveoli. As a result, the alveoli loses its ability to elastic recoil and return back to its original shape. This is an issue because the air within the alveoli is unable to move out of the alveoli to be exchanged for fresh air. Since the air in the damaged alveoli cannot be exchanged, it becomes difficult for a patient with emphysema to take a breath and bring in new air. This is why patients with emphysema have shortness of breath. In addition, since old air in the lungs is not being exchanged for new air, there is very little exchange of gases due to the pressure gradient no longer being present.

Pulmonary Edema: individuals with this condition have excess fluid in their lungs, making it difficult to inhale the appropriate amount of air. Patients with pulmonary edema also experience shortness of breath because they are not able to fully inhale due to the fluid present in their lungs.

Asthma: asthma is a condition in which the airways narrow and swell, making it more difficult to breath. Coughing, wheezing, and shortness of breath are common symptoms.

Gas Transport in the Blood-Hemoglobin

Oxygen is transported in the blood in primarily two ways:

1. Oxygen can be dissolved in the plasma.

2. Oxygen can be bound and carried by **hemoglobin**.

Figure 6.11:
Hemoglobin Structure.
Hemoglobin is made of 4
subunits. Each subunit has
a heme group with an iron atom.
The iron atom reversibly attaches
to an oxygen molecule.

At the pulmonary capillaries, oxygen diffuses down its pressure gradient from the alveoli into the blood. Around 98.5% of the oxygen is attached to hemoglobin in red blood cells and 1.5% of oxygen dissolves in the plasma.

Hemoglobin Structure

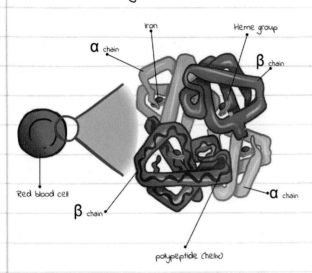

Hemoglobin special structure allows it to perform its very important job. Hemoglobin has four globular protein chains (or four subunits) (**Figure 6.11**). Each subunit contains a **heme** group. Look at the drawing: a heme group is a **porphyrin ring** that has an **iron** atom in the center. The iron atom of each heme group can bind reversibly with one oxygen molecule. This means that four oxygen molecules bind to each hemoglobin molecule. Once four oxygen molecules are bound to hemoglobin, the complex is called **oxyhemoglobin**. The concentration of oxygen influences how it binds with hemoglobin. The higher the concentration of oxygen in the blood, the more oxygen molecules bind to hemoglobin to form oxyhemoglobin. This is a good example of **Le Chatelier's Principle**. This property of hemoglobin allows us to better understand how hemoglobin functions in environments of different oxygen concentrations. For that, we need to take a look at hemoglobin's dissociation curve.

Hemoglobin dissociation curve

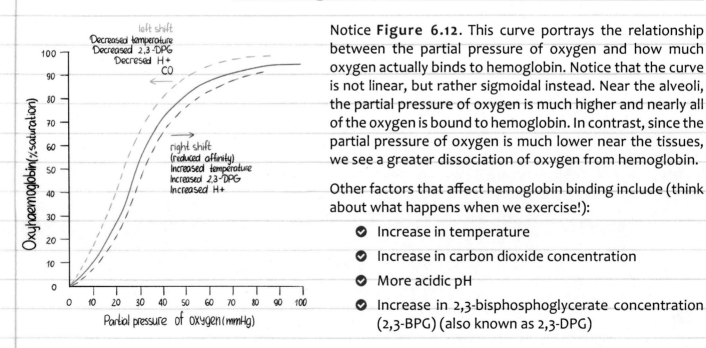

Notice **Figure 6.12**. This curve portrays the relationship between the partial pressure of oxygen and how much oxygen actually binds to hemoglobin. Notice that the curve is not linear, but rather sigmoidal instead. Near the alveoli, the partial pressure of oxygen is much higher and nearly all of the oxygen is bound to hemoglobin. In contrast, since the partial pressure of oxygen is much lower near the tissues, we see a greater dissociation of oxygen from hemoglobin.

Other factors that affect hemoglobin binding include (think about what happens when we exercise!):

- ✅ Increase in temperature
- ✅ Increase in carbon dioxide concentration
- ✅ More acidic pH
- ✅ Increase in 2,3-bisphosphoglycerate concentration (2,3-BPG) (also known as 2,3-DPG)

Figure 6.12:
Hemoglobin Dissociation Curve.

All of these factors push the dissociation curve to the right. This means that a higher concentration of oxygen would be needed to achieve the same levels of saturation under normal circumstances. For example, under normal circumstances, 50% of hemoglobin molecules will be bound to four oxygen molecules when the partial pressure of oxygen is 28 mmHg. However, if there is an increase in temperature of the hemoglobins' surroundings, it will take the partial pressure of oxygen to be around 32 mmHg for 50% of hemoglobin molecules to be bound by four oxygen molecules. The opposite of these factors (i.e. a decrease in temperature, decrease in CO2, basic pH, and decrease in 2,3 DPG) will push the dissociation curve to the left.

The special name given to the shift in the hemoglobin saturation due to a change in pH is "Bohr Shift."

2,3-biphosphoglycerate (2,3-BPG), also known as 2,3-diphosphoglycerate (2,3- DPG) (conjugate base of 2,3 BPG), is a compound that is made from an intermediate of glycolysis. 2,3 BPG binds to an allosteric site on hemoglobin and causes a decrease its the binding affinity for oxygen; thus, an increase in 2,3 BPG shifts the dissociation curve to the right.

Fetal vs. Adult Hemoglobin

The main difference is structural.

We mentioned that hemoglobin has 4 subunits. But, the identity of these subunits can differ. The common forms of the subunits are alpha, beta, and gamma. The most common form of hemoglobin in adults is a molecule that is composed of two alpha subunits and two beta subunits. Fetal hemoglobin, however, contains two alpha chains and two gamma chains. The gamma subunits have higher affinity for oxygen than the beta subunits. This allows for the transfer of oxygen from the maternal hemoglobin to the fetal hemoglobin. After birth, the fetal hemoglobin gets replaced with the adult hemoglobin configuration (two alpha and two beta subunits) (Figure 6.13).

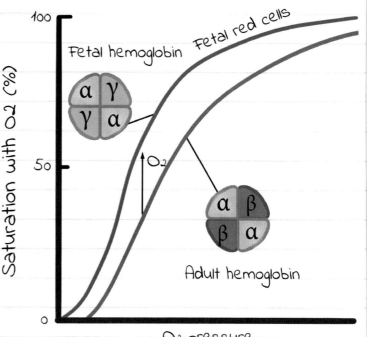

Figure 6.13:
Fetal Hemoglobin vs. Adult Hemoglobin Affinities.

Carbon Dioxide

Hemoglobin also transports carbon dioxide. Remember, carbon dioxide is one of the products of cellular respiration (this carbon originates from the glucose that we breakdown). Similarly to oxygen, very little of the overall carbon dioxide actually dissolves in the blood. Most carbon dioxide diffuses into red blood cells, where a large proportion will be converted into bicarbonate ions. The carbon dioxide that does not get converted, binds to hemoglobin. The main reason removing carbon dioxide from the body is so critical is due to carbon dioxide's ability to influence pH. Notice **Figure 6.14.** Higher carbon dioxide levels cause a decrease in pH: carbon dioxide reacts with water to form bicarbonate and hydrogen ions. The increase in hydrogen ions increases acidity and decreases pH. Some of the hydrogen ions can be picked up by the amino acids of hemoglobin, thereby neutralizing the acidity. Likewise, when pH is too basic, hemoglobin can donate hydrogen ions. Thus hemoglobin can help buffer the changes in pH that occur in a red blood cell. This is important as the effects of an environment that is too acidic can be disastrous to proteins, enzymes, and molecules alike.

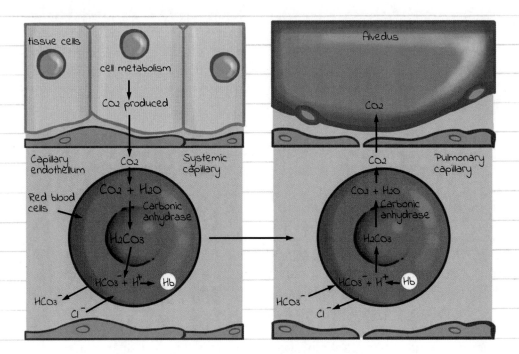

**Figure 6.14:
Carbon Dioxide Exchange.**

What's the purpose of a bicarbonate ion? Bicarbonate is capable of also acting as a buffer and provides an additional way for regulating pH via the **bicarbonate buffer system.** We will cover this system more in depth later on.

The reaction on **Figure 6.15** shows the conversion of carbon dioxide to bicarbonate. Please know this reaction as well as the name of the enzyme that catalyzes it. The enzyme is called **carbonic anhydrase** and is primarily found in red blood cells.

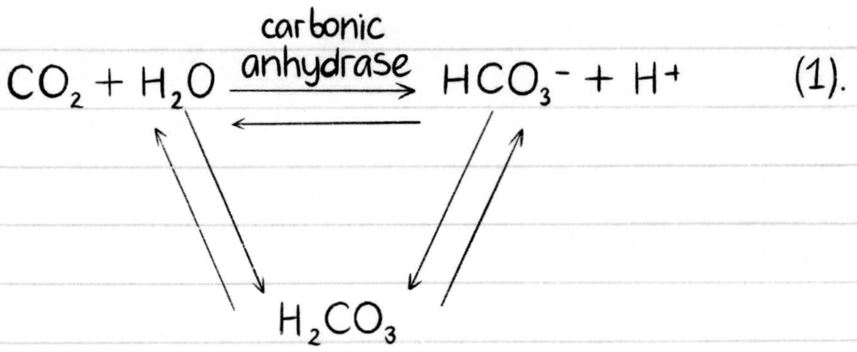

$$CO_2 + H_2O \xrightarrow{\text{carbonic anhydrase}} HCO_3^- + H^+ \qquad (1).$$

$$H_2CO_3$$

**Figure 6.15:
Bicarbonate Buffer System.**

In order to keep producing bicarbonate, bicarbonate must be continuously removed from the cytoplasm of the red blood cell due to Le Chatelier's Principle (we will cover later on). How do we accomplish this? We know that cell membranes are normally impermeable to ions due to the nonpolar nature of the membrane. One way we can overcome this is via an antiport protein in the cell membrane that exchanges a bicarbonate ion for a chloride ion. This process is called a **chloride shift**.

Regulation of pH

We mentioned earlier that one of the functions of the bicarbonate buffer system plays an important role in regulating pH. How so?

In the bicarbonate buffer system, we see carbon dioxide react with water to form carbonic acid. Carbonic acid then becomes bicarbonate and hydrogen ions (**Figure 6.16**). When there is an excess of hydrogen ions, the pH drops, and the environment is considered acidic. One way we can neutralize this problem is by increasing our breathing rate. In doing so, we are expelling more carbon dioxide than normal. Well, how does that help? According to Le Chatelier's Principle, if a change in concentration of a reactant occurs to a system in equilibrium, the equilibrium will shift to counteract that change in concentration. By removing carbon dioxide, the equation shifts to the left: hydrogen ions will combine with bicarbonate to form carbonic acid, which will form carbon dioxide and water. By forcing hydrogen ions to react with bicarbonate, we are removing free hydrogen ions from our blood, thus raising the pH.

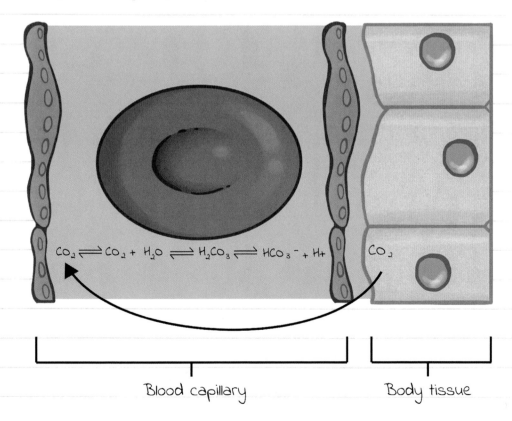

$$CO_2 \rightleftharpoons CO_2 + H_2O \rightleftharpoons H_2CO_3 \rightleftharpoons HCO_3^- + H+$$

Blood capillary   Body tissue

Figure 6.16:
Carbon Dioxide contribution to pH. As you can see in the diagram, the more carbon dioxide produced, the more the Le Chatlier's equation gets shifted to the right, causing an increase in hydrogen ion concentration. The increase in hydrogen ion concentration decreases pH!

What if we have the opposite scenario? What if the blood is too alkaline? This can occur, for example, when someone is hyperventilating. The intense breathing results in excess carbon dioxide leaving the blood and the consequent decrease in hydrogen ion concentration. The reason breathing into and out of a paper bag is a remedy for hyperventilation is because you are rebreathing the exhaled carbon dioxide and returning levels to normal. Another remedy is by holding one's breath for longer before exhaling. By bringing carbon dioxide levels back to normal, hydrogen ion levels normalize, and blood pH will return back to normal.

How are we able to control our breathing rate?

A special structure in the brain controls ventilation. This structure is called the **respiratory center** and is located in the medulla and pons of the brainstem. Here, breathing is maintained in an unconscious, involuntary manner. How does the brain center know how to control breathing? The control depends on the concentration of oxygen and carbon dioxide as well as the pH of the arterial blood. Special receptors called **chemoreceptors** located in the arteries can detect changes in these concentrations and either increase or decrease ventilation as needed.

Protection

The airways also play a role in filtering the air we breathe to ensure that foreign invaders like viruses and bacteria do not enter our bodies. Our airways contain **cilia**, hair-like projections that move microbes and debris out of the airways (**Figure 6.17**). Our airways also contain goblet cells that secrete mucus that traps microorganisms. When we cough, we use the combination of mucus and our cilia to push out unwanted particles.

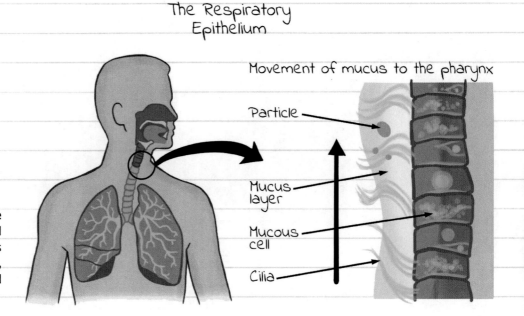

Figure 6.17:
Protective Function of the Respiratory System. Particles and microbes get trapped in the mucus of the airways. When we cough, our cilia pushes these unwanted particles and microbes out.

Chapter 6 The Respiratory System

Thermoregulation by the respiratory system

The respiratory system plays a role in regulating heat, which can be truly appreciated when looking at dogs. When dogs run around a lot, they begin to heavily pant. For us humans, this form of heat control is not as significant because we are capable of sweating whereas dogs cannot.

But even in humans cooling via respiration occurs. How? Our lungs warm the air that we breathe, making it equal to body temperature. When we exhale, we expel that warm air.

Questions

1) Which of the following is the correct order of pleurae membrane localization from most to least proximal to the lungs?

    a. intrapleural space → visceral pleura → parietal pleura → chest wall

    b. chest wall → visceral pleura → intrapleural space → parietal pleura

    c. Visceral pleura → intrapleural space → parietal pleura → chest wall

    d. parietal pleura → intrapleural space → visceral pleura → chest wall

2) What is the first mechanism the respiratory tract utilizes to protect itself from pathogens?

    a. Vibrissae trap particulate matter in the nares

    b. Lysozymes kill bacteria in the nasal cavity

    c. Macrophages engulf pathogens

    d. Mast cells trigger an inflammatory response

3) What factors are the main reasons why gas exchange is so efficient in the lungs?

    I. The branching nature of bronchiole and alveoli

    II. The small size of the alveoli

    III. The lungs are located in the chest cavity

    IV. There is a left lung and a right lung

    a. I only

    b. I and II only

    c. III only

    d. III and IV only

4) The diaphragm separates which two cavities?

    a. Thoracic cavity and abdominal cavity

    b. The dorsal body cavity and the thoracic cavity

    c. The abdominal cavity and the pelvic cavity

    d. The thoracic cavity and the pelvic cavity

5) If the intrapleural space is filled with more fluid than usual, as in pleural effusion, what are the effects on respiration?

    I. There is no effect on respiration.

    II. Lung expansion is restricted due to increased pressure in the intrapleural space

    III. There is a decrease in pH in lung capillaries.

    a. I only

    b. II only

    c. III only

    d. II and III

6) What is the name of the mechanism for breathing?
   a. Intrapleural oscillation breathing
   b. Pressure-variance breathing
   c. Negative-pressure breathing
   d. Pressure-dependent breathing

7) In a patient's lungs, if the residual volume is 2 L and the vital capacity is 4 L, what is the total lung capacity?
   a. 6 L
   b. 2 L
   c. 8 L
   d. 4 L

8) If the vital capacity is 5 L, the inspiratory reserve volume is 3 L, and the expiratory reserve volume is 1 L, what is the tidal volume?
   a. 1 L
   b. 9 L
   c. 3 L
   d. 4.5 L

9) What lung volume can be measured using a spirometer?
   a. Total lung capacity
   b. Residual volume
   c. Complete lung volume
   d. Tidal Volume

10) Respiratory rate can be influenced by which of the following conditions?
   I. Hypercarbia
   II. Hypercapnia
   III. Hypoxemia
      a. I only
      b. II only
      c. I, II, and III
      d. None of the above

11) Which of the following are functions of the lungs?
   I. Immune function
   II. Thermoregulation
   III. pH control
   IV. Blood filtration
      a. I only
      b. I and III
      c. I, II, and III
      d. IV only

12) Which of the following most correctly pairs the specific pulmonary blood vessel with its function.
   a. Pulmonary arteries transport oxygenated blood from the right ventricle of the heart
   b. Pulmonary arteries transport deoxygenated blood from the left ventricle of the heart

    c. Pulmonary veins transport deoxygenated blood to the right atrium of the heart

    d. Pulmonary veins transport oxygenated blood to the left atrium of the heart

13) **What is the driving force for gas exchange in the lungs?**

    a. The thin membrane that separates the alveolus from the lung capillaries

    b. The pressure differential of the gasses

    c. Liquid in the intrapleural space

    d. The elasticity of the chest wall

14) **Which of the following most correctly pairs the specific gas with its proper movement in gas exchange?**

    a. CO_2 flows down its partial pressure gradient from the pulmonary capillaries to the alveoli

    b. CO_2 flows down its partial pressure gradient from the alveoli to the pulmonary capillaries

    c. O_2 flows down its partial pressure gradient from the pulmonary capillaries to the alveoli

    d. O_2 flows up its partial pressure gradient from the alveoli to the pulmonary capillaries

15) **Which of the following mechanisms does the human body NOT regularly use for thermoregulation?**

    a. Panting

    b. Vasodilation

    c. Vasoconstriction

    d. Rapid muscle contractions

16) **Which of the following correctly displays the bicarbonate buffer system in blood that is relevant to gas exchange in the lungs?**

    a. $CO_2 + H_2O \rightarrow H_2CO_3 \rightarrow H^+ + HCO_3$

    b. $C_2O_4 + H_4O_2 \rightarrow H_4C_2O_6 \rightarrow H_2 + H_2C_2O_6$

    c. $CO_2 + H_2O \rightarrow H_2CO_3$

    d. $H_2CO_3 \rightarrow H^+ + HCO_3$

17) **Which of the following is NOT a major part of the immune function in the lungs?**

    a. Mucociliary escalator

    b. Mast cells

    c. Lysozymes

    d. Cytochrome P450

18) **Which of the following is NOT a mechanism by which the respiratory system defends itself from outsider invaders in the nasal cavity?**

    a. Mucociliary escalator

    b. Lysozymes

    c. Mast cells

    d. Vibrissae

19) **What would be the result of increased carbon dioxide levels in the lung capillaries?**

    a. Decreased pH in the lung capillaries
    b. Increased pH in the lung capillaries
    c. No change in the pH in the lung capillaries
    d. Decreased respiratory rate

20) **Why is surfactant so important on alveoli?**

    a. Surfactant kills off pathogens and helps the immune function of the lungs
    b. Surfactant prevent alveoli from collapsing upon expiration
    c. Surfactant allows hemoglobin to bind more tightly to oxygen in the pulmonary capillaries
    d. Surfactant binds to CO_2 which allows it to more efficiently be expelled from the body

Answers

1) **Answer: C**

   Explanation: Pleurae membranes surround each lung. When the lung expands, it pushes on this membrane. The visceral pleura is the most proximal to the lung, followed by the intrapleural space, and the parietal pleura. The intrapleural space contains a small amount of fluid and is known as a potential space. The outermost part of the membrane is the chest wall. Only (C) gives the correct order of the structure.

2) **Answer: A**

   Explanation: The very first contact the respiratory system has with air is when the air enters the nares (nostrils). Here, vibrissae, long hairs lining the nares, filter out contaminants from the air (A). The other options (B), (C), and (D) are all real mechanisms that the respiratory tract utilizes. However, they occur after vibrissae function in the nares.

3) **Answer: B**

   Explanation: The branching network and small size of the alveoli allow them to have a large surface area which increases efficiency of gas exchange (A). The lungs are located in the chest cavity, but this is not one of the main reasons why gas exchange is so efficient, eliminating (C) and (D). Additionally, having a left and right lung is important for respiration, but it is not specifically important for gas exchange, eliminating (D).

4) **Answer: A**

   Explanation: The diaphragm is a muscle under somatic control that is extremely important for proper respiration. It contracts and relaxes which allows the lungs to properly function. The diaphragm separates the thoracic cavity and the abdominal cavity (A). The other options are not accurate.

5) **Answer: D**

   Explanation: If more fluid fills the intrapleural space than usual, the pressure in the intrapleural space will remain high which will prevent the lung from expanding and respiration will be affected. This supports II and eliminates I. Additionally, with decreased respiration, CO_2 will build up in lung capillaries, which will result in increased H+ ions in the blood and decreased pH in lung capillaries, supporting III and option (D).

6) **Answer: C**

> **Explanation:** The correct name of the mechanism for breathing is negative-pressure breathing (C) which describes the driving force behind breathing: lower pressure in the intrapleural space than in the lungs. The other options are not real mechanisms and thus are not correct answers.

7) **Answer: A**

> **Explanation:** The total lung capacity is defined as the maximum possible volume of air in the lungs when an individual inhales. The vital capacity is the difference between the minimum and maximum volume of air in the lungs. The residual volume is the volume of air remaining in the lungs after complete exhalation which prevents the lungs from collapsing. Total lung capacity is equal to the vital capacity plus the residual volume. In this scenario, the vital capacity is 4 L and the residual volume is 2 L, thus the total lung capacity is 6 L, option (A).

8) **Answer: A**

> **Explanation:** The vital capacity is the difference between the minimum and maximum volume of air in the lungs. The inspiratory reserve volume is the volume of air that can be inhaled after normal inhalation, whereas the expiratory reserve volume is the volume of air that can be exhaled after normal exhalation. The tidal volume is the volume of air inhaled and exhaled when breathing normally. Inspiratory reserve volume plus expiratory reserve volume plus tidal volume equals vital capacity. Thus, vital capacity minus inspiratory reserve volume minus expiratory reserve volume equals tidal volume (5-3-1=1), option (A).

9) **Answer: D**

> **Explanation:** A spirometer cannot measure residual volume, which eliminates (A) and (C). Complete lung volume is not a real lung volume measurement term. Tidal volume is the only lung volume that can be tested using a spirometer from the last above, option (D).

10) **Answer: C**

> **Explanation:** Hypercarbia and hypercapnia both define conditions of high carbon dioxide partial pressure in the blood. These conditions result in increased respiratory rate to increase exhaled carbon dioxide, resulting in decreased carbon dioxide in the blood. Thus, I and II are sufficient answers. Furthermore, hypoxemia is a condition of low oxygen concentration in the blood. This condition also increases respiratory rate through chemoreceptor signaling. Thus, (C) is the best option.

11) Answer: C

Explanation: The lungs are not only responsible for respiration, but they also have several other roles in the body. The lungs come in direct contact with the outside environment so they act to prevent infection from reaching the bloodstream. The lungs can control thermoregulation via vasodilation and vasoconstriction. They also control blood pH by getting rid of excess CO_2 or bringing in O_2 depending on blood conditions. Out of the options above, the only function that the lungs do not do is filter blood (this is the job of the liver). Thus, option (C) is the best.

12) Answer: D

Explanation: Pulmonary arteries transport deoxygenated blood from the right ventricle of the heart, which eliminates (A) and (B). The pulmonary veins transport oxygenated blood to the left atrium of the heart, which eliminates (C) and supports (D).

13) Answer: B

Explanation: The thin layer that separates the alveolus from the lung capillaries makes gas exchange more efficient, but it is not the driving force, eliminating (A). There is only a small amount of liquid in the intrapleural space. This space is responsible for allowing negative-pressure breathing to occur, but once again it is not the driving force behind gas exchange, eliminating (C). The elasticity of the chest wall allows the lungs to expand when they bring in more oxygen, but the pressure differences between O_2 and CO_2 are what actually drive the gas exchange between the alveolus and the lung capillaries. This eliminates (D) and supports (B).

14) Answer: A

Explanation: Hemoglobin delivers deoxygenated blood with high concentrations of carbon dioxide to the lungs. Inside the alveoli of the lungs, fresh air that was breathed in contains high concentrations of O_2 and low concentrations of CO_2. Thus, CO_2 will flow down its partial pressure gradient from the pulmonary capillaries (where it is high in concentration) to the alveoli (where it is low in concentration), option (A).

15) Answer: A

Explanation: Vasodilation and vasoconstriction are the expansion and reduction of capillary size which influences how much blood can pass through them and thus how much thermal energy is dissipated. Options (B) and (C) are correct. Furthermore, rapid muscle contractions, also known as shivering, can allow humans to produce heat in their bodies supporting (D). The only option not regularly used by humans for thermoregulation is panting, option (A).

Chapter 6 The Respiratory System

16) Answer: A

Explanation: The full bicarbonate buffer system shows the relationship between hydrogen ions and carbon dioxide that is facilitated by carbonic acid, supporting option (A). Both parts of the equilibrium are important, which eliminates (C) and (D). Option (B) is also incorrect because the ratio of atoms is incorrect and will not be seen in the human body.

17) Answer: D

Explanation: Cytochrome P450 enzymes are primarily located in the liver. They are responsible for proper immune function in the liver, but are not a major part of immune function in the lungs, which is why (D) is the correct answer.

18) Answer: C

Explanation: Mast cells are a part of the immune function of the lungs, however, they are not utilized until the air reaches the lungs, which is why option (C) is correct. The mucociliary escalator, lysozymes, and vibrissae all have a role in immune function in the nasal cavity.

19) Answer: A

Explanation: An increase in carbon dioxide in the lung capillaries would result in an increase in H+ ions present in the blood due to the bicarbonate buffer system. Increased H+ ions in the blood would increase acidity and decrease the pH in the lung capillaries. This is why option (A) is true and option (B) is not. Option (C) is incorrect because an increase in carbon dioxide levels in the blood would definitely have a chemical effect. Lastly, option (D) is incorrect because an increase in carbon dioxide in the blood would actually result in an increased respiratory rate.

20) Answer: B

Explanation: The main role of surfactant is to lower the surface tension between the air and liquid of the alveoli. By doing this it prevents the alveoli from collapsing in on itself when exhalation occurs. This is why option (B) is correct.

Chapter 7
Lymphatic System

Chapter 7
Lymphatic System

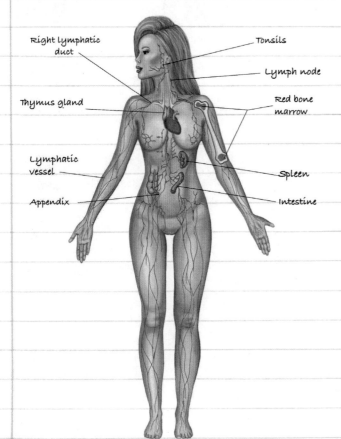

Right lymphatic duct

Tonsils

Lymph node

Thymus gland

Red bone marrow

Lymphatic vessel

Spleen

Appendix

Intestine

Figure 7.1:
The Lymphatic System

We have discussed previously about a system that moves fluids throughout the body called the circulatory system. The circulatory system is a **closed system**, in which all of its vessels are connected and there is a continuous flow of blood. The lymphatic system, on the other hand, is an **open system** in which fluid enters at one end and leaves out the other. While the circulatory system consists of blood, the lymphatic system contains a clear liquid that is known as **lymph.** Let's look at the flow of lymph through the lymphatic system.

Lymph is propelled through the lymphatic system by smooth muscle contractions of the vessels, skeletal muscle contractions around the vessels, activity of the body, and external compressions. Valves are also present to prevent the backflow of lymphatic fluid.

Lymph collected from all parts of the body is brought to the **thoracic duct** and **right lymphatic duct**, where it is emptied back into the circulatory system (**Figure 7.1**). Lymph from the right arm and the head is emptied into the right lymphatic duct, and lymph from everywhere else in the body is emptied into the thoracic duct.

The main functions of the lymphatic system include:

1. Returning fluid and proteins filtered out of the capillaries back into the circulatory system

2. Absorbing the fat which the small intestines are unable to absorb and transferring it to the circulatory system

3. Serving as a filter to help capture and destroy foreign pathogens.

Maintaining Fluid and Protein Balance

The lymphatic system acts as a recycling system. In the circulatory system chapter, we discussed the exchange of fluid and molecules that occurs between the capillaries and the tissues across interstitial fluid. While most of the material is retained by the tissues or capillaries, some fluid

IN-TEXT QUESTION:
How would the blockage of lymphatic vessels affect the distribution of fluids within the body?

Answer:
The lymphatic system is vital to the drainage of the fluid in the tissues throughout the body and to the return of these fluids to the circulatory system. However, if the lymphatic vessels are blocked, this fluid would remain in the tissue, resulting in a disruption of the distribution of fluid in the body. This blockage causes edema, the swelling caused by fluid collecting in the tissues that is not drained into the circulatory system.

and molecules are left in the interstitial fluid. This can lead to a fluid imbalance in the body, as well as a loss of beneficial materials. The lymphatic system is able to prevent these complications by returning these materials back into the circulatory system (**Figure 7.2**). As the pressure within the interstitial space builds up due to the accumulation of molecules and excess fluid, interstitial fluid is pushed into lymphatic vessels to be transported to the thoracic duct and right lymphatic duct.

Absorption and Transport of Fats

Let's review what we learned from the digestive system chapter. Fats are not as easily absorbed as carbohydrates and proteins. Fatty acids and glycerols that enter the enterocytes (a type of cell in the small intestine) via a micelle are converted back into triacylglycerides. The triglycerides are sent to the golgi apparatus, where they are clumped together with cholesterol, phospholipids, and proteins to form a **chylomicron**. Chylomicrons are then absorbed by lacteals, which are finger-like projections of the lymphatic system (Figure 7.3). These fat aggregates travel through the lymphatic system until they drain into the thoracic duct. From the thoracic duct, chylomicrons will empty into the circulatory system, travel through the blood, and transport fat effectively through the body.

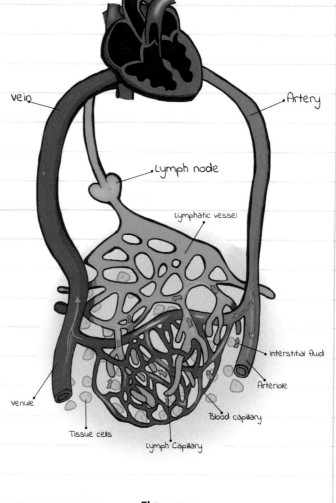

Figure 7.2:
Interstitial Fluid Drainage. The lymphatic system acts as a recycling system by collecting all excess fluids and materials, and returning them back to the circulatory system.

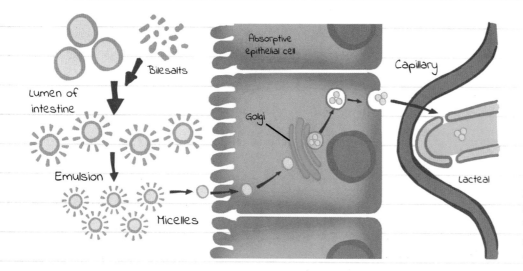

Figure 7.3:
Fat Transport through the Lymphatic System. Chylomicrons from the small intestine enter into lacteals, which are part of the immune system, to be transported into the circulatory system.

Role in Immune Response

The lymphatic system has many lymph nodes, which are concentrated regions of lymphocytes (white blood cells). As we will cover in the next section, lymphocytes are cells that play a significant role in the immune response against pathogens. Thus, the lymphatic system serves as a filter to capture and destroy foreign pathogens (**Figure 7.4**).

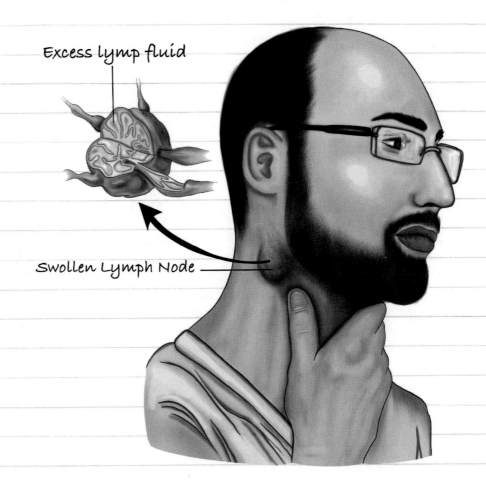

Excess lymp fluid

Swollen Lymph Node

Figure 7.4:
Lymph Nodes. At lymph nodes are a collection of white blood cells that are ready to fight off infection. When an infection is present, lymph nodes will tend to swell up, indicating that your body is attempting to fight off the pathogen.

Questions

1) **Which of the following most correctly pairs the directionality of fluid in the lymphatic vessels and the size of the vessels as they move toward the center of the body?**

    a. Lymphatic vessels are one-way vessels that become smaller as they approach the center of the body.
    b. Lymphatic vessels are one-way vessels that become larger as they approach the center of the body.
    c. Lymphatic vessels are bidirectional vessels that become smaller as they approach the center of the body.
    d. Lymphatic vessels are bidirectional vessels that become larger as they approach the center of the body.

2) **What are the main functions of the lymphatic system?**

    I.   It returns fluid that was filtered out of the capillaries to the circulatory system
    II. It comprises a vital part of immunity in the human body
    III. It carries blood to extremities throughout the body
    a. I only
    b. II only
    c. I and II
    d. I, II, and III

3) **How is the lymphatic system involved in the body's immune response?**

    I.   T-cells are created from hematopoietic stem cells in lymph nodes.
    II. B-cells proliferate and mature in germinal centers in lymph nodes.
    III. Antigen-presenting cells and lymphocytes interact at lymph nodes.
    a. I only
    b. I and III
    c. II and III
    d. I, II, and III

4) **Where do B-cells proliferate and mature after they leave the bone marrow?**

    a. Germinal centers
    b. Lymphatic centers
    c. Leukocyte centers
    d. Edema centers

5) **What are the name(s) of the ducts that lymphatic vessels empty into?**

    I.   Right Lymphatic Duct
    II. Left Lymphatic Duct
    III. Thoracic Duct
    a. II only
    b. II and III
    c. I and III
    d. III only

6) Which of the following most correctly pairs the Starling force with its function as it pertains to lymphatic vessels?

    a. Oncotic pressure of the blood draws water back into the vessel at the arteriole end

    b. Oncotic pressure forces water out of the vessel at the venule end

    c. Hydrostatic pressure forces water out of the vessel at the arteriole end

    d. Hydrostatic pressure of the blood draws water back into the vessel at the arteriole end

7) The lymphatic system is responsible for transporting fats from the digestive system into the blood-stream. Where do the fats that undergo this transportation originate?

    a. Stomach

    b. Esophagus

    c. Large intestine

    d. Small intestine

8) What is the name of the units of fat that are packaged by intestinal mucosal cells and transported via lacteals?

    a. Chylomicrons

    b. Lymphocytes

    c. Germinal centers

    d. Virions

9) What is a common procedure that medical professionals perform to determine if you may be fighting infection that pertains to the lymphatic system?

    a. Examine sites of lymph nodes to look for swelling

    b. Take your temperature

    c. Take a urine sample

    d. Check your nostrils for congestion

10) What would be the result of a blockage of lymph flow in a lymph node in the arm?

    1. The arm would swell

    2. The trapped fluid in the lymph node in the arm would not be able to be transported to the thoracic duct and thus would not reach the circulatory system.

    3. Antigen-presenting cells would not be able to efficiently reach the lymph node and the leukocytes in the lymph node would not be involved in an immune response

    a. I and II

    b. I and III

    c. II and III

    d. I, II, and III

Answers

1) **Answer: B**

   Explanation: Lymphatic vessels wrap around the blood capillaries in tissues and transport lymph fluid to the thoracic duct in the posterior chest. The lymphatic vessels are one-way vessels that get larger as they move toward the center of the body, making option (B) correct. The other options mix up the two variables in question, the directionality of the lymphatic vessels or their size change as they move toward the center of the body.

2) **Answer: C**

   Explanation: The lymphatic system carries water and proteins that are filtered out in blood capillaries to the thoracic duct where this fluid is reintegrated into the circulatory system. Lymph nodes are a part of the lymphatic system and are locations in which antigen-presenting cells and lymphocytes interact. Thus, options (I) and (II) are correct and option (C) is the best answer. Option (III) can be eliminated because lymphatic vessels are one-way vessels that carry lymph to the thoracic duct.

3) **Answer: C**

   Explanation: The lymphatic system is involved in the body's immune response because it contains lymph nodes. Lymph nodes are the location in which B-cells proliferate and mature (II) and where antigen-presenting cells interact with lymphocytes to mount an organized immune response (III). This is why (C) is correct. Option I can be eliminated because T-cells are actually created from hematopoietic stem cells in bone marrow and then they mature in the thymus.

4) **Answer: A**

   Explanation: Germinal centers (A) are the location in which B-cells proliferate and mature once they leave the bone marrow. B-cells remain naive in lymph nodes until they are activated by helper T-cells. The rest of the options do not exist in human anatomy.

5) **Answer: C**

   Explanation: Lymphatic vessels are one-way vessels that carry lymph from blood capillaries in tissues to the center of the body. In the center of the body the lymphatic vessels empty into the right lymphatic duct and the thoracic duct (C). The thoracic duct is actually responsible for collecting over 50% of the lymph from the lymphatic vessels. Surprisingly, it is not named the left lymphatic duct, and thus option II is incorrect.

6) **Answer: C**

Explanation: Starling forces are responsible for allowing the lymphatic system to be involved in equalization of fluid distribution. Due to unequal pressures of fluid being forced out at the arteriole end and drawn back in at the venule end, some fluid is lost. This fluid is collected by the lymphatic system and returned to the circulatory system in the middle of the body. Hydrostatic pressure is defined as the pressure of the blood on the capillary wall and forces fluid out of the vessel specifically at the arteriole end. Thus, option (C) is the best answer.

7) **Answer: D**

Explanation: Lacteals are small lymphatic vessels that are located at the center of each villus in the small intestine. These vessels are responsible for transporting the fat from the small intestine toward the center of the body where it will be integrated into the bloodstream. Thus, option (D) is the best answer.

8) **Answer: A**

Explanation: Intestinal mucosal cells package fats into chylomicrons. The chylomicrons are then absorbed by lacteals, transported via lymphatic vessels to the thoracic duct, and then absorbed into the circulatory system. The fats can then be distributed throughout the body. Thus, (A) is the correct answer. Lymphocytes (B) are white blood cells involved in the immune response. Germinal centers (C) are the locations in lymph nodes in which B-cells mature and proliferate. Virions (D) are viruses that are living outside of cells in the body.

9) **Answer: A**

Explanation: A common result of infection is to have swollen lymph nodes. Lymph nodes are distributed throughout the body and some common locations are just below the jaw and in one's armpits. Medical professionals oftentimes check these locations to determine if their patient is suffering from a symptomatic or asymptomatic infection. The other procedures are also commonly performed by medical professionals to determine the likelihood of infection, but the only procedure pertaining to the lymphatic system is (A).

10) **Answer: D**

Explanation: All of the above conditions may arise if the flow of lymph through a lymph node in the arm was blocked. First off, the arm would swell as there would be trapped fluid at the lymph node, similar to when the lymph nodes in one's neck swell when they are sick. The trapped fluid would not be able to flow through the lymphatic vessels to the thoracic duct. Lastly, antigen-presenting cells would be unable to reach the lymph node and thus the leukocytes within the lymph node would not be able to be activated and a proper immune response would not be mounted.

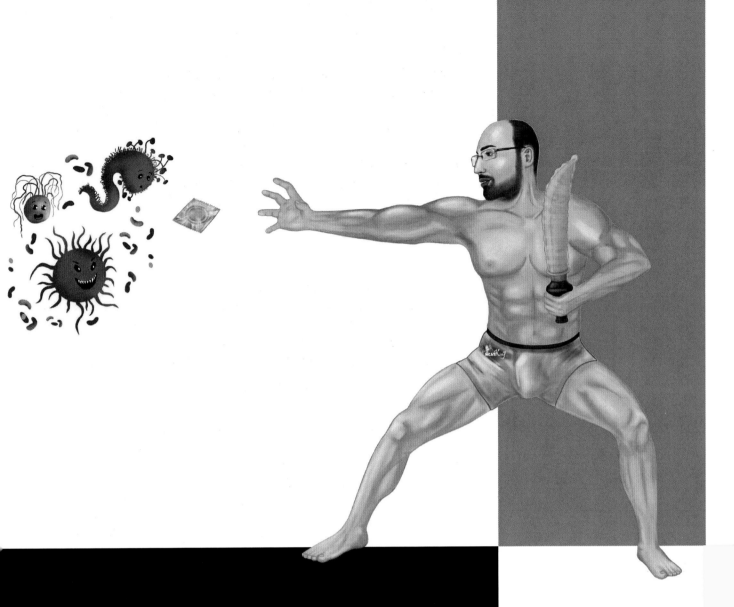

Chapter 8
Immune System

Chapter 8

The Immune System

If you've ever walked in the subways of New York, you know that the world is a very dirty place. According to researchers, there are about 1,000,000,00 0,000,000,000,000,000,000,000 bacteria living on Earth. That's more than the number of stars in the Universe, and does not even include all of the other potential pathogens like viruses, parasites, fungi, toxins, etc. Don't even think about considering this insane number! But an interesting question arises: with all of these pathogens surrounding us, how are we alive? How are we not always sick? Well, you can thank your immune system for that! It's functioning 24/7 to protect you! This wonderful system is our defense against the world, as well as a defense against ourselves. Our immune system is responsible for removing dead and abnormal cells that could potentially lead to illnesses such as cancer. While the immune system is highly effective at keeping us safe, it is not perfect. A hypervigilant immune system can lead to autoimmune diseases, while a lax immune system increases the body's vulnerability to infection. The task of the immune system is huge and therefore, as one can imagine, this system is complex. The immune system is able to accomplish its tasks through its two branches: innate immunity and adaptive (acquired) immunity. Follow along on **Figure 8.1** as we cover all cells of the immune system and understand where they come from.

Figure 8.1: Cell Tree.

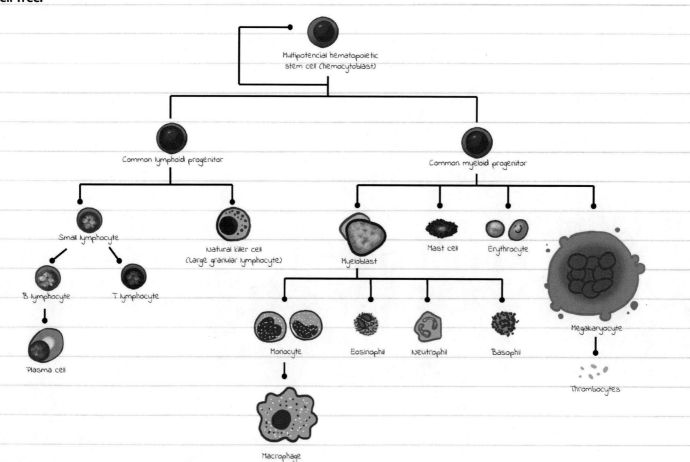

Chapter 8 The Immune System

Innate Immunity

Think of **innate immunity** as the first line of defense. Innate immunity prefers to keep the invaders out rather than fighting them once they're in the body. Therefore, the body's innate immune defenses include barriers such as our skin, nose hairs, eyelashes; tracts of the respiratory and digestive systems; and secretions such as tears, sweat, saliva, mucous, and stomach acid. Innate immunity is responsible for keeping those illness-causing rascals out.

The barriers mentioned above are not always successful and sometimes invaders manage to get through, resulting in a general, nonspecific immune response called **inflammation**. Why is inflammation important? Inflammation results in the accumulation of immune cells at the location of infection by increasing the blood flow to that area. By localizing the infection, inflammation also prevents the spread of infection to other areas of the body.

Let us discuss the cells involved in the innate immune response to better understand what happens if invaders manage to survive past the body's physical defenses (**Figure 8.2**).

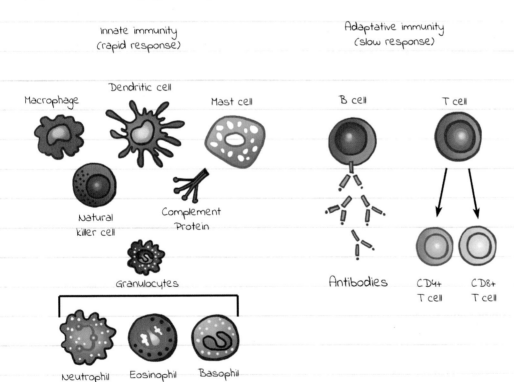

Figure 8.2:
Cells of the Innate and Adaptive Immune System.

1. **Macrophages:** macrophages derive from **monocytes**, which are **agranulocytes**. Agranulocytes are white blood cells that lack **granules** within their cell. Granules are tiny sacs that contain various enzymes and components that are used to defend against pathogens and destroy cells. Macrophages are phagocytic cells that engulf bacteria by phagocytosis and destroy them.

2. **Mast cells:** these cells release cytokines and granules to create an inflammatory cascade that directs immune cells to the location of an infection.

3. **Cytokines:** molecules used for cell signaling or cell-to-cell communication.

4. **Granulocytes:**
    a) **Neutrophils:** most common granulocyte. Phagocytic cell.

    b) **Eosinophil:** secretes highly toxic proteins and free radicals that kill bacteria and parasites.

    c) **Basophils:** releases histamine. Histamine is an inflammatory agent that causes blood vessels to dilate to increase blood flow to the area of infection.

5. **Dendritic cells:** antigen-presenting cells. They recognize antigens and present them to **lymphocytes,** cells that make up a part of the adaptive immune response. **Antigens** are proteins or polysaccharides found on the surface of pathogens. The body uses the antigens to recognize and neutralize the pathogen. Dendritic cells bridge the innate and adaptive immune system, which we will see later on.

6. **Natural killer cells:** destroy infected host cells that display the antigen of the pathogen.

Adaptive (Acquired) Immune System

Whereas the innate immune response is general and nonspecific, the adaptive immune response is a very specific response. What do we mean by specific? We mean antigen specific! Each pathogen displays unique antigens on its membrane that are recognized and selectively attacked by the adaptive immune system. Don't think that the innate and adaptive immune responses occur in a mutually exclusive way. The processes can overlap. As we mentioned above, the innate immune response initiates the inflammatory response, causing the release of cytokines. These cytokines attract cells involved in the adaptive immune response to the area of infection. These cells of the adaptive immune system are **lymphocytes** called **B-cells** and **T-cells.** Both B-cells and T-cells have their own unique functions that culminate in a specific and effective attack against foreign invaders.

Acquired immunity can be further split into two categories: **active immunity** and **passive immunity.** The only difference between these two types of immunity is where the antibodies originate. If the body produces its own antibodies to fight a foreign invader, the process is called **active immunity.** This occurs whenever we get sick or receive a vaccination. On the other hand, if we obtain antibodies that are made by a source other than our body, it is called **passive immunity.** An example of passive immunity is when a mother transfers immune cells through the placenta to the fetus during pregnancy. Another example is when we are given the antibodies needed to combat a specific pathogen such as when we are ill and as a treatment receive blood plasma from donors who had previously combatted and recovered from that specific illness. (**Figure 8.3**).

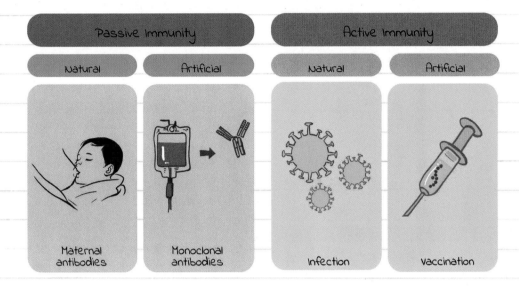

Figure 8.3:
Passive vs. Active Immunity.

B-cell Immunity

B-cells are produced in the bone marrow and mature in the spleen. Once fully mature and differentiated, B-cells are able to secrete antibodies, also called **immunoglobulins**. Interestingly, antibodies are not only secreted by B-cells, but are also inserted into B-cell membranes to function as surface receptors. Thus, B-cell immunity is referred to as antibody-mediated or **humoral immunity.**

But what exactly are **antibodies**?

First and foremost, antibodies are proteins that recognize antigens. Antibodies are "antigen-specific," meaning that an antibody is functional only if it can bind to a particular antigen (**Figure 8.4**).

Figure 8.4:
Antibody Specificity. The antibody can only bind to the antigen that is specific to the antibody's shape.

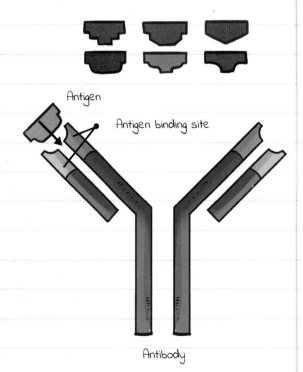

There are five different groups of antibodies: IgG, IgA, IgM, IgE, and IgD. We will briefly discuss the differences between the ones you should know for the MCAT exam.

1. **IgG:** The most common antibody found in the body. It activates the immune cascade and fights against many viruses, bacteria, and toxins. This antibody is also capable of crossing the placental barrier. Thus, a mother's IgGs can be used to combat an infection in her infant.

2. **IgA:** Found in mucosal areas such as the lungs, stomach, and intestines. They are also found in secretions such as tears, saliva, mucus, and breast milk. IgAs fight against pathogens that have breached the mucosal surface and are trying to enter epithelial cells.

3. **IgE:** Specialized for allergic responses.

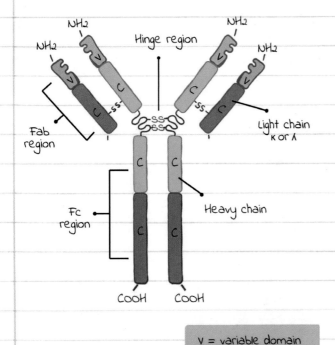

Figure 8.5:
Antibody Structure.

V = variable domain
C = constant domain

Figure 8.5 shows the structure of an antibody molecule. We will discuss the features of the structure and how these relate to the immune system. Antibodies are made of four polypeptide chains. Two of these chains are identical and are called **heavy chains**; the two other chains are also identical and are called **light chains**. The terms "heavy" and "light" refer to the sequence of these polypeptides and their length. As you can see in the picture, **heavy chains** are longer than **light chains.**

The most obvious thing is that the antibody looks like a Y. Antigen binding sites, known as the **variable region(s)**, are at the "top" tips of the Y. The variable region, which includes both light and heavy chains, creates antigen-specific binding sites. Below the variable region is the **constant region**, made also of heavy and light chains. The constant region determines the antibody's type (i.e. IgG, IgA, IgG, etc.).

An antibody can be categorized into two distinct regions: the **Fab region** and the **Fc region.** The Fab region consists of the variable region and a constant region. Since the Fab region has the variable region, it determines the specificity of the antibody to an antigen. The Fc region consists only of constant regions. The Fc region binds to the membrane of B-lymphocytes and can interact with some proteins of the complement system (covered later in chapter). An organism's antibodies all have the same constant region.

Antibody Function

Now that the structure is out of the way, let's get into the function. Antibodies fight off invaders in three main ways (**Figure 8.6**):

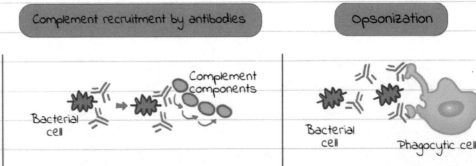

Antibodies bind to inactivate viruses and toxins. These antibodies are called "neutralizing antibodies"

Antigen-antibody complexes activate the complement system (the classical pathway), triggering its antibacterial activity

Phagocytic cells grab the antibodies bound to the surface of foreign substances, for efficient phagocytosis.

Figure 8.6:
Antibody Mechanism of Action.

1. Neutralization: antibodies bind to toxins and a pathogen's antigen(s). In doing so, antibodies prevent the ability of pathogens to infect cells.

2. Opsonization: antibodies bind to antigens on the surfaces of foreign substances, making them more recognizable for phagocytes.

3. Activation of complement system: antigen-antibody complex activates the complement system. Activation of the complement system causes lysis of the microbe, inflammation, and/or phagocytosis of the microbe opsonized with complement fragments. We discuss the complement system in greater detail later on.

As you can see, antibodies do not directly kill pathogens. Instead, antibodies neutralize and/or make the pathogen more visible to the immune system's actual killer cells. Antibodies are a lot like the wingman coordinating the joining of two people!

Now that we have covered antibodies, let us dive into how B-cells carry out their function in the adaptive immune system using antibodies.

Naïve B-cells that have just finished maturing in the spleen contain a number of different **B-cell receptors (BCRs)** derived from the DNA of the organism. The BCRs are shaped like antibodies, each one specific to a different antigen. Once one of these BCRs binds to an antigen of a foreign particle, the B-cell engulfs the antigen and the antigen reappears on the surface of the B-cell (**Figure 8.7**). This time, however, the antigen is displayed with a membrane-

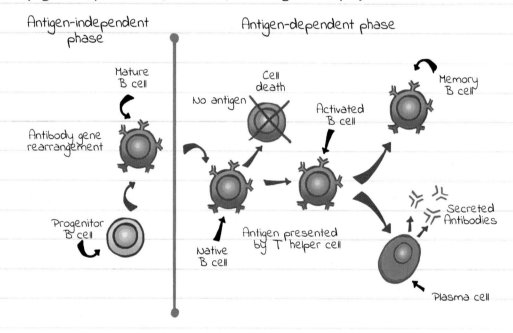

Figure 8.7:
Development of B-Cells into Plasma B-Cells and Memory B-Cells.

bound protein receptor called a **major histocompatibility complex class II (MHC class II).** Simultaneously, a dendritic cell from the innate immune system displays the same antigen on its MHC class II molecule to a helper T-cell, activating the helper T-cell. The activated helper T-cell binds to the antigen-MHC class II complex on the B-cell, causing the B-cell to divide into many **memory B-cells** and a **plasma B-cell** (**Figure 8.8**). A memory B-cell expresses an antibody on its membrane that is similar to the BCR on the parent cell. The plasma B-cell begins to secrete that same antibody (**Figure 8.7**). The presence of the antibodies secreted by the plasma B-cell triggers the same series of responses described above (neutralization, opsonization, and complement system activation). If the foreign invaders ever return, the antibody on the memory B-cell will recognize the antigen and divide into thousands of plasma cells. The vast amount of plasma cells secrete large amounts of antibodies which aid in the quick and effective destruction of the pathogen (**Figure 8.9**). Think of it like relationships: it may take 3 or more dates before a couple hooks up for the first time. However if that couple breaks up and were ever to come back together, there will likely be fewer dates before that couple hooks up again.

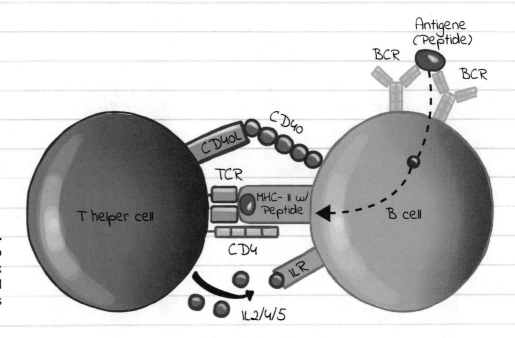

Figure 8.8:
Activation of B-Cell by Helper T-Cell. The activated helper T-Cell binds to the antigen-MHC Class II complex on the B-Cell. This causes the B-Cell to divide into many memory B-Cells and a Plasma B-Cell.

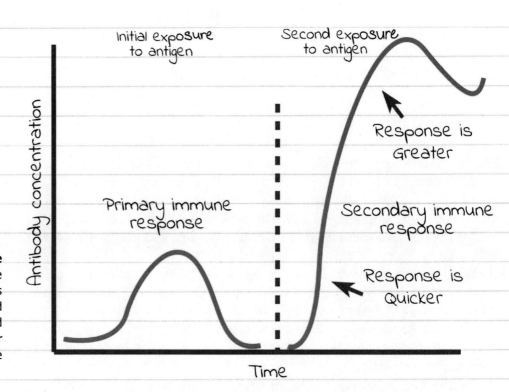

Figure 8.9:
Initial vs. Second Exposure Response Timing. Due to the abundance and speed at which antibodies are produced during the second exposure, our body is able to rid itself of the infection much quicker and effectively the second time around.

T-lymphocytes

When foreign particles are able to bypass the attack from antibodies, they are able to invade host cells. Once a host cell gets infected, antibodies are no longer useful, and it is as if the antigen of the pathogen is invisible. Luckily, we have our special forces combat unit, the **T-lymphocytes** that carry out **cell-mediated immunity.**

T-lymphocytes are produced by bone marrow and mature in the thymus. Once matured, all T-cells express **T-cell receptors (TCRs)** and one of three co-receptors. The three co-receptors are **CD4, CD8,** and **CD25. Helper T-cells** express CD4, **Cytotoxic T-cells** express CD8, and **T-regulatory cells** express both CD4 and CD25.

TCRs only recognize antigens bound to major histocompatibility complexes I and II. We briefly mentioned MHC's when discussing B-cell immunity, but now let us take a deeper look at what exactly MHCs are. In doing so, we can gain a better understanding of how T-cell immunity works.

Major histocompatibility complexes (MHCs) are a group of proteins on the cell membranes that present antigens. MHCs function to help the immune system differentiate one's own healthy cells from foreign invaders. There are two MHCs you should know for the MCAT exam: **MHC class I** and **MHC class II**.

MHC class I: these are proteins that are found on the surface of every nucleated cell (remember, this does not include red blood cells). Healthy cells bind a normal peptide that represents a "self-antigen" to an MHC class I. As white blood cells travel throughout the body, they recognize the self-antigen on healthy cells and ignore them. If a cell becomes infected, it produces a peptide that represents a "viral antigen" and binds it to an MHC class I. White blood cells can now recognize this cell as being infected with a foreign pathogen and take measures to destroy it.

MHC class II: these proteins are found only on cell membranes of immune cells (B-lymphocytes, macrophages, dendritic cells, and T-lymphocytes) and function to help immune cells communicate with each other. An example of MHC class II in action was mentioned previously: both B-cells and dendritic cells engulf the foreign antigen and present it on its cell surface with MHC class II.

Shown on **Figure 8.10** is an image demonstrating how T-cells use both T-cell receptors and co-receptors to bind to MHC proteins.

So how does cell-mediated immunity work?

As you read, follow **Figure 8.11.** An **antigen-presenting cell (APC),** such as a dendritic cell, presents the foreign antigen, bound to an MHC class II, to

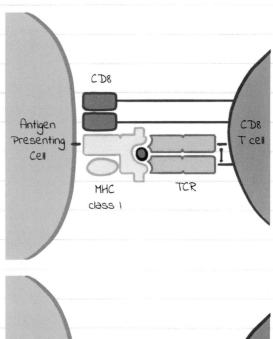

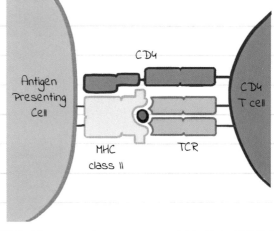

Figure 8.10:
T-Cell Receptors and Co-Receptors. Cytotoxic T-Cells express CD8 co-receptors and bind to cells (non-immune cells) using MHC class I receptors. These cells are non-immune cells. Helper T-Cells express CD4 co-receptors and bind to cells (immune cells) using MHC class II receptors.

a **naïve T-cell**. This activates the naïve T-cell and induces some naïve T-cells to turn into **cytotoxic T-cells (killer T-cells)** and others into **helper T-cells**. The cytotoxic T-cell clones itself multiple times. One group of these clones stay as active cytotoxic **T-cells;** the other group becomes inactive **memory T-cells**. The active cytotoxic **T-cells**, with their TCR and CD8 co-receptors, bind to the antigens on the MHC class I of infected cells. The active cytotoxic **T-cells** then trigger apoptosis of these infected cells. The memory **T-cells** remain in the body so that if the same antigen is ever recognized in the future, the adaptive immune response can be activated immediately. This is similar to how the secondary response is much stronger and effective in B-cell immunity.

The **helper T-cells**, expressing TCRs and CD4 coreceptors, bind to MHC class II of APCs and respond by secreting cytokines to signal macrophages and natural killer cells to seek out and kill pathogen-infected cells. The cytokines also stimulate cytotoxic T-cells to clone themselves As mentioned earlier in the B-cell immunity section, helper **T-cells** additionally bind to the antigen-MHC class II complex on B-cells and cause them to divide into many **memory B-cells** and a **plasma B-cells**.

The final type of T-cell we need to discuss is the **T-regulatory cell**. These cells express CD4 and CD25 co-receptors. T-regulatory cells function to "regulate" **T-cells** by helping them distinguish between self and foreign molecules. In doing so, T-regulatory cells reduce the risk of autoimmune disease.

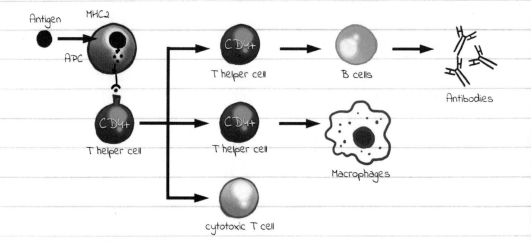

Figure 8.11:
Differentiation of T-Cells.

Regulation of T-cells

We count upon our immune system to defend against the outside world. Thus, we must make sure our **T-cells** are fit to perform their job. While **T-cells** are maturing in the thymus, they undergo a selection test. The **positive selection test** consists of determining whether the **T-cells** are able to recognize MHC antigens/receptors. Without this ability to recognize MHC antigen/receptor complexes, **T-cells** are deemed useless since they cannot determine if a particle is foreign or part of the self. If a **T-cell** is unable to pass this test, it undergoes apoptosis.

Chapter 8 The Immune System

The **negative selection test** is when the **T-cells** must be able to show they will not attack host cells that are not infected. Specifically, they must be able to show that they won't attack cells that display "self-antigens" on the MHC class I proteins. This test is highly important in preventing autoimmune diseases. If a **T-cell** is unable to pass this test, it also undergoes apoptosis.

The Complement System

We briefly mentioned the complement system involved in B-cell immunity. The complement system helps (complements) the ability of the innate and adaptive immune system to destroy pathogens. The complement system consists of proteins that patrol the blood in an inactive form. Upon activation, the proteins come together and perform the following functions:

1. **Opsonization:** in this step, antigens on the surfaces of foreign substances are marked for phagocytosis.

2. **Inflammation:** the complement system attracts macrophages and neutrophils to the sight that antigens originate from.

3. **Cell lysis:** the proteins of the complement system destroy the membranes of the foreign cells and thereby prevent further spread of the infection.

Questions

1) **An abnormally low number of helper T-cells in an individual may affect them in which of the following ways?**

    a. Reduced activation of cytotoxic T-cells that induce apoptosis
    b. Decreased expression of major histocompatibility complex proteins
    c. The release of histamine to regulate an allergic response
    d. Increased level of antibody production

2) **A group of patients were administered monoclonal antibodies as treatment for their multiple sclerosis. The antibodies used in this treatment are composed of:**

    a. A constant region that binds to the antigen
    b. One light chain and one heavy chain
    c. Two light chains and two heavy chains that vary in their polypeptide sequences
    d. Two identical polypeptide light chains and two identical polypeptide heavy chains

3) **Which of the following serves as the site for B-cell maturation?**

    a. Bone Marrow
    b. Spleen
    c. Thymus
    d. Lymph nodes

4) **"Guillain-Barre" syndrome is a condition in which the destruction of healthy nerves occur. A failure in which one of these processes can result in this autoimmune disorder?**

    a. Negative selection
    b. Positive selection
    c. Presentation of antigens
    d. B-cell activation

5) **During an allergic reaction, which of the following would most likely be responsible for the release of histamine?**

    a. Macrophages
    b. Natural killer cells
    c. T-cells
    d. Mast cells

6) **Humoral immunity is provided by:**

    a. Immunoglobulins
    b. Mucociliary escalator
    c. Digestive enzymes
    d. Killer T-cells

7) **A decrease in the number of CD⁴⁺ cells is LEAST likely to impact the:**

   a. Activation of cytotoxic T-cells
   b. Stimulation of B-cells to secrete antibodies
   c. Likelihood of a surge in infected cells
   d. Recognition of antigens presented on MHC I

8) **An organism experiencing a recurrent pathogen will display an immune response involving:**

   a. Memory B-cells
   b. Macrophages
   c. Neutrophils
   d. Basophils

9) **B-lymphocytes differ from T-lymphocytes in which of the following ways:**

   a. They are involved in humoral immunity rather than cell-mediated immunity
   b. Their maturation occurs within the thymus
   c. They are not involved in the production of immunoglobulins
   d. They destroy virally infected cells

10) **A tumor in which of the following organs would affect T-lymphocyte maturation?**

   a. Lymph Nodes
   b. Bone marrow
   c. Parathyroid
   d. Thymus

11) **Which of the following components of the immune system has a role in both adaptive immunity and innate immunity?**

   a. Lysozyme
   b. MHC I
   c. Macrophages
   d. Memory Cells

12) **Which of the following statements regarding antibodies is FALSE?**

   a. Antibodies can neutralize certain toxins
   b. The antigen binding region of the antibody is only made up of heavy chains
   c. A wide array of antibodies are produced due to the ability of antibody genes to undergo genetic rearrangements
   d. Antibodies are produced by B-lymphocytes

13) **An allergic response occurs when the immune system responds to a foreign substance. Which components of the immune system mediates the allergic response, and which type of immunity does it fall under?**

   a. Complement system; innate immunity
   b. Complement system; adaptive immunity
   c. Immunoglobulins; innate immunity
   d. Immunoglobulins; adaptive immunity

14) Scientists warn that a newly discovered herpes virus is highly contagious. The majority of those infected are unaware, and the virus easily integrates itself into the host genome. For most of an infected individual's life, it remains dormant. This information suggests which of the following is true?

    a. Most individuals infected with the virus are elderly

    b. Individuals with healthy immune systems will be capable of clearing the virus from their immune systems, whereas immunocompromised individuals won't

    c. The immune response generated by infection will assist infected individuals from clearing out other strains of the herpes virus as well

    d. The virus can only be spread by direct contact with the viral reservoir. However, person-to-person contact is safe.

15) The immune system response generated by a strain of rotavirus is temporary. This suggests which of the following statements is TRUE?

    a. An individual can only be infected by rotavirus once in their life

    b. An individual can only be infected by a particular strain of rotavirus just once

    c. An individual can be infected by the same strain many times, just not in immediate succession

    d. An individual can be infected by the same strain many times, even in immediate succession

16) In most individuals infected with tuberculosis, the infection lies dormant. Latent infections are characterized by the appearance of granulomas in infected tissue. Granulomas are areas of inflammation surrounded by immune cells in an attempt to contain the infection. Granulomas can persist permanently without advancement of the disease. Most of these patients are unaware that they are positive for tuberculosis. Which of the following is most likely the reason for granuloma development?

    a. Tuberculosis bacteria form granulomas as a means of protection from the immune system

    b. The immune system maintains the granulomas to prevent infection from other, more destructive bacteria

    c. Unable to eliminate the causative bacteria, macrophages surround and contain the infectious agent to prevent it from spreading.

    d. Granulomas are formed by the plasma cells in response to the bacteria.

17) A 50 year-old man is informed by his physician that he has Neutropenia, a condition characterized by low neutrophil levels. Which of the following is least likely to cause this condition?

    a. Exposure to radiation

    b. Drug induced damage to the bone marrow

    c. An autoimmune condition resulting in the destruction of white blood cells

    d. An excess of hematopoietic stem cells

18) Which of the following is true of the major histocompatibility complex?

   a. There are five groups of histocompatibility complex
   b. MHC I signals intracellular, viral infection
   c. MHC I and MHC II display protein fragments on the cell surface for recognition by B-cells
   d. B-cells detect infections through the major histocompatibility complex

19) Multiple Myeloma is a blood cancer that is detected when testing suggests a high concentration of abnormal antibodies in the bloodstream. The structure of these antibodies suggest that they were produced by a single clonal cell that has proliferated profusely. From which of the following cell types does this cancer arise?

   a. Plasma Cells
   b. Cytotoxic T-cells
   c. Helper T-cells
   d. Monocytes

20) Major histocompatibility complex class I (MHC I) molecules are found in which of the following cell types?

   I.   T-cells
   II. Dendritic Cells
   III. Macrophages
      a. I only
      b. I, II, and III
      c. II and III
      d. I and III

Answers

1) **Answer: A**

   Explanation: Helper T-cells detect foreign antigens that are displayed on MHC proteins of cells such as macrophages, dendritic cells, and B-lymphocytes. They also increase immune responses such as antibody production by B-cells and cytotoxic T-cell activation. Thus, the correct answer is (A). Expression of the major histocompatibility complex proteins are regulated at the transcriptional and translational level. Therefore, cells can display antigens regardless of helper T-cell count, making B incorrect. Option (C) can be eliminated as it best describes the function of a mast cell. A low number of helper T-cells will *decrease* the amount of antibodies produced, making choice (D) false.

2) **Answer: D**

   Explanation: Antibodies are Y-shaped proteins that bind antigens to neutralize and mark them for destruction. Each antibody consists of two identical light chains, two identical heavy chains, a variable region and a constant region. Therefore, option (D) is correct. Option (A) can be eliminated as the *variable* region binds to the antigen, not the constant region. Options (B) and (C) are incorrect as there are two of each of the light and heavy chains and their polypeptide sequences must be identical.

3) **Answer: B**

   Explanation: Choice (B) is the correct answer. B cells are produced in the bone marrow and matured in the spleen. Thymus (C) is the site for T-cell maturation. Choice (D) is incorrect as lymph nodes are nodular tissues that modulate activation of lymphocytes and detect antigens in lymphatic fluid.

4) **Answer: A**

   Explanation: Autoimmune disorders are primarily a result of the immune system's failure to recognize and destroy cells that respond too strongly to self-antigens. Negative selection facilitates the destruction of immature B-cells and T-cells that bind to self-antigens. Thus, (A) is the correct answer. Positive selection (B) is not the best answer choice because in this process only T-cells that can successfully identify MHCs survive. Choices (C) and (D) do not result in autoimmunity.

5) **Answer: D**

   Explanation: Choice (D) is the best answer. Mast cells are granulocytes that can release inflammatory chemicals such as histamine causing an allergic response. Histamine increases vasodilation causing an inflammatory response. Options (A), (B), and (C) describe cells that do not release histamine.

6) **Answer: A**

Explanation: Immunoglobulins, otherwise known as antibodies, are mainly involved in the humoral immune system which is specific and adaptive. Choice (B) is unrelated, the mucociliary escalator plays a role in initiating respiratory defense mechanisms. Digestive enzymes (C) are involved in nonspecific innate immunity. Choice (D) can be eliminated because killer T-cells are included in cell mediated immunity, not humoral.

7) **Answer: D**

Explanation: Choice (D) is the best answer. CD^{4+} cells or helper T-cells recognize antigens presented on MHC II, not MHC I. CD^{8+} T-cells or cytotoxic T-cells are responsible for recognizing antigens presented on MHC I. Choices (A), (B), and (C) are more likely to be impacted by a decrease in CD^{4+} cells.

8) **Answer: A**

Explanation: The key word here is *recurrent*, memory (B) cells are formed after a primary infection. They play an important role in the adaptive immune system by creating an accelerated antibody-mediated response that is specific to the pathogen involved. Choices (B), (C), and (D) represent cells of the innate immune system that are involved in providing a nonspecific response.

9) **Answer: A**

Explanation: (A) is the correct answer because B-lymphocytes are involved in humoral immunity as they produce antibodies. The other options are incorrect because they are characteristics of T-lymphocytes.

10) **Answer: D**

Explanation: The Thymus (D), is the location of T-lymphocyte maturation. If a tumor disrupts T-cell maturation in the thymus, autoimmune diseases can arise.

11) **Answer: C**

Explanation: Lysozyme (A) is a nonspecific defense only (innate immunity). Both memory cells and MHC I (B and D), are only involved in the specific (adaptive), immune response. Macrophages, however, can act as both a nonspecific and specific defense. These phagocytes can eliminate pathogens and foreign bodies they suspect may cause an infection. They can also specifically respond to antibody coated antigens.

12) Answer: B

> **Explanation:** The genes for antibodies are capable of undergoing genetic rearrangements (C is TRUE). Antibodies are also capable of neutralizing toxins (A is TRUE). Antibodies are produced by B-lymphocytes as a component of humoral immunity (D is TRUE). Remember, the antigen binding region of any antibody is made up of both heavy chains and light chains (B is FALSE). Review **Figures 8.4** and **8.5** for further detail.

13) Answer: D

> **Explanation:** Immunoglobulins are antibodies. Therefore, they are a component of the adaptive immune system and serve to activate the immune response when one is exposed to an allergen. The complement system is not activated when one is exposed to allergens.

14) Answer: A

> **Explanation:** Based on the given information, (A) is the most likely answer. The question stem does not dive into the body's immune response to this specific virus, so it would be hard to determine how healthy immune systems would react compared to immunocompromised ones (B). Furthermore, (C) and (D) cannot be concluded from the given information as well.

15) Answer: C

> **Explanation:** A temporary immune response indicates that the body can combat the rotavirus repeatedly over a short time period. But after this short lived immunity subsides, the individual can become infected again. The question stem gives no information regarding how infection with this particular strain of the virus affects an individual's immunity to other strains (B and D).

16) Answer: C

> **Explanation:** Choice (A) can be eliminated as it is clear from the questions stem that granulomas are formed by the immune response, not tuberculosis bacteria. Plasma cells are responsible for antibody development not the inflammatory pathway, therefore choice (D) is wrong. Choice (B) is unlikely because the use of pathogens to protect against infection against more destructive bacteria is usually done with relatively benign bacteria (kind of like taking a vaccine). These benign organisms only cause disease in immunocompromised individuals and other rare instances. Therefore, choice (C) is the most likely answer. Granulomas form when the immune system attempts to wall off substances it perceives as foreign but is unable to eliminate. They are typically made up of collections of macrophages.

17) Answer: D

Explanation: Choices (A), (B), and (C) would all damage the body's ability to produce neutrophils. An excess of hematopoietic stem cells would not inhibit the ability to produce neutrophils.

18) Answer: B

Explanation: There are only two classes of major histocompatibility complex. T-cells are responsible for recognizing MHC complexes on the surface of cells. CD^{4+} T-cells recognize MHC II complexes and CD^{8+} T-cells recognize MHC I complexes. MHC class I complexes are responsible for signaling intracellular, viral infections and are found in all nucleated cells of the body.

19) Answer: A

Explanation: Plasma cells are responsible for producing antibodies. Plasma cells are differentiated B-cells capable of secreting immunoglobulin, or antibodies. These cells play an important role in the adaptive immune response, namely, being the main cells responsible for humoral immunity. A cancerous mutation and resulting proliferation of these cells can lead to the abnormal antibody production (A).

20) Answer: B

Explanation: Major histocompatibility complex class I (MHC I) molecules are expressed by all nucleated cells in the body (in essence, all cells except red blood cells). Therefore, the answer is (B).

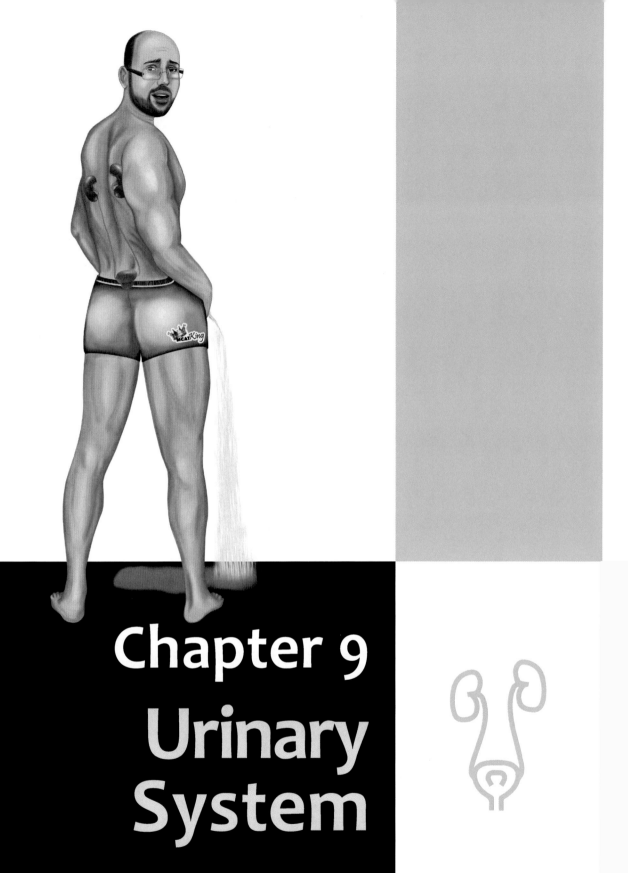

Chapter 9
Urinary System

Chapter 9

Urinary System

The **urinary system** functions to filter out and eliminate waste in the form of **urine**, informally known as "pee". However, the urinary system, or the **renal system**, plays a significant role in other bodily processes besides just filtration and excretion. These functions include:

1. Regulating blood volume and composition (i.e. Na^+, K^+, and Ca^{2+} concentrations)

2. Regulating blood pressure

3. Regulating pH

4. Contributing to blood cells production

5. Synthesizing and secreting calcitriol

The kidney is the main organ of the urinary system. In this chapter, we will cover all the information you need to know about the urinary system and the kidney for the MCAT exam. Before we discuss all the complex details, let us first look at the structure of the system itself.

Structure of the Urinary System

Front view of the Urinary System

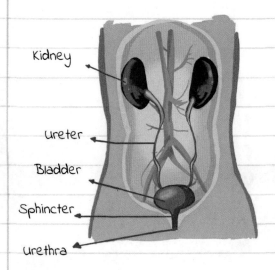

Kidney

Ureter

Bladder

Sphincter

Urethra

Figure 9.1:
The Urinary System.

Imagine that you just drank an ice-cold glass of water. The water is absorbed into the blood at the small and large intestine. The blood travels to the kidneys, where it is passed through the **nephron,** the basic unit of the kidney (**Figure 9.1**). The nephron filters the blood and collects the filtrate. The nephron processes the filtrate and turns it into **urine**. The urine then leaves the nephron of the kidney and enters into a tube called the **ureter** (**Figure 9.2**). A single ureter from each kidney leads to the **bladder**. As the bladder fills with fluid, it relaxes and expands. Eventually, the bladder fills to a point that initiates a reflex response that gives us the feeling of needing to urinate. At this point, you rush to the bathroom and the urine is expelled through a tube called the **urethra.**

To control when we urinate, we have two **sphincter** muscles located between the bladder and the urethra. Sphincters are muscles that control the opening and closing of a tube. Take a look at **Figure 9.3.**
    The first sphincter is made of smooth muscle and is thus under our involuntary control. This sphincter, called the internal sphincter of the urethra, opens in response to stretch receptors in the bladder that notify the brain about the increase in volume of urine in the bladder. The second

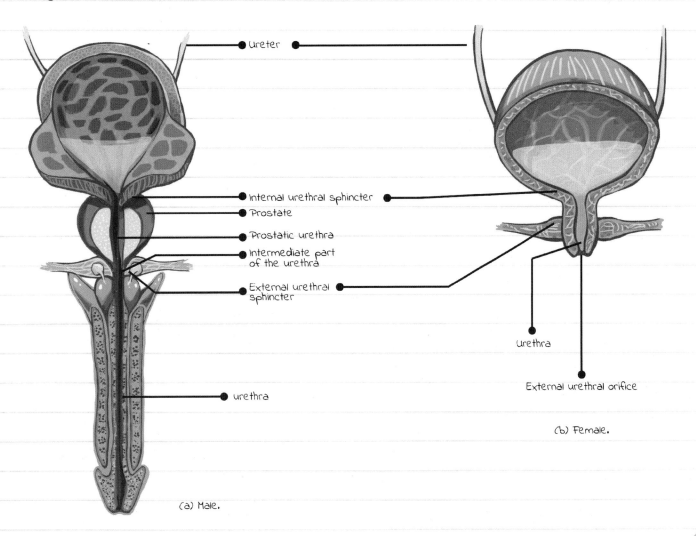

Figure 9.2:
The Kidney and the Nephron

Renal Artery (carries unfiltered blood)

Kidney

Nephron

Blood

Urine

Renal Vein (carries filtered blood)

Ureter

sphincter, called the external sphincter of the urethra, is made of skeletal muscle and is thus under voluntary control. When we want to urinate, our brain will signal to open the external sphincter and allow for urine to enter the urethra. In addition, upon urination, the brain signals the bladder muscles to tighten in order to squeeze the urine out and empty the bladder.

Figure 9.3:
The Bladder and Urethra

Ureter

Internal urethral sphincter

Prostate

Prostatic urethra

Intermediate part of the urethra

External urethral sphincter

urethra

Urethra

External urethral orifice

(b) Female.

(a) Male.

The urinary system also consists of two important blood vessels that you must know: the **renal artery** and the **renal vein**. Let us do a quick review of the cardiovascular system to understand these blood vessels. Oxygenated blood from the lungs enters the left side of the heart, via the pulmonary vein, and exits the heart via the aorta, an artery. Blood in the aorta travels to tissues and organs in the body to supply them with oxygen and nutrients. After gas and nutrient exchange, the blood travels to the right side of the heart via the vena cava, a vein. Blood from the right side of the heart then travels the lungs via the pulmonary artery and the cycle begins anew.

Notice the names of the vessels described. What do all the arteries have in common? What do all the veins have common? If you notice, all the arteries are blood vessels that move blood AWAY from the heart while all the veins are blood vessels that move blood TOWARDS the heart. How does this apply to renal arteries and renal veins? Oxygenated blood exits the left side of the heart via the aorta, which splits into many different arteries. These arteries travel to the various tissues and organs, including the kidney. The **renal artery** is the name of the artery that supplies oxygenated blood to the kidney in **Figure 9.2**. After the blood has been filtered in the kidneys, blood exits via the renal vein, which connects to the vena cava.

Alright, so we understand the flow of blood and the anatomy of the urinary system, but how exactly does the urinary system carry out the functions we described earlier? It all begins at the nephron.

Nephron

Figure 9.4:
The Nephron in the Kidney

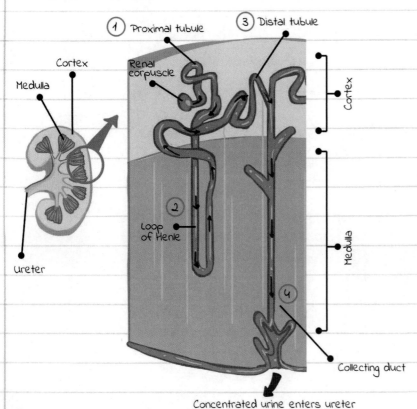

① Proximal tubule
③ Distal tubule
Cortex
Medulla
Renal corpuscle
Cortex
②
Loop of Henle
Medulla
④
Ureter
Collecting duct
Concentrated urine enters ureter

The nephron is the functional unit of the kidney, meaning that it is the smallest structure that can perform the functions of the organ. The outer layer of the kidney is called the **cortex** and the inner layer is called the **medulla.** Specific parts of the nephron are located in different regions of the kidney as shown in **Figure 9.4**.

The blood enters the kidney through the renal artery which divides into subsequent smaller arteries and arterioles that are located in the cortex. The blood flows into the nephron via the **afferent arteriole** into a network of capillaries known as the **glomerulus**. In the glomerulus, the blood is filtered, and a fluid is produced called the **filtrate**. The filtrate is picked up by a tubule that surrounds the glomerulus called the **Bowman's capsule**. The Bowman's capsule is continuous with the nephron. Together, the glomerulus and Bowman's capsule make up a structure known as the

renal corpuscle. The blood that has been filtered at the **renal corpuscle** exits via the **efferent arterioles.** From the efferent arteriole, the blood continues into the **peritubular capillaries** and the **vasa recta.** The peritubular capillaries partakes in exchange with the proximal and distal convoluted tubules; the vasa recta partakes in exchange with the **loop of Henle.** Following exchange, blood exits the kidney in the renal vein. See **Figure 9.5.**

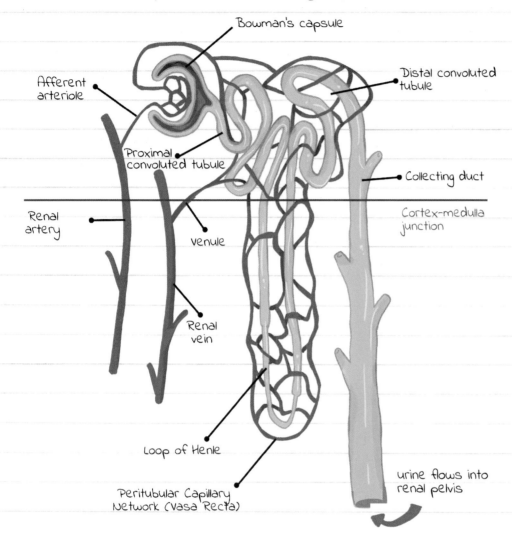

Figure 9.5:
Blood Vessels of the Nephron

Now let's backtrack a little bit to the nephron itself. The blood from the afferent arteriole enters the glomerulus, where fluid is transferred to the Bowman's capsule. About 1/5th of all blood plasma passing through the kidney enters the glomerulus. From the Bowman's capsule, the filtrate enters the **proximal tubule** in the cortex. The filtrate then slides down into the medulla as the **loop of Henle.** The loop of Henle is just that: a loop. A descending limb projects into the medulla and an ascending limb climbs back up towards the cortex. The filtrate continues to the **distal tubule** in the cortex and drains into the **collecting duct** in the medulla. The filtrate in the collecting duct is then sent to the bladder as urine.

We mentioned a lot of new structures of the nephron, each of which plays a significant role in forming urine and contributing to the overall function of the urinary system. Let us now take an in depth look at what happens at each of the locations of the nephron.

Renal Corpuscle

The nephron continually goes through cycles of filtration, reabsorption, and secretion. Filtration in the nephron occurs at the renal corpuscle, made of the Bowman's capsule and the glomerulus (**Figure 9.6**). How does the glomerulus allow certain substances into the Bowman's capsule, but not others? Fenestrations! Recall in the cardiovascular system chapter that capillaries can either be continuous or fenestrated. **Fenestrated capillaries**, such as those found in the glomerulus, have pores that allow the passage of molecules of a certain size and smaller. After passing through the fenestrations, the molecules must face two other filters known as the **basement membrane** and **podocytes**. Ultimately, water, salts, glucose, urea, amino acids, and small proteins enter the Bowman's capsule; no blood cells enter.

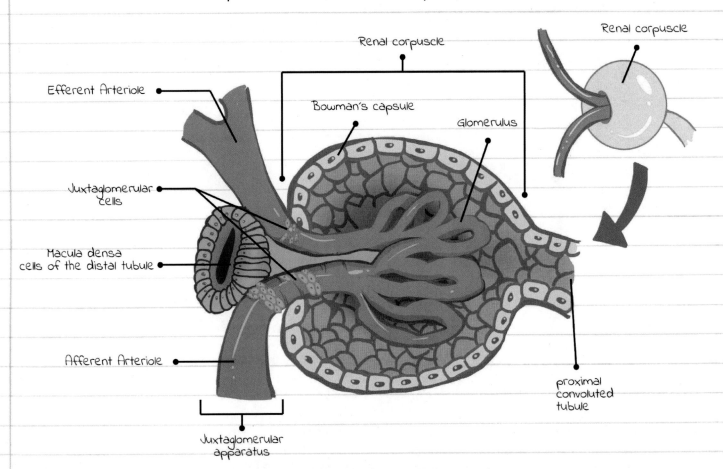

Figure 9.6:
Renal Corpuscle. The afferent arteriole brings blood to the glomerulus where it is filtered out and into the Bowman's capsule, which is part of the nephron. Blood leaves the glomerulus via the efferent arteriole.

Before we continue, it is important that we discuss the term **osmolarity**, which is the amount of dissolved particles per liter of water (mOsm/L). The greater the osmolarity, the greater the solution's solute concentration. When two solutions are separated by a semipermeable membrane and the osmolarity of one solution is greater than the osmolarity of the other, an **osmotic gradient** is formed and water will flow via osmosis to the solution with the greater osmolarity to create an **isotonic** solution. Isotonic solutions are two solutions with the same osmolarity. The solution with the higher osmolarity is known as being hypertonic to the other solution; likewise, the solution with the lower osmolarity is known as being hypotonic to the other solution.

Pressure causes water to flow across a semipermeable membrane. Specifically, **osmotic pressure**. Osmotic pressure is the tendency of a solution to draw in a solvent by osmosis. A more concentrated solution (greater osmolarity) has more osmotic pressure than a less concentrated solution (less osmolarity). Since the solution with greater osmolarity has a larger driving force (osmotic pressure) to take in water, water will flow into the more concentrated solution. Notice **Figure 9.7**.

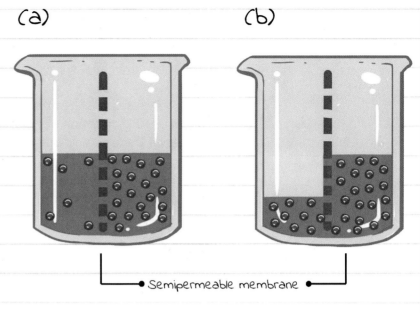

Figure 9.7:
Osmolality and Osmosis.

In (a), the right side has a greater osmolarity (mOsm/L) than the left side because it has more particles per amount of water. The right side is considered hypertonic while the left side is considered hypotonic. Water will travel from the left side to the right side via osmosis as shown in (b). By adding more water to the right side, the ratio of the amount of particles to water becomes the same on both sides. The solutions in (b) are isotonic.

The osmolarity of the fluid that enters the Bowman's capsule is around 300 mOsm/L; the osmolarity of the blood in the glomerulus is the same. How can this be if blood was filtered at the glomerulus? Remember we said that both solutes AND water enter the Bowman's capsule? When solutes enter, water follows by osmosis to create a solution in the Bowman's capsule that is **isotonic** to the blood in the glomerulus.

Glomerular Filtration Rate

What causes fluid to flow from the glomerulus into the Bowman's capsule? Pressure baby! Remember in the cardiovascular system and respiratory system chapters how fluids are able to move when there is a pressure differential across a membrane.

There are three types of pressure that are involved in filtration at the renal corpuscle:

1. **Hydrostatic pressure**: the pressure exerted by the blood against the capillary walls of the glomerulus. Remember, a fluid in its container applies a force on the walls of the container and causes pressure in the container.

2. **Colloid osmotic pressure**: the pressure for water to enter a container due to the presence of plasma proteins and other solutes. The term "colloid" refers to plasma proteins, such as albumin, as the solutes determining the osmotic pressure. The colloid osmotic pressure is higher in the capillaries than it is in the Bowman's capsule due to the lack of plasma proteins in the Bowman's capsule; thus, fluid is drawn into the glomerular capillaries.

3. **Hydrostatic pressure** in the **Bowman's capsule**: the Bowman's capsule is an enclosed space and therefore acts like a container. As a result, the fluid inside also applies a pressure against its surroundings, or hydrostatic pressure.

Fluid always flows from an area of high pressure to an area of lower pressure. The direction of fluid (in or out of the glomerulus) depends on the values of the above 3 pressures (**Figure 9.8**) As you can see in the figure, when the hydrostatic pressure of the capillary is greater than the sum of the colloid osmotic pressure and the hydrostatic pressure of the Bowman's capsule, blood can be filtered into the Bowman's capsule.

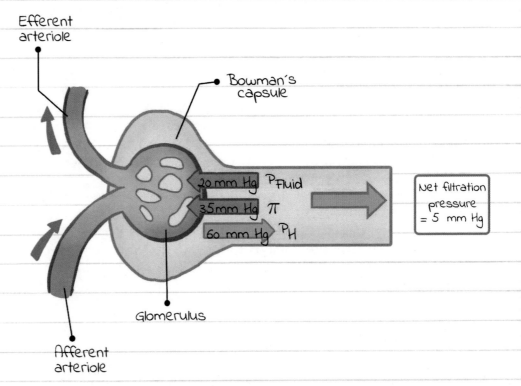

Figure 9.8:
Glomerular Filtration. P_{fluid} indicates the fluid pressure created by the fluid within the Bowman's capsule. π indicates the colloid osmotic pressure gradient due to proteins in the plasma but not in the Bowman's capsule. The hydrostatic pressure, or blood pressure, is indicated by P_H. The Net Filtration Pressure = $P_H - \pi - P_{fluid}$. In the case illustrated above, the net filtration pressure equals 5 mm Hg (Net Filtration Pressure = 60 mm Hg – 35 mm Hg – 20 mm Hg = 5 mm Hg).

The above three pressures determine the **glomerular filtration rate (GFR)**. This is the rate (volume/time) at which the kidney filters the blood at the glomerulus. The higher hydrostatic pressure of the glomerular capillaries, relative to the sum of P_{fluid} (**Figure 9.8**) and colloid osmotic pressure, the greater the filtration rate. Another factor that affects glomerular filtration rate is the **filtration coefficient,** which is dependent on the surface area and the permeability of the filtering membrane.

The MCAT wants you to understand the interrelated nature of the cardiovascular and urinary systems. For example, if the afferent arteriole which brings blood to the glomerulus has an increase in resistance, then the hydrostatic pressure in glomerulus decreases due to the decreased blood flow to the area. This results in a decrease in GFR. On the other hand, if you have an increase in resistance in the efferent arteriole, it is like a plug that has clogged up a drain! This increases the glomerular hydrostatic pressure and thereby increases the GFR. The MCAT may test your understanding on how changes in blood vessel resistance can affect the GFR.

The next parts of nephron that we cover have a lot of detail. We include specific mechanisms of how reabsorption and secretion occurs so that you get a thorough understanding of how the nephron works. We also include a lot of numbers to help guide you through specific processes and to grasp the relative amounts of ions and fluids that are reabsorbed vs secreted. However, memorizing all these details and numbers are not necessary for the MCAT exam. Instead, you may find it more beneficial to simply understand which solutes get reabsorbed/secreted at certain locations; where water is reabsorbed/secreted; and the amount of water and sodium that is secreted/reabsorbed relative to each location in the nephron. Then tie this information together and connect it to the overall function of the nephron, kidney, and urinary system! Alright, ready? Let's go!

Proximal Tubule

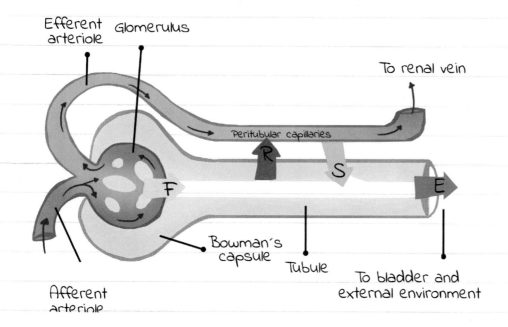

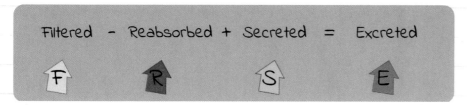

Figure 9.9:
The Proximal Convoluted Tubule. Urinary excretion depends on filtration, reabsorption, and secretion. At the proximal tubule, reabsorption and secretion occurs.

From the Bowman's capsule, the filtrate enters the **proximal convoluted tubule (PCT),** where both reabsorption and secretion occurs (**Figure 9.9**). Just as a reminder, reabsorption refers to the transfer of fluids and solutes back into the blood; secretion refers to the transfer of fluids and solutes into the nephron's tubule. In reabsorption, fluids and solids leave the PCT, enter the interstitium, and then the peritubular capillaries shown in **Figure 9.5**. Fluid reabsorption is necessary because a great amount of fluid enters the Bowman's capsule. Why do we need to reabsorb this fluid? Well if we don't, we would constantly be urinating out much of the fluid in our body. This can cause a myriad of problems such as low blood volume and low blood pressure. Reabsorption of the solutes is important because there are many valuable solutes that have passed through the filters of the glomerulus, but are needed by the body. So, what are the solutes that get reabsorbed? How much fluid gets reabsorbed?

At the PCT, 100% of glucose, 100% of amino acids, 65% of potassium, 65% of chloride, and 65% of sodium, 65% of water, 50% of urea, and 80% of phosphate is reabsorbed. You do not need to memorize these numbers for the MCAT; just understand that most of the fluid, ions, and urea are reabsorbed while ALL of the glucose and amino acids are reabsorbed. Solutes that are unable to diffuse out of the PCT are driven out via active transport and cotransport mechanisms. An example would be an Na^+/K^+ ATPase transporter (active transport) on the basolateral side of a cell in the PCT (**Figure 9.10**). When we refer to the basolateral side of the cell, we are referring to the side that is further away from the lumen of the nephron and closer to the extracellular space containing interstitial fluid. The transporter will pump sodium out of the cell into the interstitial fluid, creating a concentration gradient for sodium to want to enter the cell. Cotransporters on the luminal side will use this concentration gradient to move other solutes, such as glucose and amino acids, into the cell as shown on **Figure 9.10**.

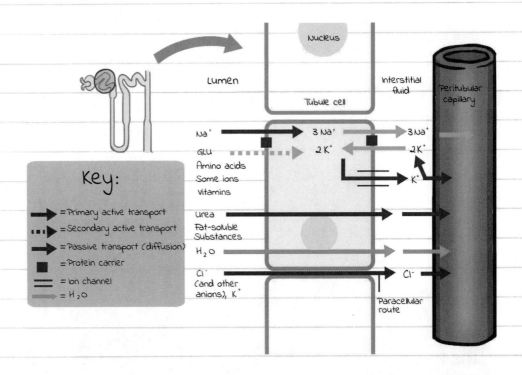

Figure 9.10:
Reabsorption at the Proximal Tubule.

Looking at **Figure 9.10**, we see that water is reabsorbed at the PCT; 65% to be exact. What causes this? As ions and solutes move out of the PCT, water in the lumen of the PCT follows via osmosis. Thus, the osmolarity of the filtrate entering and leaving the PCT does not change and remains at around 300 mOsm.

Secretion, or the movement of solutes and fluid from the blood into the lumen, also occurs at the PCT. The main solutes that are secreted are drugs (for excretion), organic acids and bases (uric acid and bile salts), and hydrogen ions. Drugs and organic acids and bases are secreted via active transport. The hydrogen ions are secreted into the lumen of the PCT using a cotransporter mechanism similar to the ones we have described above. However, instead of a symporter like we used for glucose and amino acids, an antiporter is used. An antiporter, on the lumen side, uses the concentration gradient of sodium created by the Na^+/K^+ ATPase on the basolateral side, to move sodium into the cell while simultaneously moving hydrogen into the lumen.

Loop Of Henle

After the proximal tubule, the filtrate enters the loop of Henle: a literal loop that extends downward into the medulla then back up towards the cortex. The function of the loop of Henle is to allow for the reabsorption of water and sodium chloride from the tubule to concentrate the filtrate that will be excreted out of the body as urine. There are three parts to the loop of Henle: the **thin descending limb, thin ascending limb,** and the **thick ascending limb.** Follow along on **Figure 9.11** as we take a journey through the roller coaster ride that is the loop of Henle.

The thin descending limb is highly permeable to water, moderately permeable to **urea**, and IMPERMEABLE to ions. As the filtrate (300 mOsm/L) travels down the thin descending limb, water is removed from the tubule and the filtrate becomes more **concentrated** (1200 mOsm/L). The filtrate then travels up the thin and thick ascending limbs which are impermeable to water but are permeable to ions. Ions are actively removed from the tubule, **diluting** the filtrate (100 mOsm/L) as it enters the distal convoluted tubule. But wait! Isn't the whole point of the loop of Henle to concentrate the urine? Yes it is! When we say we want to "concentrate" the urine, we are referring to the focus our nephron puts into expelling what we do not need into urine and removing what we do need from urine. Since water is something our body needs, we are concentrating the urine when we remove water from the nephron. However, the ratio of solutes- to water at the end of the loop of Henle is still less than the ratio of solutes to water at the beginning of the loop of Henle.

What is the mechanism behind this phenomena? Introducing... the kidney countercurrent system!

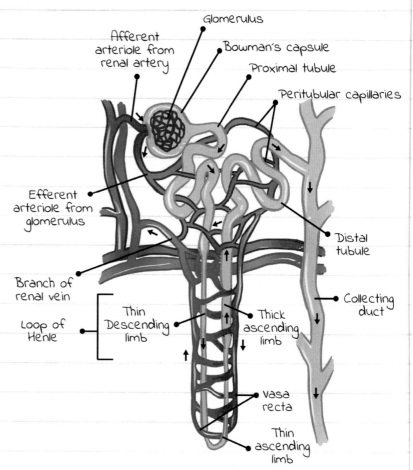

Figure 9.11:
Loop of Henle

Kidney Countercurrent Multiplier

The kidney countercurrent multiplier creates the osmotic gradient in the interstitium that allows for the removal of water and sodium chloride from the nephron for their eventual reabsorption. The countercurrent system has two players: the loop of Henle and the vasa recta. The vasa recta are special blood capillaries that surround the loop.

Follow along on **Figure 9.12**. To create the osmotic gradient, sodium chloride gets actively pumped from the thick ascending limb into the interstitial space of the medulla. This causes the osmolarity of the interstitial fluid to increase and an osmotic gradient to form between the interstitial fluid and the filtrate. As the filtrate travels down the water permeable descending limb, water travels out and into the interstitium until the filtrate in the descending limb and the interstitial fluid are isotonic (same osmolarity). New filtrate is continuously created and shoveled into the descending limb, pushing the older and more concentrated filtrate further down the loop. The ascending limb will continue to pump out ions out of the filtrate and into the interstitium to create an osmotic gradient. The cycle repeats until the gradient becomes steady. At this steady state, the osmolarity of the filtrate and its adjacent interstitial fluid is 300 mOsm/L at the top of the descending limb; 1200 mOsm at the bottom of the loop, and 100 mOsm/L at the top of the ascending limb.

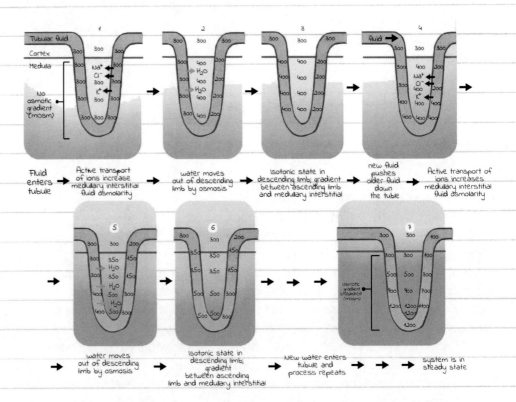

Figure 9.12:
Osmotic Gradient

The length of the loop of Henle determines the size of the gradient: the longer the loop, the greater the osmotic gradient will be. How so? The longer the loop, the more solutes are able to be pumped out and the more water will follow by osmosis. Since more water is leaving the tubule and is therefore being conserved, the urine can get more concentrated. Now it should make sense why desert animals have a longer loop of Henle; their survival relies on water conservation and so their urine needs to be extremely concentrated.

Vasa Recta

We said that the kidney countercurrent multiplier has two parts. So what role does the vasa recta play in all of this? The vasa recta functions to supply the cells of the nephron with oxygen and nutrients WITHOUT disturbing the osmotic gradient of the interstitial fluid created by the loop of Henle. The vasa recta are capillaries and are thereby highly permeable to water and solutes. If the vasa recta were like normal capillaries and simply ran across the medullary interstitium, the ions in the interstitial fluid would be absorbed into the capillaries and the gradient created by the loop of Henle would be destroyed! So what unique property of the vasa recta prevents this issue? It all has to do with the structure of the vasa recta.

The vasa recta is a hairpin-like structure that runs OPPOSITE, or "countercurrent", to the direction of the loop of Henle (**Figure 9.13**). The vasa recta begins by descending into the concentrated medulla, adjacent to the ascending loop of Henle that pumps out ions into the surrounding interstitium. These ions move into the descending vasa recta and water flows out of the descending vasa recta until the blood concentration in the vasa recta is equal to the concentration of the medullary interstitium (1200 mOsm). From the inner medulla, the vasa recta moves up towards the cortex, adjacent to the descending loop of Henle, where the surrounding interstitium is less concentrated (300 mOsm). Ions move out of the ascending vasa recta and water flows into the ascending vasa recta until the concentration of the blood in the vasa recta is equal to the concentration of the cortex interstitium. Thus, the hairpin structure of the vasa recta and the opposite direction of flow in relation to the loop of Henle allow the ions and water to stay in the medullary interstitium. The vasa recta is thereby able to provide oxygen and nutrients to the cells of the nephron without disturbing the gradient formed by the loop of Henle. If the vasa recta instead simply moved across the medullary interstitium in a manner similar to that of capillaries at the alveoli, ions and water would be reabsorbed and the gradient would be ruined.

The hairpin structure of the vasa recta also SLOWS down the blood flow coming from the peritubular capillaries. The importance of this is two fold. The slowed blood flow provides enough time for oxygen and nutrients to be exchanged with cells of the nephron. Secondly, rapid blood flow in the vasa recta would remove the ions in the medullary interstitium too quickly and destroy the osmotic gradient. The slowed blood flow allows for ions

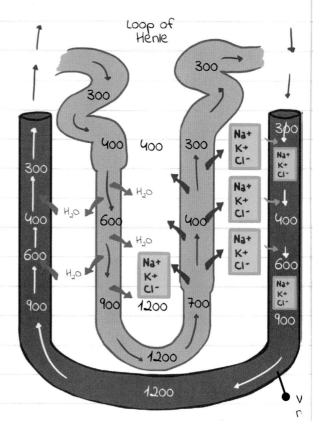

Counter Current Mechanism

Figure 9.13:
Vasa Recta

to freely enter and for water to freely leave the descending vasa recta; likewise, it allows for ions to freely leave and for water to freely enter the ascending vasa recta. The ions and water that need to stay in the medullary interstitium to maintain the osmotic gradient will stay; the rest will remain in the vasa recta and re-enter circulation. About 15% of the water that enters the nephron will be reabsorbed by the vasa recta due to the loop of Henle. By the time filtrate leaves the loop of Henle, around 80% of water of the original filtrate has been reabsorbed.

Distal Tubule

While the proximal convoluted tubule and the loop of Henle are mostly associated with bulk flow, the **distal convoluted tubule (DCT)** is focused on fine management of water and specific ions. As a reminder, you do not need to memorize all the little details that we mention in this section. Instead, it is more important to understand what gets secreted, what gets reabsorbed, and the mechanism of action of the hormones we will discuss.

The DCT can be split into two parts: the early and late distal convoluted tubules.

Early Distal Convoluted Tubule

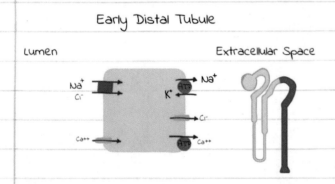

Figure 9.14:
Early Distal Convoluted Tubule

The early distal convoluted tubule is involved in the reabsorption of sodium, calcium, and chloride ions. Follow along on **Figure 9.14.** The early distal tubule is lined with epithelial cells. An Na^+/K^+ ATPase on the basolateral side of the cell pumps sodium out of the cell and potassium into the cell. This decreases the amount of sodium inside the tubular epithelial cell and creates a gradient for sodium to want to enter from the lumen. A symporter uses the sodium gradient to move sodium and chloride into the cell. Chloride ions then leave the cell using a uniporter on the basolateral side. The sodium and chloride ions that have moved out of the epithelial cell and into the extracellular space on the basolateral side are absorbed by the peritubular capillaries and re-enter circulation.

Calcium is moved out of the epithelial cell via active transport on the basolateral side. This decrease in intracellular calcium levels creates a gradient for calcium to want to enter from the lumen of the nephron. Using a uniporter on the luminal side, calcium enters the cell. You may recall in the *Endocrine Chapter* that **parathyroid hormone (PTH)** works on the kidneys to increase calcium reabsorption. Well, this is where it occurs! PTH increases the activity of the calcium uniporter on the luminal side to increase calcium movement into the cell. Calcium is then pumped out of the cell and into the extracellular fluid on the basolateral side to be picked up by the peritubular capillaries.

Late Distal Convoluted Tubule

The late distal convoluted tubule consists of two types of cells: **principal cells** and **intercalated cells (Figure 9.15)**

In principal cells, the Na^+/K^+ ATPase on the basolateral side decreases intracellular sodium concentration and increases intracellular potassium concentration. This sets up a gradient for sodium to enter the cell from the lumen and for potassium to be secreted into the lumen. As sodium enters into the lumen, water follows, making principal cells a significant player in water reabsorption; about 10-15% of water is reabsorbed at the DCT. The hormone, **aldosterone**, works on the Na^+/K^+ ATPase as we will soon see.

Intercalated cells help control pH in the body. There are two types of intercalated: alpha intercalated cells and beta intercalated cells. In both intercalated cells, carbon dioxide reacts with water in the presence of carbonic acid anhydrase to form bicarbonate and hydrogen ions. In alpha cells, hydrogen ions are moved into the lumen of the nephron using a ATPase pump. There is also an antiporter on the luminal side that moves potassium into the cell while moving hydrogen ions out into the lumen. Thus, alpha intercalated cells help the body compensate for increased acidity; as more hydrogen ions are secreted into the lumen, the reaction shifts to the right and more hydrogen ions are created to be moved into the lumen and excreted as urine. To prevent the accumulation of bicarbonate, there is an antiporter on the basolateral side that moves bicarbonate out while moving a chloride ion into the cell. The potassium and chloride ions that have built up in the cell are moved into the extracellular space via a symporter on the basolateral side. The bicarbonate, potassium, and chloride ions in the extracellular space are reabsorbed by the peritubular capillaries and re-enter circulation.

Beta intercalated cells help when the body is too basic by moving bicarbonate ions into the lumen to be excreted in urine in exchange for chlorine ions. Hydrogen ions are pumped into the extracellular space and chlorine ions are moved into the extracellular space using a uniporter. These ions are then reabsorbed by the peritubular capillaries and re-entered into circulation.

Late Distal Tubule and Collecting Duct

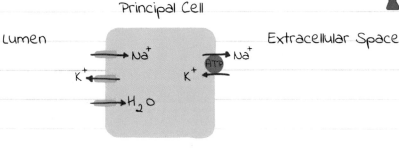

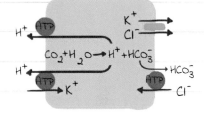

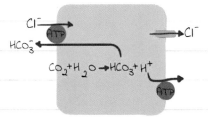

Figure 9.15:
Late Distal Convoluted Tubule, Principal Cells, and Intercalated Cells.

Collecting Duct

From the distal convoluted tubule, the filtrate enters the collecting duct. The collecting duct contains both the principal cells and intercalated cells found also in the distal convoluted tubule. Thus the collecting duct, along with the DCT, function to reabsorb ions and water, secrete ions, and mediate pH (**Figure 9.16**). However, the collecting duct is a little different from the DCT because it is a site of greater water reabsorption due to the hormone, **antidiuretic hormone (ADH),** or **vasopressin.** By varying the amount of ADH that acts on the collecting duct, we can vary the amount of water that is reabsorbed and thereby regulate blood osmolarity. The reabsorption of water at the collecting duct also increases the concentration of urine exiting into the ureter.

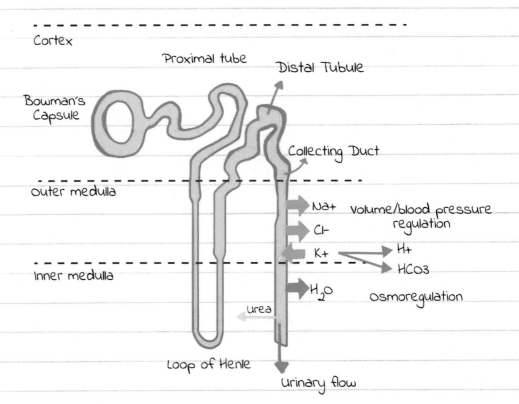

Figure 9.16:
Reabsorption and Secretion at the Collecting Duct

As we leave the collecting duct, we have accomplished our mission of concentrating the urine and reabsorbing any necessary solutes. Once urine enters the ureter, it is no longer modified and is excreted with the same composition as it left the collecting duct. We end up creating approximately 1.5L of urine per day. That is amazing considering that the kidney filters 180L/day. From these numbers alone, we can see the magnitude of just how much fluid the nephron reabsorbs!

Hormones of the Urinary System

Aldosterone

A quick review of the endocrine system will remind you that aldosterone is a steroid hormone that is synthesized in the adrenal cortex of the kidney. Since it is a steroid hormone, it enters the blood and is carried to its target by the carrier protein **albumin**. The targets are the principal cells that are located in the distal convoluted tubule and the outer medullary portion of the collecting duct.

Aldosterone stimulates principal cells to increase production of the basal Na^+/K^+ ATPase as well as the luminal Na^+ and K^+ channels. This increase in membrane proteins causes more sodium to be reabsorbed and more potassium to be secreted into the lumen of the nephron. The increased reabsorption of sodium is followed by the increased reabsorption of water via osmosis. Since more water is being reabsorbed, blood volume and pressure will increase. Thus, aldosterone plays a significant role in sodium reabsorption, potassium secretion, and blood pressure regulation!

Recall that alpha intercalated cells have an antiporter on the luminal side that moves hydrogen ions out of the cell while moving potassium ions into the cell. By aldosterone increasing potassium ion concentration in the lumen of the DCT/collecting duct, the hydrogen/potassium antiporter activity of the alpha intercalated cell is also increased. Thus, aldosterone indirectly increases hydrogen secretion.

What causes aldosterone to be secreted so that blood pressure can be increased? Introducing... the **renin-angiotensin-aldosterone pathway (RAAS)!**

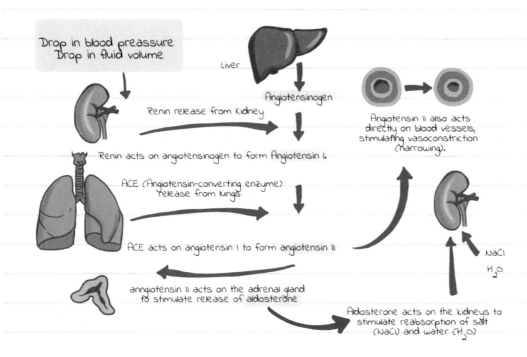

Drop in blood preassure
Drop in fluid volume

Liver

Angiotensinogen

Renin release from Kidney

Angiotensin II also acts directly on blood vessels, stimulating vasoconstriction (narrowing).

Renin acts on angiotensinogen to form Angiotensin I.

ACE (Angiotensin-converting enzyme) release from lungs

ACE acts on angiotensin I to form angiotensin II

NaCl
H_2O

anngiotensin II acts on the adrenal gland to stimulate release of aldosterone

Aldosterone acts on the kidneys to stimulate reabsorption of salt (NaCl) and water (H_2O)

Figure 9.17: Renin-Angiotensin-Aldosterone System

Follow along on **Figure 9.17.** A drop in blood pressure initiates the release of the enzyme **renin** from the kidneys, which converts **angiotensinogen** (produced in the liver) to **angiotensin I**. An enzyme called **angiotensin-converting enzyme** (ACE) converts angiotensin I to **angiotensin II**. Angiotensin II induces the **adrenal cortex** to release **aldosterone**, which travels through the blood and acts on the DCT and collecting duct to retain sodium and water. The reuptake of water increases blood volume, and thereby blood pressure. Angiotensin II also binds to receptors in blood vessels and causes them to constrict, resulting in an increase in blood pressure.

Antidiuretic Hormone

Antidiuretic hormone (ADH), or **vasopressin**, increases water reabsorption at the inner medullary portion of the collecting duct by increasing the number of **aquaporins** on the luminal side of principal cells. Remember, aquaporins are specialized membrane protein channels that allow the passage of water. As the collecting duct moves deep into the medulla, its surrounding interstitial concentration increases due to the countercurrent multiplier system. Water will be drawn out of the collecting duct and into the interstitium, where it can be osmotically reabsorbed by the vasa recta or peritubular capillaries.

ADH is produced by the **hypothalamus** and stored in the **posterior pituitary**. It is released from the posterior pituitary when **osmoreceptors** in the hypothalamus detect an increase in blood osmolarity. ADH travels to principal cells and increases its number of aquaporin on the luminal side, causing an increase in water reabsorption. The increase in water reabsorption will normalize the blood osmolarity as well as increase blood pressure. ADH also increases urea reabsorption, which we will cover later on in this chapter.

Atrial Natriuretic Peptide

We have talked a lot about hormones that act on the kidneys to increase blood pressure. How about when we need to lower blood pressure? That is where the atrial natriuretic peptide (ANP), also known as atrial natriuretic factor, comes in!

ANP is a peptide that is released by the atrias of the heart. ANPs are released in response to atrial stretching caused by high blood volume and pressure. ANPs are able to lower blood pressure in a multitude of ways. Firstly, ANP vasodilates the afferent arteriole while constricting the efferent arteriole of the nephron. This increases glomerular filtration rate and causes more filtrate to enter the nephron to be excreted. The more fluid being moved from the blood to the nephron, the lower blood volume and pressure becomes. The increased glomerular filtration rate also inhibits the kidney from releasing renin. By preventing renin release,

ANP inhibits the renin-angiotensin-aldosterone system that functions to increase blood pressure. ANP also acts directly on the principal cells of the collecting duct to decrease sodium reabsorption by lowering the amount of luminal sodium channels. By decreasing sodium reabsorption, less water is reabsorbed. If you notice, this is the OPPOSITE mechanism by which aldosterone increases blood pressure. Lastly, ANP acts directly on the blood vessels and causes them to vasodilate, reducing resistance and blood pressure in the process.

For the MCAT exam, you do not need to memorize all these mechanisms of action for ANP. Instead, understand that ANP works to lower blood pressure and opposes the action of aldosterone and the RAAS!

Other Hormones

We mentioned in the beginning of this chapter two functions of the urinary system that have not been covered yet: blood cell production and the synthesis of calcitriol.

The kidneys secrete a hormone, called **erythropoietin,** that induces red blood cell production (**erythropoiesis**) in bone marrow. Erythropoietin is typically released when the body is low on oxygen (**hypoxic**) because red blood cells carry oxygen. The more red blood cells, the more oxygen can be carried throughout the body.

The kidneys also produce **calcitriol,** the active form of vitamin D, in response to parathyroid hormone. Calcitriol increases calcium levels in the blood in a multitude of ways: calcitriol increases calcium absorption from the intestine; increases calcium release from bone by increasing osteoclast activity; and increases calcium reabsorption at the kidneys.

Urea

There is an important solute that we have briefly mentioned earlier in the chapter called urea. You may recall reading that around 50% of urea that has entered the nephron is reabsorbed at the proximal convoluted tubule. As you will soon find out, urea also plays a role at the loop of Henle and the collecting duct. But before we explore urea's entire role in the nephron, let us first answer… what exactly is urea?

Amino acids are typically used to make proteins in the body. However when cells are starving for energy, cells will use amino acids as precursors of substrates for cellular respiration to create ATP. Likewise when there is an excess of amino acids, the amino acids can be used as precursors of substrates for metabolic pathways that result in the production of glucose and later, glycogen. For amino acids to be used as precursors, deamination (removal of amino group -NH3) must occur first so that only a carbon skeleton remains. The amino group is converted into ammonia, shuttled into the urea cycle in the liver, and converted into urea (**Figure 9.18**). Urea is toxic to the blood in high amounts; therefore, excess urea is secreted into the nephron to be excreted. So what role does urea have at the loop of Henle and collecting duct?

Figure 9.18:
Urea Formation.

Other than to be excreted in urine, urea's role in the nephron is to assist in the reabsorption of water at the loop of Henle. We mentioned earlier how sodium and chloride ions form a hyperosmotic environment in the medullary interstitium so that water will travel out of the descending loop of Henle, into the interstitium, and later into the vasa recta. Recall that it is very important that we reabsorb a sufficient amount of water so that

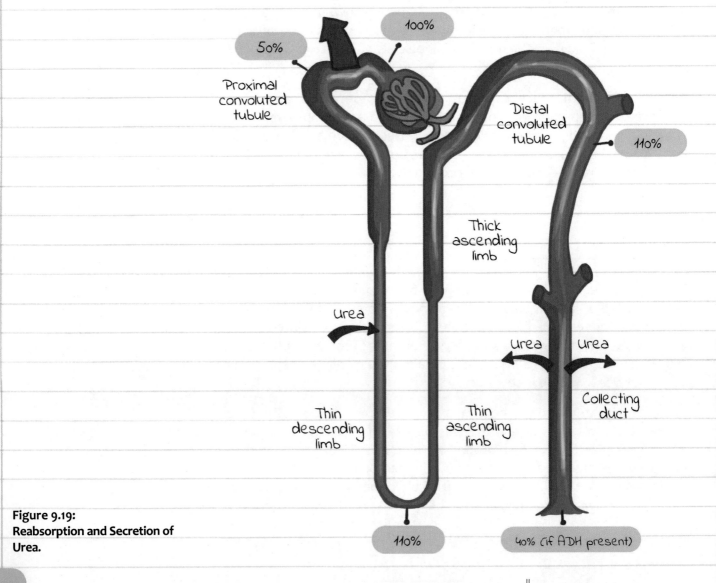

Figure 9.19:
Reabsorption and Secretion of Urea.

a sustainable blood volume and pressure is kept. Sodium and chloride ions are not the only solutes responsible for creating the hyperosmotic environment in the medulla; urea is too! As filtrate travels down the thin descending limb, the combination of sodium ions, chloride ions, and urea concentrate the medullary interstitium to about 1200 mOsm/L. This drives water out of the thin descending limb until the filtrate becomes isotonic with the interstitium. Without urea, there would still be an osmotic gradient present; however, the gradient would not be as strong (<1200 mOsm/L) or would require more ions to be secreted into the interstitium to reach an osmolarity of 1200 mOsm/L. The thin descending limb is moderately permeable to urea; thus, some urea is passively driven into the tubule from the interstitium. The thin ascending limb and thick ascending limb are not permeable to urea; the distal convoluted tubule does not reabsorb urea. As a result, the filtrate entering the collecting duct is relatively concentrated with urea. Some urea will diffuse out of the collecting duct, specifically at the medullary portion, into the interstitium. The urea that has entered the interstitium contributes towards the osmotic gradient that enables water reabsorption at the thin descending limb (**Figure 9.19**).

ADH plays a significant role in how much urea is reabsorbed. As mentioned earlier, ADH increases the amount of water reabsorbed at the collecting duct. Thus in the presence of ADH, a substantial amount of water is removed from the filtrate and the concentration of urea at the medullary portion of the collecting duct is increased. More urea will then be driven out of the collecting duct and into the interstitium, where it can contribute to the osmotic gradient or be reabsorbed by the vasa recta. ADH also increases the number of urea transporters on principal cells in the collecting duct to further aid in the movement of urea out of the tubule. When ADH is not present, the opposite will occur: less water is reabsorbed, the concentration of urea in the tubule decreases, less urea enters the interstitium, and the contribution of urea to the osmotic gradient decreases.

Questions

1) **Which of the following is/are function(s) of the urinary system?**
   - I. Release hormones in response to activity from the parathyroid gland
   - II. Regulate blood pH
   - III. Detoxify the blood
     - a. I only
     - b. II only
     - c. I and II only
     - d. I, II, and III

2) **All of the following are true of the urinary system except:**
   - a. Three sphincter muscles located between the bladder and the urethra control the opening and closing of a tube
   - b. The renal artery supplies oxygenated blood to the kidney
   - c. The filtrate from the glomerulus feeds into the Bowman's capsule
   - d. Blood exits the kidney via the renal vein

3) **Which of the following components of blood would you possibly find in the filtrate of a healthy individual when taken from the Bowman's capsule?**
   - I. Glucose
   - II. Regulate blood pH
   - III. Bicarbonate
     - a. I only
     - b. III only
     - c. I and III only
     - d. I, II, and III

4) **Which of the following represent the correct pathway of the filtrate through the nephron?**
   - a. Bowman's capsule → Distal tubule → loop of Henle → proximal tubule → collecting duct
   - b. Bowman's capsule → proximal tubule → loop of Henle → distal tubule → collecting duct
   - c. Bowman's capsule → proximal tubule → loop of Henle → collecting duct → distal tubule
   - d. Proximal tubule → Bowman's capsule → loop of Henle → distal tubule → collecting duct

5) **Which of the following is true regarding osmotic gradients?**
   - a. A less concentrated solution is hypertonic to a more concentrated solution
   - b. A less concentrated solution exerts more osmotic pressure than a more concentrated solution
   - c. Isotonic solutions only occur when there is a net flow of water from one solution to another
   - d. A more concentrated solution has a higher osmotic pressure than a less concentrated solution

6) **What is true of the relationship between the osmolarities of the fluid that enters the Bowman's capsule and the blood in the glomerulus?**
   a. The osmolarity of the fluid in the Bowman's capsule is greater than that of the blood in the glomerulus because the capsule pulls in solutes from the blood
   b. The osmolarity of the blood in the glomerulus is greater than that of the fluid in the Bowman's capsule because the blood retains many of the plasma components
   c. They are the same because when solutes enter the Bowman's capsule, water follows by osmosis to create a solution in the Bowman's capsule that is isotonic to the blood in the glomerulus
   d. None of the above

7) **What would be the effect of an increase in the resistance of the efferent arteriole of the glomerulus on the glomerular filtration rate?**
   a. The osmotic pressure would decrease
   b. The osmotic pressure would increase
   c. The hydrostatic pressure would decrease
   d. The hydrostatic pressure would increase

8) **All of the following would increase glomerular filtration rate EXCEPT:**
   a. Dilation of afferent arterioles to the glomerulus
   b. Increased concentration of sodium in the filtrate
   c. Constriction of efferent arterioles from the glomerulus
   d. Increased blood flow rate

9) **Which of the following is not secreted at all at the proximal convoluted tubule?**
   a. Amino acids
   b. Potassium
   c. Urea
   d. Chloride

10) **Which of the following methods of transport are used to reabsorb solutes?**
   I. Primary active transport
   II. Secondary active transport
   III. Passive diffusion
   a. I and II only
   b. I and III only
   c. II and III only
   d. I, II, and III

11) **Which of the following statements is true of the loop of Henle?**
   a. The ascending limb is permeable to water and the descending limb is permeable to ions
   b. The ascending limb is permeable to ions and the descending limb is permeable to water
   c. Both the ascending limb and the descending limb are permeable to water
   d. Both the ascending limb and the descending limb are permeable to ions

12) In which region of the kidney will the filtrate reach its maximum concentration?

    a. Distal tubule
    b. Proximal tubule
    c. Ascending loop of Henle
    d. Collecting duct

13) The hairpin structure of the vasa recta slows down the blood flow coming from the peritubular capillaries:

    I.   To allow quick removal of ions from the medullary interstitium
    II. To provide enough time for oxygen and nutrients to be exchanged with cells of the nephron
    III. To prevent the destruction of the osmotic gradient
        a. II only
        b. I and II only
        c. II and III only
        d. I, II, and III

14) Which of the following statements are true of intercalated cells?

    a. Alpha intercalated cells transfer hydrogen ions into the lumen of the nephron using an ATPase pump
    b. Beta intercalated cells remove bicarbonate ions from the lumen of the nephron
    c. In both intercalated cells, carbonic anhydrase combines bicarbonate ions with hydrogen ions to form carbon dioxide and water
    d. Alpha intercalated cells help compensate for increased alkalinity

15) Which of the following is a target of aldosterone?

    a. Bowman's capsule
    b. Proximal convoluted tubule
    c. Distal convoluted tubule
    d. Loop of Henle

16) Which of the following would be true of a dehydrated individual with respect to a healthy individual?

    a. Decreased levels of renin
    b. Increased levels of ANP
    c. Decreased levels of vasopressin
    d. Increased levels of aldosterone

17) Uremia is the condition of having high levels of urea in the blood. Which of the following could be the cause of that in an otherwise healthy individual?

    a. Increased levels of insulin
    b. Diminished activity of glucose transporters
    c. Increased fatty acid biosynthesis
    d. Reduced consumption of meat

18) Which of the following is/are responsible for creating the hyperosmotic environment in the medulla?

I. Sodium
II. Potassium
III. Urea

    a. I and II only
    b. I and III only
    c. II and III only
    d. I, II, and III

19) What would happen if you injected vasopressin into a healthy individual?

    a. The osmolarity of the filtrate would decrease
    b. The amount of urea in the interstitium would decrease
    c. The amount of water in the filtrate would increase
    d. None of the above

20) A patient presents with symptoms of type 1 diabetes mellitus, including presence of glucose in the urine. What could be a cause of that?

    a. Excess secretion of glucose by the proximal tubule
    b. Reduced number of glucose channels on the ascending loop of Henle
    c. Inability to reabsorb excess glucose at the proximal tubule
    d. Increased expression of glucose transporters

Answers

1) **Answer: C**

   Explanation: The kidneys produce calcitriol , the active form of vitamin D, in response to parathyroid hormone input, making statement I true and eliminating choice (B). Kidneys regulate blood pH via selective reabsorption of bicarbonate, making statement (II) true and eliminating choice (A). The livers are responsible for detoxifying the blood, not the kidney, making statement (III) false, eliminating choice (D) and making choice (C) correct.

2) **Answer: A**

   Explanation: Choices (B), (C), and (D) are all true statements, eliminating them as answer choices. To control when we urinate, we have two sphincter muscles located between the bladder and the urethra, not three, making choice (A) false and the correct answer.

3) **Answer: C**

   Explanation: After passing through fenestrations, the basement membrane and podocytes, only glucose and salts like bicarbonate remain in the Bowman's capsule along with other solutes, making (I) and (III) viable and eliminating choices (A) and (B). However, blood cells do not pass through, eliminating statement (II) and choice (D), making choice (C) correct.

4) **Answer: B**

   Explanation: Only choice (B) illustrates the correct pathway of the filtrate through the nephron. All of the other choices are incorrect.

5) **Answer: D**

   Explanation: A less concentrated solution is hypotonic to a more concentrated solution, not hypertonic, eliminating choice (A). When solutions are isotonic, there is no net flow of water as the osmotic pressure between the two solutions are equal, eliminating choice (C). Osmotic pressure is directly proportional to concentration, eliminating choice (B) and making choice (D) correct.

6) **Answer: C**

   Explanation: Osmosis dictates that so long as there is permeability to both, the flow of water follows the flow of solutes. This lends to the osmolarity remaining constant, as any movement of solute is accompanied by a movement of water, eliminating choices (A), (B), and (D) and making choice (C) correct.

7) **Answer: D**

   Explanation: Osmotic pressure is only dependent on the osmolarity of the fluid, eliminating choices (A) and (B). As per Poiseuille's law from the chapter on circulation, an increase in peripheral resistance results in an increase in the hydrostatic pressure, eliminating choice (C) and making choice (D) correct.

8) **Answer: B**

   Explanation: Dilation of afferent arterioles to the glomerulus would increase overall blood flow to the region, increasing glomerular filtration rate, eliminating choices (A) and (D). Constricting efferent arterioles from the glomerulus causes a buildup of hydrostatic pressure which would also increase the glomerular filtration rate, eliminating choice (C). Sodium concentration has no effect on the hydrodynamics of the filtrate, making (B) the correct answer.

9) **Answer: A**

   Explanation: Only small molecules and ions like potassium, chloride, and urea are secreted at the proximal convoluted tubules, eliminating choices (B), (C), and (D). Amino acids are generally fully reabsorbed, making choice (A) correct.

10) **Answer: D**

   Explanation: Primary active transport is utilized to reabsorb solutes through pumps, making statement I true and eliminating choice (C). Secondary active transport is also utilized through the creation of electrochemical gradients, making statement (II) true and eliminating choice (B). Passive diffusion is also achieved via flow down concentration gradients, eliminating (A) and making choice (D) correct.

11) **Answer: B**

   Explanation: In the loop of Henle, only the ascending limb is permeable to ions and the descending limb is permeable to water. Only choice (B) reflects this, making it the correct answer.

12) **Answer: D**

   Explanation: The goal of the nephron is to concentrate the urine in a stepwise manner by slowly selectively reabsorbing water and just some solutes. This concentration reaches its maximum at the collecting duct, where there is the final stage of water reabsorption, making choice (D) correct.

13) **Answer: C**

   Explanation: The hairpin structure of the vasa recta and the opposite direction of flow in relation to the loop of Henle allow the ions and water to stay in the medullary interstitium, not come out of it, making statement (I) false and eliminating choices (B) and (D). The purpose of the vasa recta is to provide oxygen and nutrients to the cells of the nephron without destroying the concentration gradients, making statements (II) and (III) true and choice (C) correct.

14) Answer: A

Explanation: Beta intercalated cells (not alpha) help when the body is too basic by moving bicarbonate ions into the lumen, not out of the lumen, eliminating choices (B) and (D). In both intercalated cells, carbonic anhydrase converts CO_2 and water into bicarbonate and protons, not the other way around, eliminating choice (C). Alpha intercalated cells transfer hydrogen ions into the lumen of the nephron using an ATPase pump to compensate for increased acidity, making choice (A) correct.

15) Answer: C

Explanation: Aldosterone only targets the principal cells of the distal convoluted tubule to cause increased sodium reabsorption, making (C) the correct answer.

16) Answer: D

Explanation: ANP is released in response to high blood volume, which would not be the case for a dehydrated individual, elimination choice (B). Low water levels would stimulate an increase in vasopressin to increase water reabsorption at the collecting duct, not a decrease, eliminating choice (C). A dehydrated individual would have increased levels of renin to stimulate aldosterone release and subsequent water reuptake, eliminating choice (A) and making choice (D) the correct answer.

17) Answer: B

Explanation: When cells are starving for energy, they start to rely on amino acids as precursors of substrates for metabolic pathways. The oxidative deamination of amino acids leads to the production of urea as a byproduct. To a greater enough extent, this can lead to uremia. Increased fatty acid biosynthesis occurs in response to excess energy, eliminating choice (B). Reduced consumption of meat would result in lower amino acid intake which would reduce urea in the blood, not increase it, eliminating choice (D). Increased levels on insulin allow for added glucose uptake and occur in response to excess glucose, which does not lead to a starvation of energy for the cells, eliminating choice (A). Diminished activity of glucose transporters, however, would result in the body looking to amino acids as an energy source as cells are unable to take up glucose, making choice (B) correct.

18) Answer: B

> **Explanation:** Only sodium, chloride, and urea are involved in creating the hyperosmotic environment in the medulla, making choice (B) correct.

19) Answer: D

> **Explanation:** Vasopressin causes reabsorption of water at the collecting duct, which would increase the osmolarity of the filtrate and decrease the amount of water in the filtrate, eliminating choices (A) and (C). Vasopressin also indirectly results in the increased reuptake of urea, causing the amount of urea in the interstitium to increase, eliminating choice (B). Choice (D) is the correct answer.

20) Answer: C

> **Explanation:** There is no secretion of glucose by the proximal tubule, eliminating choice (A). There are no glucose channels in the loop of Henle, eliminating choice (B). Increased expression of glucose transporters would stimulate uptake of glucose, not release, eliminating choice (D). Inability to reabsorb excess glucose at the proximal tubule would cause it to remain in the filtrate and eventually detected in the urine, making choice (C) correct.

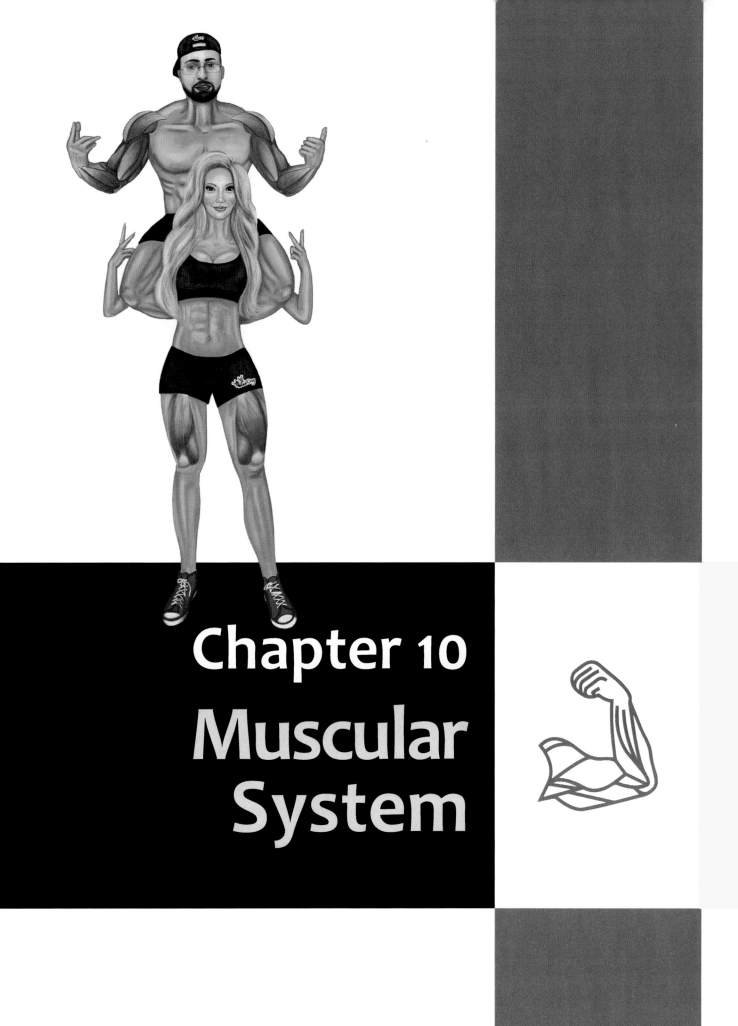

Chapter 10
Muscular System

Chapter 10

Muscular System

Humanity is obsessed with muscles! We've all been to history museums and looked at the statues of Greek heroes in awe. Aside from making us look attractive, muscles provide us with the indispensable ability to move around. Muscles are also critical for organ function and for regulating our body heat. Next time your friend looks at you and asks "do you even lift bro?" think about this chapter. You'll soon be able to confidently explain that our muscles are used for way more than just lifting!

Skeletal		Voluntary	Striated	Multinucleated	Non-branched
Cardiac		Involuntary	Striated	Single Nucleus	Branched
Smooth		Involuntary	Nonstriated	Single Nucleus	Tapered

Figure 10.1:
Muscle Types and their Properties

There are three muscle types in the human body: **skeletal, cardiac,** and **smooth muscle (Figure 10.1). Skeletal muscle** is a form of **striated** muscle tissue and is under voluntary control. Striated muscles are muscles with fibers that are aligned in parallel bundles. Skeletal muscles are attached to bones via **tendons,** and **ligaments** attach different bones together. Most of our voluntary bodily movements are thanks to the skeletal muscles. **Cardiac muscle** is only found in the heart and is also a form of striated muscle, but it is under involuntary control. **Smooth muscle** is located on the walls of many internal organs and around blood vessels. This muscle type is also under involuntary control, but it is not striated. Let us take a deeper look into the three muscle types.

Figure 10.2:
Origin and Insertion of Muscles via Tendons

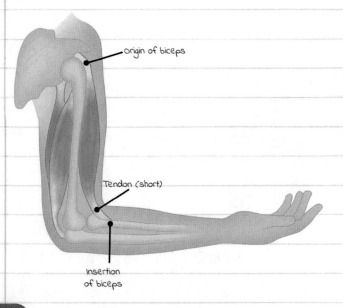

origin of biceps

Tendon (short)

Insertion of biceps

Skeletal Muscle

Most of the muscle in the body is skeletal muscle. Like we mentioned above, attachments of skeletal muscle to the bones via tendons enable the bones to move in different ways. There are two points of connection between the muscle and bone that you must know: **origin** and **insertion** of a muscle.

A shown in **Figure 10.2,** the **origin** is a fixed attachment of the skeletal muscle to bone via the tendon. The origin does not move during muscle contraction. In contrast, the **insertion** is the point at which the tendon attaches to the bone that does move during contraction. Let's look at the example in **Figure 10.2**: when we contract our biceps and flex our arm, our forearm (insertion) moves while our shoulder (origin) stays put. In summary, while both the origin and insertion are points where the tendon attaches to the muscle, the origin is a **fixed attachment** and the insertion **moves**. Let's use a real world example to describe origin and insertion. Say you have a rope attached to an object and you are standing 10 feet away with the other end of the rope in your hand. When you pull on the object, it gets closer to you. You have not moved from your original spot. In this situation, the origin is where your hand is attached to the rope while the insertion is where the rope is attached to the object.

Muscles are also categorized based on the type of motion they cause. If contraction of the muscle brings the bones closer together, it is called a **flexor**. The biceps are an example of a flexor because they bring the bones of the forearms closer to the bones of the upper arm. If contraction of the muscle results in the bones moving away from one another, the muscle is called an **extensor**. The tricep muscle, for example, moves the bones of the forearm away from the bones of the upper arm, making it an extensor. Many joints of the body, such as the elbow, contain both flexor and extensor muscles. These pairs of muscles are **antagonistic muscle groups,** since they exert opposite effects on the movement of bone (**Figure 10.3**).

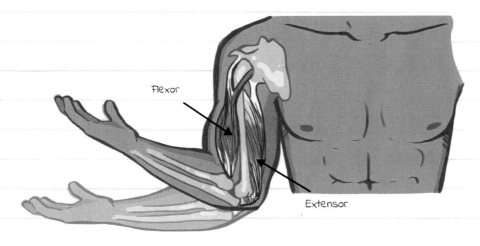

Figure 10.3:
Flexor and Extensor Muscles. The biceps are flexor muscles and the triceps are extensor muscles.

Skeletal Muscle Structure

Skeletal muscle cells are called **muscle fibers**. They are unique in that they contain hundreds of nuclei, thereby being **multinucleated**. Muscle fibers,

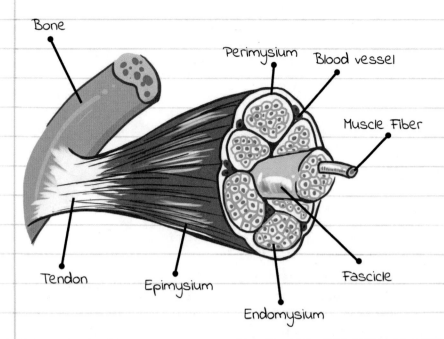

interestingly, are the largest cells in our body. Groups of fibers join together to form an even larger unit called a **fascicle;** and many fascicles form skeletal muscle themselves. Look at **Figure 10.4!**

Let us take a moment to zoom in to analyze the anatomy of a muscle fiber in order to understand how muscle contraction occurs (**Figure 10.5**). Although the muscle fiber is physiologically similar to other cell types, there are some differences. Additionally, muscle fiber organelles are named differently than the organelles of other cells. For example, a muscle fiber's cell membrane is called the **sarcolemma;** the cytoplasm is referred to as the **sarcoplasm;** and the endoplasmic reticulum is called the **sarcoplasmic reticulum.** Within the muscle fibers are structures called **myofibrils** which are bundles of contractile and elastic proteins that carry out the contractions. The process by which contractions occur will be discussed more in depth below.

Figure 10.4:
Skeletal Muscle Structure. Many muscle fibers (skeletal muscle cells) make up a fascicle. Many fascicles form skeletal muscle.

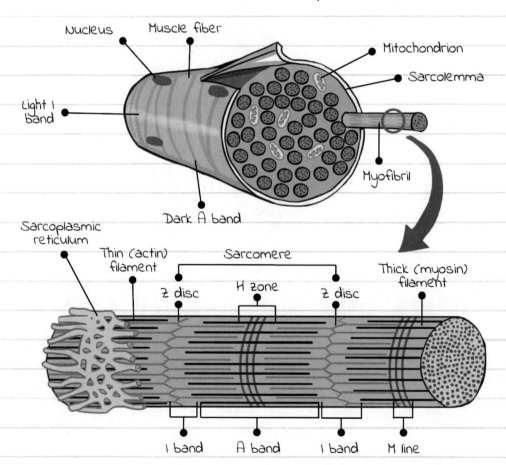

Figure 10.5:
Anatomy of the Muscle Fiber. Muscle fibers are made of myofibrils that carry out contraction.

The sarcoplasmic reticulum contains an enlarged portion called **terminal cisternae,** which stores **calcium ions** that are critical for contraction. An additional network of tubes is associated with the terminal cisternae, called

Chapter 10 Muscular System   Copyright © 2019 MCAT King

the **transverse tubules (t-tubules),** that are involved in the transmission of a muscle contraction. The T-tubules are continuous with the sarcolemma, which allows an action potential to move from the cell surface to the inside of the fiber at a much faster rate. Together, the t-tubules and the terminal cisternae make up a **triad (Figure 10.6).**

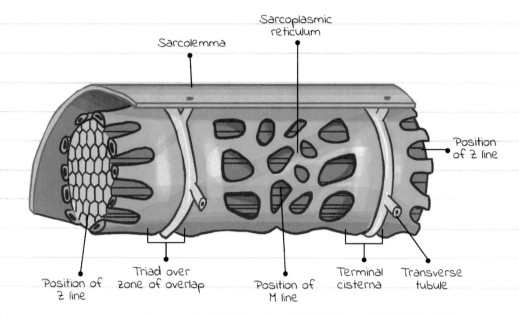

Sarcoplasmic reticulum

Sarcolemma

Position of Z line

Position of Z line

Triad over zone of overlap

Position of M line

Terminal cisterna

Transverse tubule

Figure 10.6:
The Sarcoplasmic Reticulum (SR) and Transverse Tubule. The T-tubule is continuous with the sarcolemma and moves action potentials from outside the fiber to inside the fiber. This will initiate release of calcium stored in the terminal cisternae of the SR to be used for contraction.

Let us discuss the proteins that make up the muscle fibrils and how they contribute to contraction.

First, we have **myosin.** Myosin is classified as a motor protein due to its ability to create movement. Notice the anatomy of myosin. Each myosin has protein chains that have a circular "head" and "tail" (**Figure 10.7**). The heads have a hinge that allows them to crank back and bend forward when need be. The many myosin molecules together create the **thick filament.**

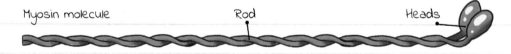

Myosin molecule

Rod

Heads

Figure 10.7:
Myosin Molecule.

The other protein in muscle is **actin.** The monomeric form of actin is called G-actin. Many G-actin units polymerize to form F-actin. The F-actin polymers twist together to form the **thin filament**. Together, the thick and thin filaments are connected by **cross-bridges**. When **cross-bridges** form, a myosin head binds to the myosin-binding site on actin. At any point in time, the cross-bridges are either relaxed or are contracting. When contraction occurs, the actin and myosin together are termed the **sliding filament model (Figure 10.8).**

We can recognize other structures when looking at a myofibril under the microscope. In myofibril, there are repeating patterns of light and dark bands called **sarcomeres (Figure 10.9).** Sarcomeres are the smallest functional unit of the muscle. The list below includes structures of the sarcomere that you should be able to recognize for the MCAT.

Figure 10.8:
Sliding Filament Model.

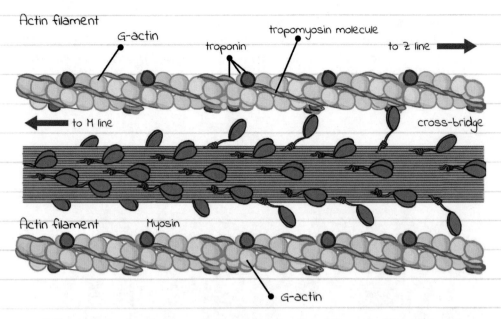

1. **Z Line:** serves as the attachment site for the thin actin filaments. There is one at the end of each end of a sarcomere.
2. **I Band:** the region of the sarcomere that is made up of the thin actin filaments only. Notice how a Z-line runs through each I Band; half of each I Band belongs to a different sarcomere.
3. **H Zone:** the region of the sarcomere that is made up of the thick myosin filaments only. It is the central region of the A band.
4. **A Band:** the darkest band. Runs along the entire length of the thick filament. The band specifically refers to the entire length of the myosin filament, including where the actin filament overlaps with the myosin. This is the only part of the sarcomere that does not change size when a muscle contracts.
5. **M Line:** refers to the middle of the sarcomere. The thick filaments attach to this line of proteins. The M line divides the A band in half.

Figure 10.9:
Sarcomere.

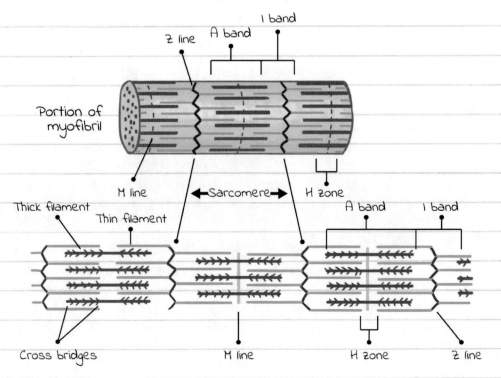

Chapter 10 Muscular System   Copyright © 2019 MCAT King

Skeletal Muscle Contraction

Muscle contraction requires energy in the form of ATP. For the MCAT, you should become familiar with the process of contraction and the events that occur in the myofibril. Study the steps along with the diagram! (Figure 10.10)

1. **Acetylcholine** is released from the somatic motor neuron and binds to cholinergic (nicotinic) receptors on the muscle cell.

2. An action potential is generated and travels down the T-tubule.

3. Calcium ions within the T-tubule are transported into the cell and trigger a channel on the sarcoplasmic reticulum to release calcium into the cell and cause contraction.

How does the release of calcium into the cell induce contraction? There are two proteins to know to answer this question: **troponin** and **tropomyosin.** When a muscle is at rest, the tropomyosin blocks the myosin-binding sites on actin. This prevents myosin from binding to actin. In order for contraction to take place, the myosin-binding sites on actin need to be uncovered. Thus....

1. Calcium ions will bind to troponin.

2. The calcium bound to troponin will alter the conformation of tropomyosin, uncovering the myosin-binding sites located on actin.

3. The myosin head binds to the actin filament, creating a cross-bridge, and completes a **power stroke**, resulting in the movement of the actin filament. Specifically, the myosin head bends and pulls the thin actin molecules inward, resulting in contraction.

4. The bent myosin head releases itself from actin. Simultaneously, calcium ions leave their binding sites on troponin and tropomyosin recovers the myosin-binding sites on actin.

5. The myosin head returns to its original position until contraction is needed again.

During contraction, actin and myosin slide past each other. The sarcomere shortens and the Z lines begin to move closer together. When the muscle cell is fully contracted, the I band and H zone are not visible. Interestingly, the A band length remains constant even though the sarcomere shortens (**Figure 10.9**).

Let us take a look at the molecular mechanisms that occur during contraction. At the end of contraction, before relaxation and a subsequent cycle, the myosin heads are still tightly bound to actin and are said to be stiff. This stiff position is called the **rigor state**. The following steps occur (**Figure 10.11**):

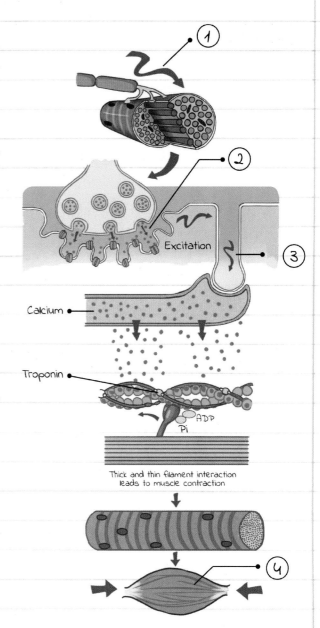

Figure 10.10:
Muscle Contraction.
1) An action potential arrives at the neuromuscular junction.
2) ACh is released, binds to receptors, and opens sodium ion channels, leading to an action potential in sarcolemma.
3) Action potential travels along the T-tubule.
4) Thick and thin filament interaction leads to muscle contraction. Thus, the muscle shortens and produces tension.

IN-TEXT QUESTION:
What happens if the sarcoplasmic reticulum is unable to release calcium ions?

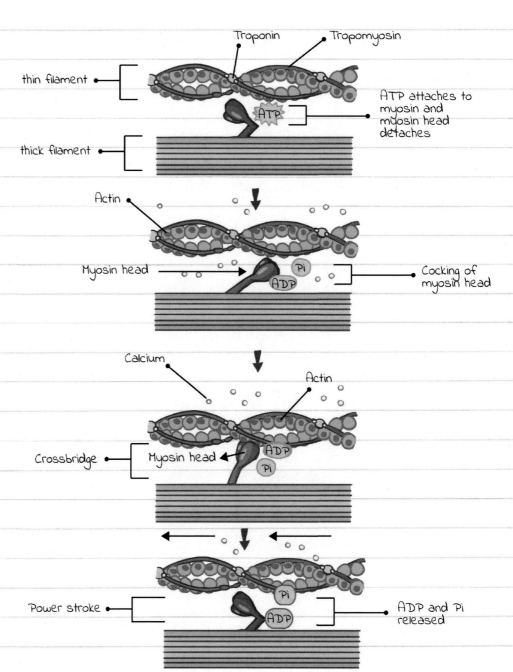

Answer:
No muscle contraction will occur. Calcium ions are required to uncover the myosin-binding sites. Without calcium, contraction will be prevented.

Figure 10.11:
Mechanism of Muscle Contraction

1. **ATP** (adenosine triphosphate), a high energy molecule, binds to the myosin head and causes the myosin head to be released from actin.

2. The myosin hydrolyzes ATP to ADP and a molecule of inorganic phosphate. Myosin uses the released energy from the hydrolysis of ATP to rotate and attach to actin in a "cocked" position. This position is analogous to bringing your arm back, or "cocking" it, before throwing a baseball forward.

3. The release of ADP and inorganic phosphate from the myosin head causes the myosin head to change position and move the actin filament. This is the **power stroke.** The power stroke is analogous to the actual act of throwing the baseball forward.

4. ATP attaches to myosin and causes its release from actin. Myosin returns back to its original position until contraction is initiated again.

Neural Control of Muscle Contraction

What initiates the contraction? How does the electrical signal of the neurons get translated into a physical movement? You may have heard the term **"EC coupling."** This stands for **excitation-contraction coupling** and is the process by which an electrical signal from a neuron stimulates muscle fiber contraction. The following happens (**Figure 10.12**):

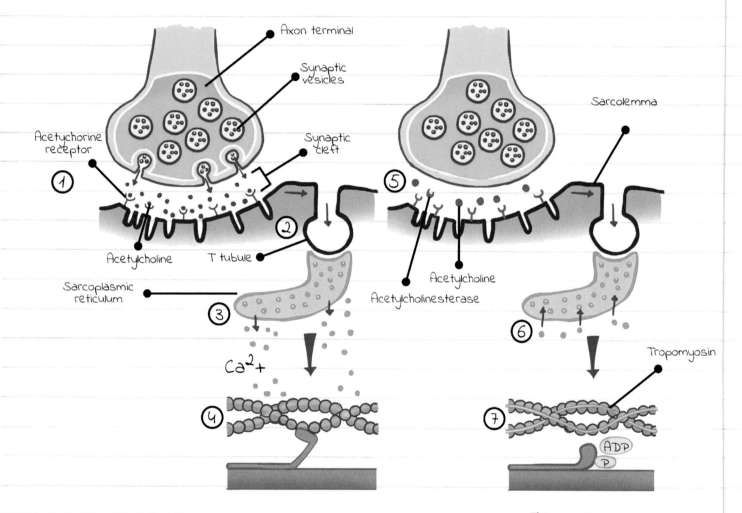

Acetylcholine is released into the synapse at the neuromuscular junction, the space between the neuron and muscle, and binds to receptor channels on the **motor end plate** of the muscle fiber. This causes the membrane channels to open and allow sodium and potassium to cross the membrane. Since the sodium influx is greater than the rate at which that potassium leaves, the cell will depolarize. If depolarization reaches a certain threshold, an action potential occurs. The action potential spreads down to the **T-tubule,** opening a calcium channel on the T-tubular membrane. Calcium enters the cell and triggers the opening of another calcium channel on the sarcoplasmic reticulum. The opening of these channels allows calcium to rush into the cytoplasm. Calcium binds to troponin and allows the sliding filament model discussed earlier to occur.

Upon relaxation, the calcium is pumped back into the sarcoplasmic reticulum using a protein called **Ca²⁺ ATPase.**

Figure 10.12:
Calcium's Role in Muscle Contraction.
1) Acetylcholine released from the axon terminal binds to receptors on the sarcolemma of the muscle fiber.
2) An action potential is generated and travels down the T-tubule.
3) Ca^{2+} is released from the sarcoplasmic reticulum.
4) Ca^{2+} binds troponin; actin and myosin attach forming a "cross-bridge."
5) Acetylcholinesterase removes acetylcholine from the synaptic cleft.
6) Ca^{2+} goes back into the sarcoplasmic reticulum.
7) Tropomyosin covers over myosin binding sites, causing cross-bridge to detach.

Now we finally understand the molecular and physiological events that occur during a single cycle of contraction. A single cycle is called a **twitch**.

The Importance of ATP in Muscle Contraction

Considering that contraction relies upon ATP, the muscles need a lot of energy. A muscle fiber only has enough ATP for about 8 cycles. Not to worry, the cell has backup storage! The muscle's backup energy comes in the form of **phosphocreatine**: a molecule made from creatine and ATP to form high-energy phosphate bonds (**Figure 10.13**). Phosphocreatine is created in the cell when the muscles are at rest. When muscles become active, the high energy phosphate from phosphocreatine is transferred to ADP to create ATP. The enzyme that accomplishes the phosphate transfer is called **creatine kinase**.

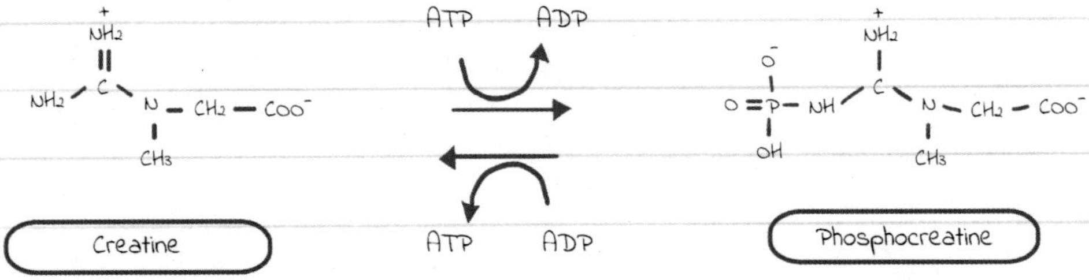

Figure 10.13:
Phosphocreatine.
Phosphocreatine serves as a storage for high energy phosphate bonds to be readily available to combine with ADP to form ATP. ATP can then aid in muscle contraction.

Muscle Fatigue

Since studying for this exam has most of us out of shape, you may currently be able to relate to **muscle fatigue**. Fatigue does not simply mean tired. The technical definition for muscle fatigue is that the muscle is no longer able to generate the power output it needs. In other words, the muscle can no longer generate force. This is often due to two factors: the lack of available energy and/or the accumulation of metabolites. As we discussed earlier, muscle contractions rely on ATP. Thus a shortage of ATP will not allow as strong a muscle contraction as desired. A muscle contraction also produces waste products, known as metabolites, that interfere with the release of calcium from the sarcoplasmic reticulum. Without calcium to uncover actin, myosin cannot bind and cause contraction.

The speed at which fatigue occurs depends on the muscle fiber type as well as the intensity of the activity. It also depends on the individual's fitness. Several specific disorders result in issues in the contraction cycle that can cause abnormal fatigue.

Types of Skeletal Muscle Fibers

There are three different types of fibers you should know: **slow-twitch**, and two types of **fast-twitch** fibers.

IN-TEXT QUESTION:
What are two built-in ways that the muscles have in order to reduce the onset of muscle fatigue?

Answer:
The muscles have creatine phosphate that can be converted into ATP. Additionally, the muscles have myoglobin stores, so that oxygen can be used for oxidative phosphorylation, even when strenuous exercise requires more oxygen than the lungs can provide.

Chapter 10 Muscular System   Copyright © 2019 MCAT King

1. **Slow-Twitch Fibers (Type I)** or **slow oxidative fibers.**

2. **Fast-Twitch Fibers (Type IIA)** or **fast oxidative fibers.**

3. **Fast-Twitch Fibers (Type IIB)** or **fast glycolytic fibers.**

As you can see from the names, one of the main differentiating factors between these fibers is the speed at which they contract. But, what determines the speed of contraction? The speed is dependent on how fast myosin is able to hydrolyze ATP to initiate the cross-bridge cycle. The fast fibers are appropriately named because they are capable of hydrolyzing ATP much faster than the slow fibers. Additionally, the above fibers are categorized as oxidative or glycolytic. Oxidative and glycolytic fibers differ in the metabolic pathway the fiber uses to produce ATP. The oxidative fibers use aerobic pathways such as the citric acid cycle and electron transport chain. If you remember correctly, more ATP is produced via these aerobic pathways than by anaerobic processes. Oxidative fibers, therefore, do not get fatigued as quickly as glycolytic fibers. What provides the oxygen needed for aerobic respiration to occur in the muscle fibers? **Myoglobin!** Myoglobin is an oxygen carrying molecule in muscles, similar to hemoglobin in blood cells. It gives the oxidative fibers a red color. Slow oxidative fibers have more myoglobin than fast oxidative fibers and are therefore redder. Glycolytic fibers use the anaerobic pathway, glycolysis, to produce ATP. Since glycolysis produces less ATP per cycle, these muscles fatigue more quickly. Glycolytic fibers do not contain myoglobin and therefore appear white in color.

Once you understand the above differences, the remaining variations make much more sense. Since the oxidative fibers use aerobic pathways to create energy, and these aerobic pathways occur in the mitochondria, the oxidative fibers have more mitochondria than their glycolytic friends. Additionally, the oxidative fibers contain more blood capillaries that supply the fibers with the oxygen needed for aerobic respiration.

Figure 10.14:
Muscle Fiber Types. Long distance running requires less force/tension, but more energy supply to last the distance; thus slow twitch oxidative fibers are mainly used. Sprints require great amounts of force and are for brief periods of time; thus, fast twitch glycolytic fibers are used. The 400 meter dash and 800 meter dash fall in between and thus, require fast twitch oxidative fibers.

The characteristics of each fiber allow it to perform a specific function in our body. Since the slow oxidative fibers can function for long periods without fatigue, they are useful for movements that do not require a great amount of tension or energy such as maintaining posture. Fast oxidative fibers can produce more tension, compared to slow oxidative fibers, and have the benefit of abundant ATP production. Fast glycolytic fibers can produce the most tension and are thus used for movements that require rapid and forceful contractions such as throwing a punch (**Figure 10.14**).

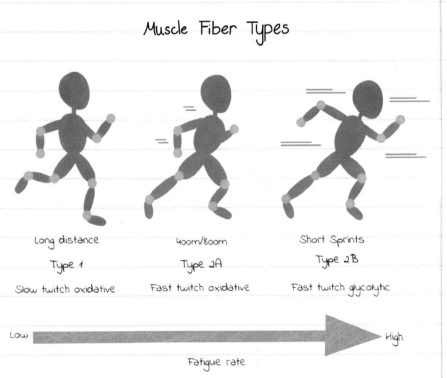

Muscle Fiber Types

Long distance	400m/800m	Short Sprints
Type 1	Type 2A	Type 2B
Slow twitch oxidative	Fast twitch oxidative	Fast twitch glycolytic

Low ———————————————————→ High

Fatigue rate

Motor Unit

A term that comes up a lot in regards to muscles is **"motor unit."** A motor unit is a group of muscle fibers that function together, or simply put, as a "unit". It also involves a somatic motor neuron that controls the group of muscle fibers. The somatic motor neuron initiates an action potential and the muscle fibers contract as a result!

Please note that each fiber is only innervated by a single neuron! A single motor neuron, however, can innervate multiple fibers (**Figure 10.15**).

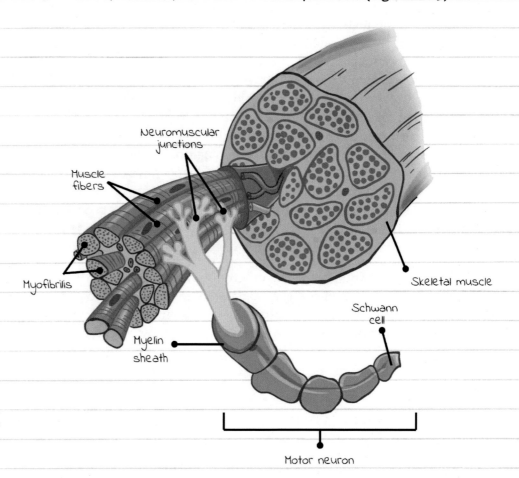

Neuromuscular junctions

Muscle fibers

Myofibrilis

Myelin sheath

Skeletal muscle

Schwann cell

Motor neuron

Figure 10.15:
Motor Unit. In a motor unit, a motor neuron innervates a group of muscle fibers to work together.

Different motor units have varying numbers of fibers depending on the type of control that muscle exerts. For example, muscles that have very fine movement, like the hand, have fewer muscle fibers per motor unit. Bigger muscles with less fine control, such as the muscles involved in posture, can contain hundreds of fibers per motor unit. Keep in mind, the muscle fibers in a motor unit belong to the same fiber type. You will not find both fast twitch and slow twitch muscle fibers in the same motor unit.

Like action potentials, the contraction of motor units is an **all-or-nothing** event. If that is the case how then can our contractions have varying strengths? Shouldn't then all contractions be the same amount of force?

Skeletal muscles have many motor units of different types that allow them to conduct contractions of variable strengths. When a powerful contraction is needed, more motor units are fired. When a weak contraction is needed, fewer motor units are fired. Likewise, the speed at which the muscle contraction needs to occur will dictate the type of motor units (slow-oxidative, fast-oxidative, fat-glycolytic) that will be engaged. This process of selectively choosing the appropriate muscle fiber for contraction is called **recruitment**.

Cardiac Muscle

Cardiac muscle is found in the heart and functions to make the heart a pumping machine. Cardiac muscle is similar to skeletal muscle in many aspects. For example, actin and myosin filaments are arranged in rectangular-like sarcomeres that make cardiac muscle appear "striated." Cardiac cells also contract mechanistically similar to skeletal muscle cells: an action potential travels down a T-tubule and triggers the release of calcium from the sarcoplasmic reticulum to bind to troponin. The binding of calcium to troponin shifts tropomyosin and unveils the binding site for myosin on actin. The rest of the sliding filament model ensues.

Cardiac muscle differs in some respects to skeletal muscle as well. Cardiac muscle cells, or cardiomyocytes, are **mononucleated**, bearing some resemblance to smooth muscle. While skeletal muscle contraction is typically voluntary, cardiac muscle is not. Cardiac muscle is instead controlled by a pacemaker called the sinoatrial node (SA node). Cardiac muscle also has a unique connection between its cells called **intercalated discs** that allow cardiac muscle to work as a single unit, or in **syncytium.** The cells are connected via gap junctions at the intercalated discs, enabling the quick passage of an action potential from one cell to another. Cardiac muscle and cardiomyocytes are covered in greater detail in the circulatory system.

Smooth Muscle

Smooth muscle is different from skeletal muscle in both its structure and the way in which contraction occurs.

The muscle fibers in smooth muscle are much smaller than they are in skeletal muscle. Smooth muscle is **mononucleated,** whereas skeletal muscle tends

Figure 10.16:
Cardiomyocites. Cardiac muscle cells, or cardiomyocytes, have sarcomeres that give it the striated appearance. Cardiomyocytes are connected via gap junctions that allow quick communication between cells.

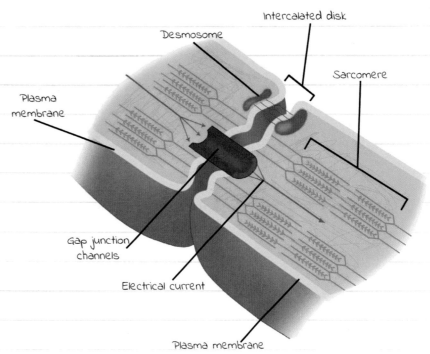

Labels in figure: Intercalated disk, Desmosome, Sarcomere, Plasma membrane, Gap junction channels, Electrical current, Plasma membrane

IN-TEXT QUESTION:
How does cardiac muscle resemble skeletal muscle? How about smooth muscle?

Answer:
Like skeletal muscle, cardiac muscle appears striated and can have more than one nucleus in each cell. However, like smooth muscle, cardiac muscle is innervated by the autonomic nervous system, and is involuntary. Interestingly, cardiac muscle does not require innervation from the nervous system in order to contract (smooth muscle also displays this when it contracts due to stretching). This phenomenon is known as myogenic activity and is limited to the smooth muscle and cardiac muscle. All three types of muscles require calcium ions in order for contraction.

to be multinucleated. Smooth muscle also differs in the manner they are stimulated by the nervous system. While somatic motor neurons release only acetylcholine into the neuromuscular junction in skeletal muscle, various neurotransmitters are released into an area called the **synaptic trough** in smooth muscle. The synaptic trough is bigger and less isolating than the neuromuscular junction. Thus, a neurotransmitter that is released into the synaptic trough can bind to membrane receptors on any of the smooth muscle cells. Since multiple types of neurotransmitters are released into the synaptic trough, smooth muscle cell membranes have a wide array of receptors compared to only nicotinic receptors on the motor end plate (**Figure 10.17**).

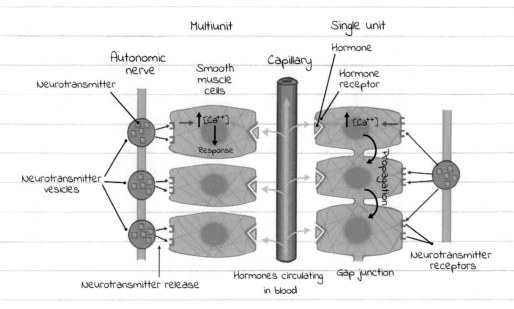

Figure 10.17:
Synaptic trough.

Smooth muscle gets its name from its lack of sarcomeres, giving it a "smooth" appearance. Smooth muscle cells do, however, contain actin and myosin that function mostly in the same way as these proteins do in skeletal muscle. One difference is that smooth muscle contains a protein called **calmodulin** instead of **troponin** that binds to calcium. Instead of

Figure 10.18:
Smooth Muscle Contraction. Intermediate and thin filaments are connected to dense bodies, which are anchored to the sarcolemma of the smooth muscle cell. During smooth muscle contraction, thin and thick filaments slide past each other in a similar way to skeletal muscle contraction. The entire smooth muscle cell will contract as the dense bodies connect multiple parts of the cell.

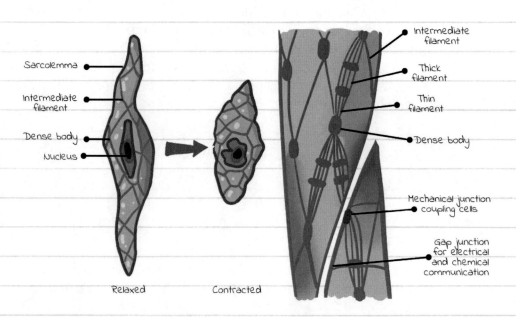

the Z-lines in skeletal muscle, smooth muscle thin filaments are anchored to a structure called a dense body. The dense body itself is anchored to the sarcolemma of smooth muscle cells and is connected to intermediate and thin filaments (**Figure 10.18**). When contraction occurs, cross bridges form between thin and thick filaments. As the myosin head shifts, the thin filament slides past the thick filament and causes contraction. The dense bodies and intermediate filaments are pulled in the process which causes the entire muscle fiber to contract.

Smooth Muscle Contraction

To summarize the molecular events of smooth muscle contraction:

1. The binding of a neurotransmitter from the interstitial fluid triggers depolarization, and ultimately an action potential, to occur.

2. The action potential causes calcium channels on the sarcolemma to open, allowing the influx of calcium into the cell.

3. Calcium channels from the sarcoplasmic reticulum open and cause the influx of calcium into the sarcoplasm.

4. Calcium binds to a protein called **calmodulin.**

5. The calcium-calmodulin complex activates a protein known as **myosin light chain kinase (MLCK).**

6. **MLCK** phosphorylates myosin heads and causes an increase in **myosin ATPase** activity.

7. This "activated" myosin head forms a cross-bridge along actin to create muscle tension and eventual contraction.

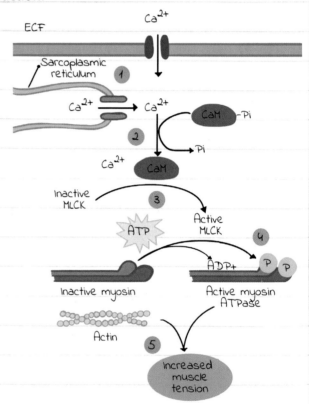

Figure 10.19:
Smooth Muscle Contraction Mechanism of Action:
1) Extracellular Ca^{2+} enters the cell and causes a release of Ca^{2+} from the sarcoplasmic reticulum
2) Ca^{2+} binds to calmodulin
3) Ca^{2+} bound to calmodulin activates myosin light chain kinase (MLCK)
4) MLCK phosphorylates myosin heads and activates myosin.
5) Active myosin cross-bridges with actin and creates muscle tension.

Thermoregulation of Muscles

Muscles play a large role in thermoregulation. Muscles can constrict or dilate blood vessels to allow more or less blood circulation to the skin for heat exchange. In hot temperatures, smooth muscles cause blood vessels near the periphery of the body to dilate and allow more heat to be released via sweat. In cold temperatures, the smooth muscle causes the blood vessels near the periphery of the body to vasoconstrict. This keeps the blood at the core of the body warm in cold temperatures. Additionally, in cold temperatures, the skeletal muscle will contract repeatedly to produce heat and warm up our bodies. This is why we shiver!

Questions

1) **Which of the following is NOT one of the three main types of muscle?**
    a. Smooth muscle
    b. Skeletal muscle
    c. Rough muscle
    d. Cardiac muscle

2) **Which of the following most correctly pairs the type of skeletal muscle fiber with its myoglobin and mitochondria content?**
    a. Red fibers have high myoglobin content and high amounts of mitochondria
    b. Red fibers have low myoglobin content and low amounts of mitochondria
    c. White fibers have high myoglobin content and low amounts of mitochondria
    d. White fibers have high myoglobin content and high amounts of mitochondria

3) **Which of the following is NOT a characteristic of red muscle fibers?**
    a. Muscles that can sustain activity
    b. High myoglobin content
    c. High amounts of mitochondria
    d. Less iron

4) **What is tonus in the context of smooth muscle cells?**
    a. When blood can no longer reach those muscle cells
    b. When muscles have been tensed for an extended period of time
    c. A state of constant low-level contractions
    d. When muscle cells are deprived of oxygen

5) **What is the name of the cell-cell interactions that take place between cardiac muscle cells?**
    a. Gap junctions
    b. Tight junctions
    c. Grand junctions
    d. Loose junctions

6) **Which of the following is the order of locations that depolarization travels during myogenic activity in cardiac muscle?**
    a. Atrioventricular node → sinoatrial node → bundle of His → Purkinje fibers
    b. Sinoatrial node → atrioventricular node → bundle of His → Purkinje fibers
    c. Purkinje fibers → atrioventricular node → sinoatrial node → bundle of His
    d. Bundle of His → Purkinje fibers → atrioventricular node → sinoatrial node

7) Which of the following muscles are responsible for involuntary movements?

I.   Smooth Muscle
II. Cardiac Muscle
III. Skeletal Muscle
   a. I only
   b. II only
   c. I and II
   d. III only

8) Which of the following muscle cells can have more than one nucleus per cell?

I.   Smooth Muscle
II. Cardiac Muscle
III. Skeletal Muscle
   a. I only
   b. I and II
   c. II and III
   d. I, II, and III

9) Which of the following muscle groups require Ca^{+2} for contraction?

I.   Smooth Muscle
II. Cardiac Muscle
III. Skeletal Muscle
   a. I only
   b. II only
   c. I and III
   d. I, II, and III

10) Which of the following muscle groups are striated?

I.   Smooth Muscle
II. Cardiac Muscle
III. Skeletal Muscle
   a. I only
   b. I and II
   c. II and III
   d. III only

11) Which region contains only thin filaments?

   a. Z-line
   b. I-band
   c. H-zone
   d. A-band

12) Which region contains thick filaments in their entirety and does not change length upon muscle contraction?

   a. Z-line
   b. I-band
   c. H-zone
   d. A-band

13) A myofibril consists of many _____ units in series?

    a. Sarcomeres
    b. Sarcolemma
    c. Sarcoplasmic reticulum
    d. Sarcoplasm

14) What structure is responsible for distributing an action potential to all sarcomeres in a muscle?

    a. Myofibrils
    b. Sarcolemma
    c. Titin
    d. Transverse tubules

15) Which ion is responsible for binding to troponin to initiate myosin binding to actin during muscle contraction?

    a. Na^+
    b. Ca^{+2}
    c. Cl^-
    d. CO_3^{-2}

16) What happens to the shape of the sarcomere as muscle contraction occurs?

    a. It increase in length
    b. It decreases in length
    c. It splits into two sarcomeres
    d. Two sarcomeres condense into one

17) Which of the following is the correct order of events that occur in the Actin-Myosin Cross-Bridge Cycle?

    a. The powerstroke occurs, the sarcomere contracts, and ADP and P_i dissociate from myosin → Resting stage in which ATP is hydrolyzed and myosin is not bound to actin → Ca^{+2} binds to troponin, tropomyosin undergoes a conformational change, and myosin binds to actin at the myosin binding site → ATP binds to myosin which causes it to detach from the actin, ATP hydrolyzes to ADP and P_i which recocks the myosin head

    b. Ca^{+2} binds to troponin, tropomyosin undergoes a conformational change, and myosin binds to actin at the myosin binding site → Resting stage in which ATP is hydrolyzed and myosin is not bound to actin → The powerstroke occurs, the sarcomere contracts, and ADP and P_i dissociate from myosin → ATP binds to myosin which causes it to detach from the actin, ATP hydrolyzes to ADP and P_i which recocks the myosin head

    c. Resting stage in which ATP is hydrolyzed and myosin is not bound to actin → Ca^{+2} binds to troponin, tropomyosin undergoes a conformational change, and myosin binds to actin at the myosin binding site → ATP binds to myosin which causes it to detach from the actin, ATP hydrolyzes to ADP and P_i which recocks the myosin head → The powerstroke occurs, the sarcomere contracts, and ADP and P_i dissociate from myosin

d. Resting stage in which ATP is hydrolyzed and myosin is not bound to actin → Ca^{+2} binds to troponin, tropomyosin undergoes a conformational change, and myosin binds to actin at the myosin binding site → The powerstroke occurs, the sarcomere contracts, and ADP and P$_i$ dissociate from myosin → ATP binds to myosin which causes it to detach from the actin, ATP hydrolyzes to ADP and P$_i$ which recocks the myosin head

18) **What enzyme is responsible for terminating the signal at the neuromuscular junction?**

    a. Acetylcholinesterase
    b. Hexokinase
    c. Phosphofructokinase
    d. Pyruvate kinase

19) **What is the name of the period in between the stimulus and the start of the contraction?**

    a. Contraction period
    b. Relaxation period
    c. Latent period
    d. Delay period

20) **What is oxygen debt?**

    a. Oxygen debt is the difference between the amount of oxygen that the muscles need at a certain moment and the oxygen actually available in the system
    b. Oxygen debt is the oxygen that the muscles must produce and return to the respiratory system after exercise
    c. Oxygen debt is the oxygen lost by the respiratory system when exhalation occurs
    d. Oxygen debt is the difference in oxygen use between red and white fibers.

Answers

1) **Answer: C**

   Explanation: The three main types of muscle in the human body include smooth muscle (A), skeletal muscle (B) and cardiac muscle (D). These muscle types share some similarities and some differences. Rough muscle does not exist and thus the correct answer is (C).

2) **Answer: A**

   Explanation: Red fibers are also known as slow-twitch fibers. These fibers primarily get their energy aerobically. To do so, they utilize their high myoglobin content and high amounts of mitochondria that can facilitate oxidative phosphorylation. This makes (A) the best answer and eliminates (B). Options (C) and (D) can be eliminated because white fibers, also known as fast-twitch fibers, contain a lower myoglobin content and mainly utilize anaerobic mechanisms to produce energy so they also have a lower amount of mitochondria.

3) **Answer: D**

   Explanation: Red muscle fibers contract slowly and thus they can sustain activity for long durations of time, eliminating (A). Red muscle fibers also have high myoglobin and mitochondria content which enables them to derive their energy aerobically through oxidative phosphorylation, eliminating (B) and (C). Lastly, red muscle fibers actually have more iron, which gives them their red color, and thus the correct answer is (D).

4) **Answer: C**

   Explanation: Smooth muscle is responsible for involuntary action and is found throughout the human body. Unlike skeletal muscle, smooth muscle performs more sustained contractions that are lower in level. This is known as tonus, or a state of constant low-level contractions (C). Muscles that have been tensed for an extended period of time without rest is known as tetanus, eliminating (B). Options (A) and (D) describe situations that are irrelevant to contractions.

5) **Answer: A**

   Explanation: One of the unique characteristics of cardiac muscle cells is how they communicate. The main way they do so is through gap junctions which connect the cytoplasms of adjacent cells. These gap junctions allow ions to pass directly between cells, which allows for rapid and coordinated depolarizations and highly efficient contractions. This makes (A) the best answer. Tight junctions (B) are another type of cell-cell interaction, but they are not relevant to this example. Grand and Loose Junctions, (C) and (D) respectively, do not exist.

6) **Answer: B**

> **Explanation:** Depolarization begins at the sinoatrial node. It then spreads to the atrioventricular node. Subsequently, it spreads to the bundle of His and then to Purkinje fibers. The option that correctly states this order of locations of depolarization is option (B).

7) **Answer: C**

> **Explanation:** Smooth and Cardiac muscle take part in involuntary movements whereas skeletal muscles are required for voluntary movements. This eliminates Option (III) and proves Options (I) and (II), making option (C) the best answer.

8) **Answer: C**

> **Explanation:** Smooth muscle cells only have one nucleus per cell, so Options (A), (B), and (D) can be eliminated. Skeletal muscle cells have many nuclei per cell and cardiac muscle cells can have 1-2 nuclei per cell.

9) **9) Answer: D**

> **Explanation:** All muscle cells require Ca^{+2} for proper contraction. Ca^{+2} binds to troponin which causes a conformational change in tropomyosin. The conformational change in tropomyosin opens up the myosin binding site on actin. Myosin can then attach to actin and the process of muscle contraction can occur. Therefore, option (D) is the best solution as every muscle cell requires Ca^{+2} to start this process.

10) **Answer: C**

> **Explanation:** Due to the repetition of sarcomeres in cardiac and skeletal muscles, they appear to be striped or striated, making (C) the best answer. Although smooth cells contain the actin and myosin that make up the sarcomere units, the fibers are not as well-organized so striations cannot be seen, eliminating (A) and (B).

11) **Answer: B**

> **Explanation:** The Z-line defines the boundaries of each sarcomere and actually does not consist of either myosin or actin, eliminating (A). The H-zone contains only thick myosin filaments, eliminating (C). Lastly, the A-band contains both thin actin and thick myosin filaments, eliminating (D). Thus, the correct answer is (B), the I-band, as it contains only actin thin filaments.

12) **Answer: D**

> **Explanation:** The Z-line defines the boundaries of each sarcomere and actually does not consist of either myosin or actin, eliminating (A). The I-band contains only actin thin filaments, eliminating (B).

The H-zone contains only thick myosin filaments but it shrinks upon contraction, eliminating (C). Lastly, the A-band (D) contains the entire myosin thick filament and does not change length upon muscle contraction, making (D) the correct answer.

13) **Answer: A**

Explanation: Sarcolemma is the cell membrane of a myocyte, eliminating (B). The sarcoplasmic reticulum is responsible for maintaining Ca^{+2} levels in the muscle cell, eliminating (C). The sarcoplasm is the muscle-cell equivalent of the cellular cytoplasm, eliminating (D). Sarcomeres (A), are the units that makeup myofibrils.

14) **Answer: D**

Explanation: Myofibrils is the term used to define sarcomeres that are lined up in a series, eliminating (A). The Sarcolemma is the cell membrane of a myocyte, eliminating (B). Titin is the spring that anchors actin and myosin filaments together and prevents excessive stretching of muscle, eliminating (C). Transverse tubules are perpendicular to myofibrils and use this orientation to distribute an action potential to many sarcomeres within a muscle (D).

15) **Answer: B**

Explanation: Calcium binds to troponin which is a regulatory subunit that causes tropomyosin to change confirmation. When tropomyosin changes confirmation, it exposes the myosin-binding sites on actin. The myosin head will then bind to actin and continue the mechanism of muscle contraction. Thus, calcium is the correct answer (B).

16) **Answer: B**

Explanation: When the myosin head connects to the actin filament, it pills on the actin which draws the thin filaments toward the M-line, which results in a shortening of the sarcomere, Option (B), which eliminates Option (A). The sarcomeres do not combine with each other or split into two different sarcomeres during this process, which eliminates Options (C) and (D).

17) **Answer: D**

Explanation: Option D is the proper series of events in the actin-myosin cross-bridge cycle that causes muscles to contract. It can be repeated several times to continue to cause muscle contractions.

18) **Answer: A**

Explanation: Acetylcholinesterase degrades acetylcholine in the synapse. This terminates the signal at the neuromuscular junction and allows the sarcolemma to repolarize. As the signal slows, less Ca^{+2} is released from the sarcoplasmic reticulum, resulting in myosin-binding sites on actin to be covered by troponin and actin-myosin binding to cease. All of the other Options (B), (C), and (D) are enzymes involved in glycolysis. This makes Option (A) the best answer.

19) Answer: C

Explanation: The contraction period is the period in which muscle contractions are occurring, eliminating (A). The relaxation period is the period after the contraction period has ended and before a new stimulus has been received, eliminating (B). The latent period is the name of the period in between the stimulus arriving and contractions starting. During the latent period, the action potential is spreading along the muscle, allowing calcium to be released. The delay period is not a term that is involved in muscle contraction, eliminating (D).

20) Answer: A

Explanation: Option (A) is the most proper definition of oxygen debt. However, Option (B) is very close to true. Another definition of oxygen debt is the amount of oxygen that is required for the body to recover from strenuous exercise. This oxygen comes from the surrounding environment, rather than muscle cells, which is why (B) is false.

Index

Symbols

A

B

C

Chapter 10 Muscular System

humoral immunity 189
Hydrostatic pressure 211, 212
Hyperopia 30
hyperpolarizes 9
hyperthyroidism 59
hypophyseal portal system 57
Hypothalamus 20, 22, 56, 222
hypothyroidism 59
hypoxic 223
H Zone 240

I

I Band 240
IgA 189
IgE 189
IgG 189
ileocecal valve 104
ileum 99
immunoglobulins 189
increases alveolar compliance 159
incus 37
inferior vena cava 121
Inflammation 187, 195
inhibitory 11
inhibitory postsynaptic potential 11
innate immunity 187
inner cell mass 85
insertion 236
Inspiratory reserve volume 157
Insulin 62
insulin-dependent diabetes 63
intercalated cells 219
intercalated discs 247
intercalated disks 123
Internal intercostal muscles 156
internodal pathway 125
intestinal phase 99
intracellular catalytic domain 17
intrinsic factor 98
iron 162
islets of Langerhans 62
isotonic 211
isovolumetric contraction 129
isovolumic relaxation 129

J

jejunum 99

K

ketogenesis 105
kinocilium 38
knee-jerk reflex 27
Krebs cycle 105
Kupffer cells 107

L

larynx 97, 153
Le Chatelier's Principle 162

Leptin 107
leukocytes 139
Leydig cells 63, 79
ligaments 236
Ligand-Gated Ion Channel 17
light chains 190
Limbic System 22
Lipase 100, 101
Lipids 105
lipoprotein 103
lipoprotein lipase 103
liver 101
loop of Henle 209
low density lipoprotein (LDL) 105
lower respiratory tract 153
lumbar 19, 24
luteal phase 83
Luteinizing hormone (LH) 57, 58, 79, 83
lymph 178
lymphocytes 139, 188

M

Macrophages 187
macula 32
Magnocellular cells 35
maintaining pH balance 152
maintenance of pH 152
major histocompatibility complex class II (MHC class II) 191
malleus 37
mass movement 105
Mast cells 188
mechanical digestion 96
Medulla 22, 208
megakaryocyte 140
Melatonin 55
memory B-cells 191, 194
menopause 81
menstrual cycle 81, 83
menstrual phase 84
Mesoderm 86
metarterioles 130
MHC class I 193
MHC class II 193
micelles 101
Microglia 4
microvilli 99
Midbrain 22
middle ear 36
Mineralocorticoids 54, 60, 61
mitral valve 123
MLCK 249
M Line 240
monocytes 139, 187
mononucleated 247
morula 85
motor control 23
motor end plate 243
motor unit 246
moves 237
mucosal cells 99
multinucleated 237
multiple neurons 11

Chapter 10 Muscular System

White matter 19, 20

Z

Z Line 240
zona pellucida 84
zonules 29
zygote 78, 81, 82
zymogens 100

Chapter 10 Muscular System

Like our method?
Join in person or virtual courses
with the one and only
MCAT KING!
For more information visit
mcatking.com/mcatcourse
and start your White Coat Journey today!

For more motivation follow us on social media and Instagram @mcatking!

Made in the USA
Coppell, TX
07 February 2023

12397584R00164